THE ADMIRABLE DISCOURSES OF BERNARD PALISSY

UNIVERSITY OF ILLINOIS PRESS / URBANA 1957

THE
ADMIRABLE
DISCOURSES
OF
BERNARD
PALISSY

TRANSLATED BY AURÈLE LA ROCQUE

He has fared better at the hands of ceramists, who hail his work as one of the glories of the French Renaissance and carefully preserve the few masterpieces from his hand that have luckily survived. He is likewise well known to scholars specializing in sixteenth-century French. His vocabulary has been analyzed and his syntax commented upon in many works dealing with this important period in the development of the French language. Agricultural scientists have recognized him as a pioneer for his treatise on marl. His ideas on geology are similarly definitive, at their best; and in any case, certainly interesting.

It is hoped that this translation into English of his major work will help to reintroduce Palissy and secure his deserved recognition among the earlier men of science. The translation is preceded by an introduction outlining the main events of Palissy's life and the information about him available in print. The text has been annotated wherever it seems to need clarification.

Grateful acknowledgment is tendered Professor Alexander H. Schutz of the Department of Romance Languages, The Ohio State University, for gracious assistance and kindly understanding in tracking down many difficult words and expressions in the text. The writer is also indebted to the following for bibliographic information: Miss Dorothy W. Bridgwater, Yale University, Mr. Robert H. Haynes, Harvard University, Miss Helen Northrup, University of Wisconsin, Mr. Basil Stuart-Stubbs, McGill University, and Miss Margaret I. Smith, University of Michigan.

Professor George W. White, head of the Department of Geology, University of Illinois, gave the translation a thorough critical reading in manuscript. His suggestions resulted in the addition of many of the critical notes on the text and his help is acknowledged with deepest gratitude.

Aurèle La Rocque

The Ohio State University
Columbus, Ohio

CONTENTS

THE ADMIRABLE DISCOURSES OF BERNARD PALISSY

INTRODUCTION

PALISSY'S LIFE

Little is known of Palissy's early life; in fact, it is impossible to say with certainty when he was born. He himself has given us no information on this point except indirectly. According to the few contemporary authors who mention him, he was born in 1499, 1510, or some time between 1514 and 1520. Leroux (1927, p. 13) accepts 1510 as the most probable date. The record is no clearer concerning the place of his birth; most probably, it was in the village of la Capelle Biron, in the diocese of Agen; some authors have argued otherwise but without convincing proof. The names of his parents, their profession or trade, his brothers and sisters, if any, are equally unknown. Certain it is that at a very early age he settled in Saintes,[1] the capital of the old province of Saintonge, where he spent the major part of his life.

His education was not neglected, for he learned to read and write and acquired, perhaps by himself, enough knowledge of mathematics and geometry to qualify later in life as a surveyor. This was more than young men of his class learned at the time and it assured him of exceptional opportunities in choosing a trade. In addition, he learned something of modeling and drawing—one wonders how—and the rudiments of sculpture.

His first choice of a trade was the making of stained glass windows. He served as an apprentice to an unknown master glazier; then, as was the custom of the day, he traveled in France, and perhaps beyond its present borders into what is now Belgium and Germany.

---

[1] Saintes is now in the department of Charente Maritime, north of the Gironde estuary, about 60 miles almost due north of Bordeaux, and about 47 miles southeast of La Rochelle. Its population was 23,441 in 1946. It still has Roman ruins, including the arch of Germanicus, baths, and an amphitheater. The Roman bridge was destroyed in 1843.

1

It was during this *tour de France* that he made many of the observations that later served as arguments and illustrations for the treatises in his books. Louis Audiat (1868) has reconstructed his route, at least in part, from places mentioned in his books. He certainly spent some time in the provinces of Guyenne, Armagnac, Brie, Champagne, Gascony, Agenais, Quercy, the Ardennes, Languedoc, Auvergne, Burgundy, and perhaps also in Bigorre and Béarn. Whatever other parts of France he visited, it is certain that as he traveled he observed plentifully and acutely; these observations were to serve him well first in his work as a ceramist, then in what we can call his scientific work.

Between 1535 and 1539 he returned to Saintes, married, and changed his trade. The change was not a voluntary one; the demand for stained glass windows was dwindling each year as the fashion in church building changed from Gothic to Renaissance. To support his wife and family—as many as six children according to his own account—Palissy had to make use of his talents in other ways. He became what one would now call a licensed land surveyor and, from his own report, earned a good living at it when his services were in demand. But he was not always employed and his income was far from assured. It was at this time that he saw or found—no one can be sure which—a porcelain cup of such outstanding beauty that he thought of reproducing it and the idea became an obsession with him. He knew little if anything about pottery-making and it is perhaps his very ignorance that induced him to attempt something that would have seemed impossible to a more experienced worker. His tireless experiments under trying conditions are told at length in his own words (pp. 188 ff.) and need not be repeated here. Suffice it to say that after sixteen years of heartbreaking failures, he managed to find what he was looking for.

His discovery was one that justly attracted him fame and modest fortune. His *rustiques figulines* are masterpieces of naturalistic depiction, ingenious casting and enameling techniques. They brought high prices, as he says himself, but his patrons seem to have thought that they were getting their money's worth. One of these patrons was Anne de Montmorency, high constable of France and governor of Saintes. He had a shop built for Palissy in one of the city towers and honored him with his patronage. Lesser nobles followed the fashion established by their superior, and Palissy not only made them ewers and platters decorated according to his designs, but branched out as a decorator of castles and even returned to his old trade of making stained glass windows for special purposes. He also obligingly designed grottoes to ornament the nobles' gardens when the fad for grottoes spread from Italy to France.

As a prosperous burgher, Palissy was in contact with the thinking men of his town. The burning topic of the day was the Reformation which had swept through Germany and Switzerland and was penetrating France and Italy. Palissy was one of the first in Saintes to adopt the new religion and his activity in that field brought him trouble, notwithstanding the protection of high personages which he owed to his artistic work. He was arrested and in spite of his powerful patrons was sent to Bordeaux to await trial. Anne de Montmorency took his case directly to the Queen Mother, Catherine de Medicis, who saved Palissy from almost certain execution by naming him *inventeur des rustiques figulines du roi,* that is, inventor or designer of the King's rustic potteries. The title carried with it direct dependence on the King's household, and therefore immunity from prosecution before the parliament of Bordeaux. No wonder Palissy proudly—and gratefully—placed this title on the title page of his book.

With the truce of Amboise in 1563 persecution ceased, at least for a time, and Palissy plied his trade in peace. His renown attracted intelligent men, lawyers, doctors, poets, and druggists to his shop and there they talked of many things, some of which are reported in Palissy's first book, the *Recepte véritable.* The full title (see annotated bibliography) is much longer and describes the contents much more fully than is customary today. It treats of geology, chemistry, philosophy, theology, history, geometry, agriculture, the building of fortifications, and even contains a history of the reformed church of Saintes.

He might have continued to enjoy limited fame in the provinces if the Queen Mother, now Regent for her fourteen-year-old son, Charles IX, had not decided to tour the realm, partly to sound out public feeling, partly to strengthen loyalty to the throne. The royal cortège arrived at Saintes in 1565. There were ceremonial presentations to the King and Queen Mother, and Palissy was among those presented. She was greatly interested in his work and two years later called him to Paris to decorate the Tuileries palace.

There he built a grotto, and his manuscript description was

discovered and published by Benjamin Fillon. The grotto itself soon disappeared for it was already in disrepair in 1569.

In Paris as at Saintes, Palissy made many friends. He names some of them in the *Discours Admirables* (see pp. 154–55), and Leroux (1927, pp. 66 ff.) has given biographic details on some of them. Although Palissy continued his work in enamelware, its manner changed to please a court particularly fond of mythological subjects. His work in this period is generally considered inferior to that of earlier times. The main criticism is that it lacked originality.

The Wars of Religion had not yet ceased, and in the great massacre of St. Bartholomew's day, August 24, 1572, Palissy escaped—by what good luck no one knows. Perhaps the Queen Mother, who saved the life of the famous surgeon Ambroise Paré, also extended her protection to Palissy. Nowhere does the latter mention the reason for his escape. Understandably, he left Paris and sought asylum at Sedan, whose sovereign ruler was a Huguenot. Audiat (1897, p. 114) has found documents on Palissy in the archives of the Protestant churches of Sedan. Among other things, they reveal that by the years of 1572 to 1576 he had three sons, Pierre, Nicolas, and Mathurin; two daughters, Catherine and Marie, and perhaps a third, Marguerite.

The peace of La Rochelle in 1573, which was supposed once more to end religious wars, induced him to return to Paris. He took up his work again, but apparently it was at this time that he felt a burning desire to publicize the information he had acquired. He lived almost in the shadow of the Sorbonne and the ideas he wished to advance ran counter to many established concepts of the day. He realized that he had little formal training and little, if any, knowledge of Latin and Greek. Yet in 1575 he gave public lectures, advertised by posters prominently displayed on the walls of Paris, on the very subjects which were later to form the major part of the *Discours Admirables*.

Perhaps his reluctance was counterbalanced by the powerful support of his followers, private physicians to the highest nobility of France, surgeons who were equally highly placed, druggists, clergymen, mathematicians, lawyers, and others described simply as gentlemen. Leroux (1927, pp. 79 ff.) gives biographic details about those whose life could be traced. They were not a mere claque of admiring followers, but men of good judgment and great learning, who would have been able to detect flaws in reasoning and errors of fact. Yet they were unable to gainsay Palissy, or so he tells us, even on those subjects whose explanation was diametrically opposed to the one then current. Palissy supported his theories and explanations with specimens, of which he apparently had a great many. The specimens, with descriptive labels, were preserved in Palissy's cabinet and he has given us (p. 233) the text of the labels in the *Discours Admirables*. The success achieved by the lessons of 1575 induced Palissy to repeat them each year at least until 1584 and to have their substance printed as the book, *Discours Admirables*.

When civil war broke out again in France in 1588, Palissy was aging and his protectors had died. He was imprisoned in the Bastille de Bussy and in 1590 he died there, an old and broken man, at least 70, perhaps even 91 years old, more probably 80. His work as an artist had not saved him this time and his renown as a scientist had not gone beyond a restricted circle of friends and admirers. His body lies in an unmarked grave and his ideas as well as his fame seemed to have been buried with him.

What did this remarkable man look like? The only portrait preserved, now in the Cluny Museum, is a formal one of a man in court dress, probably thoroughly uncomfortable in finery that he wore on the infrequent occasions when he had to. The face is long and thin, the thinness emphasized by a bald head and a long beard. The nose is strong and fine, the eyes sunken under heavy brows, the cheeks likewise sunken, the mouth with a sardonic half-smile. The general aspect is one of calm and distinction but the eyes are wide awake, as befits one who missed little and remembered everything he had observed.

We know so little of the man because he was unhonored by most of his contemporaries and immediate successors. It was more than 100 years later that Antoine de Jussieu (1718), Fontenelle, and Réaumur (1720) called attention to his works and pointed out their value. Later still, Rouelle and Guettard praised him. Almost 200 years after the first publication of the *Discours Admirables* (1777) Faujas de Saint-Fond and Gobet republished all of Palissy's works that were known at the time. Although his reputation was established in French scientific literature, he still remains little known to English-speaking scholars despite the monumental work of Morley (1852). Yet we have been reminded of his importance from time to time, most recently by Thompson

(1954). Perhaps it is because his writings have not yet been completely translated, although extracts in English have appeared, especially in Morley (1852) and Willett (1876), that he has not been given his due. Let us hope that this translation will in some measure restore him to his proper place as a pioneer in science as well as a gifted artist.

THE PRINTED RECORD

During his lifetime, Palissy had two books and one pamphlet printed. The first book appeared in 1563 and is referred to generally by the abbreviated title *Recepte véritable*. The pamphlet (Palissy, 1919) was not known to most of Palissy's biographers and was not rediscovered until the twentieth century. It is a pamphlet of 38 pages, describing the grotto built for the Duke of Montmorency, first printed in 1563, reprinted in 1919 shortly after its discovery. The second book is the *Discours Admirables* (1580). There was only one edition of each book during Palissy's lifetime and both of them are now so rare that only two copies of the first are known to exist and only a few of the second. They are treasured by the libraries fortunate enough to own them. Some data on copies of these books and the many reprints are given in the annotated bibliography. Palissy may have had other books or pamphlets printed, but if so, no copy of them has survived.

Palissy manuscripts are likewise scarce. The most important one so far discovered is a plan of a grotto for the Queen Mother, perhaps the very one that he built in the gardens of the Tuileries. The manuscript was found at La Rochelle by Benjamin Fillon and has been printed at least three times, including its incorporation in the 1880 edition of Palissy's works. There is also a receipt dated 1564 which bears his signature, reproduced in the 1880 edition (p. xxvii).

His main works, the *Recepte véritable* and the *Discours Admirables,* are similar in organization and content. Both were written in the form of dialogues, the *Recepte véritable* between two unidentified persons whose words are headed *Demande* and *Réponse,* the latter evidently the author. In the *Discours Admirables,* they are identified as *Théorique* and *Pratique* and the dialogue here is much livelier than in the first book.

There is an important difference in content between the two

books and this can best be understood by a comparison of them. The *Recepte véritable* is the description of a refuge for the just—that is, the persecuted Protestants—where they would live in peace as farmers and shepherds. From descriptions of this idyllic spot, he turns to his opinion of the best methods of farming and gives his ideas on fertilizers. In particular, he recommends collecting and using the water from manure and describes a method of constructing a reservoir for the purpose. From these practical matters, he goes on to a hodgepodge of observations and theories on natural history, including the formation of rocks, crystals, and metals, and the origin of fountains. On the subject of fountains—or springs—which he was to take up again in much greater detail in the *Discours Admirables,* he says clearly that these are fed by rain water. Then he returns to a description of the gardens that will adorn the Protestant refuge. Next, he gives an account of the reformed church of Saintes, possibly since he wishes the refugees to remember the difficult times through which they have passed. Even more, fearing perhaps that the truce of Amboise would not be the end of persecution, he dedicates to them the plan of a fortress where they may seek refuge in time of war. The fortress was to be built with spiral walls, like a snail shell. Palissy thought it would resist all attacks but Anatole France (1880 edition of Palissy's works, p. xvi) prints the opinion of an unnamed general staff officer who pointed out that even with the means available in the sixteenth century it could have been taken.

The *Discours Admirables* is the better organized of the two books. There is little history here except in digressions in the form of examples. Perhaps Palissy had given more thought to the order of presentation of his subjects through his lecturing experience; perhaps he was so concerned with the idea of convincing his reader, as he had sought to convince his hearers, that he took pains to plan his approach to each topic in the manner that he thought clearest and best. The book begins with the usual dedications and what would now correspond to a copyright notice; it ends with copies of the labels in his cabinet and a glossary of difficult words. The body of the book is divided into separate treatises on waters, particularly those of fountains and springs, rivers and the sea; on metals, various drugs, ice, salt and the method of producing it, rocks, clay, marl, and the potter's art. It is a didactic work which might well be called a textbook of geology, though it contains much information on other subjects as well.

In many cases, the *Discours Admirables* contains corrections and expansions of theories first put forth in the *Recepte véritable*. The interval of seventeen years between the publication of the two books was one during which Palissy traveled, observed, thought, lectured, and discussed his theories with able men. We must therefore take his *Discours Admirables* as the final expression of his ideas on geology and other branches of natural history. Where the *Discours Admirables* differ from the *Recepte véritable* the theories of the later work must be preferred to those of the earlier.

After the rediscovery of his work in the eighteenth century, Palissy's books were reprinted several times, with introductory statements and annotations. The earliest of these reprints seems to be that of Faujas de Saint-Fond and Gobet (1777). The others are those of Cap (1844), Fick (the *Discours Admirables* only; 1863), the Charavay edition (1880) with an introduction by Anatole France; the Audiat edition (1888), the reprint of a description of the rustic grotto of the Duke of Montmorency which was unknown to previous writers (Palissy, 1919); and finally the Corbière reprint of the *Recepte véritable* (Palissy, 1922).

Palissy has not lacked admirers and critics. Each new edition of his works was preceded by introductory information on his life, sometimes also on the value of his work, the originality and correctness of his ideas; as time passed, his vocabulary needed more and more explanation and the notes grew more copious and scholarly. The biographies, as distinguished from reprints of his works, are numerous also, in French and in other languages. The first of these, as far as could be ascertained, is that of Dumesnil (1851), followed a year later by Morley's two-volume life (1852) in English, published in London by Chapman and Hall with a second edition in 1855. An American edition was brought out by Ticknor, Reed and Fields in 1853. A third English edition was put out by Cassell, Petter, and Galpin of London, in 1869. Other biographies in French followed from time to time: Delécluze (1858), Delange (1862), Audiat (1868), Burty (1886), Dupuy (1902), Leroux (1927). Outside France, Morley was followed by Brightwell (1858 and 187-?) in English, and by Hanschmann (1903) in German. Numerous articles on particular aspects of Palissy appeared in the nineteenth and twentieth centuries; for example, a pamphlet by Jules Salles (1856) which emphasizes especially Palissy's importance in ceramic art, an article by Weiss (1896) which deals with Palissy's sojourn at Sedan, another by Sir Thomas Clifford Albutt (1919?) which deals with his importance in the revival of natural science in the sixteenth century, and one by Pimier (1934) especially concerned with Palissy's artistic work in constructing grottoes and designing gardens. Very recently, Thompson (1954) has reviewed Palissy's contributions to geography and geology.

Of books concerned with his artistic worth, the following may be cited: Enjubault (1858), known to me only by title, but dealing with Palissy's ceramic art; Sauzay (1862), a remarkable collection of paintings of Palissy's work and that of his followers; Tainturier (1863), a work that describes his glazed pottery; Larroumet (1893–96) and Verne (1923), two short articles demonstrating the continuing interest in Palissy; and the volume by Ballot (1924) in the *Documents d'art* of the Louvre.

Palissy's vocabulary has been studied and quoted as an example of sixteenth-century French in many scholarly works, for example, M. A. Eveillé's *Glossaire saintongeois* and Cotgrave's (1611) *Dictionarie of the French and English Tongues*. A special study of the syntax of the verb in Palissy's works appeared in German (Zimmermann, 1915), and Borlé (1927) has devoted an entire book to his use of conjunctions of subordination.

Palissy's life has inspired at least three plays; one in French, in verse, by Brieux (1880), one act long; one in English by Antoinette Scudder (1934), five acts; and finally, one in Spanish by Alejandro Tapia y Rivera (1944) in two parts and four acts, published in San Juan, Puerto Rico.

Palissy's style is neither elegant nor grammatical by present-day French standards. He wrote at a time when the French language was much richer in vocabulary and much freer in expression than it became later under the influence of the seventeenth-century writers and reformers. Some of Palissy's syntactical devices give his language a clumsiness that would call forth a veritable storm of blue-penciling from a twentieth-century editor. On the other hand, he has a certain quaintness that does not translate easily, if at all, and produces approximately the same effect as the outmoded but picturesque language of Shakespeare and Ben Jonson in English. The comparison with Thomas Heriot's English is even more striking, for Heriot also wrote on science, in

Virginia, at almost the same time (1588). His punctuation is haphazard but perhaps this is the printer's fault more than Palissy's. It has been changed in this translation only where the change seemed necessary for clarity; otherwise it has been left as it stands in the 1580 edition.

PALISSY'S ORIGINALITY

Palissy claimed that he knew neither Latin nor Greek and he shows repeatedly that he had little respect for the printed word of accepted authority when it contradicted his observations. Thompson (1954, p. 161) has shown that the claim may have been only a pose, and some doubt still remains on this point, as indicated by the existence of translations into French of many of the works which Palissy says he has never read.

His biographers do not agree on just what he did or did not read. Because of the importance of this point in evaluating his originality, let us first list the works that Palissy himself mentions in his books. The following list is compiled from the various biographies of Palissy and the pages quoted are those of the 1880 edition of his works.

Aristotle is mentioned (p. 184) but not as an author. He is quoted as teaching Antipater to collect noxious waters in a donkey's hoof, as reported by Plutarch in the life of Alexander the Great. Had Palissy known Latin, for example through studies at a university, he could not have failed to mention this highest of authorities on many of the subjects discussed in his book. We may conclude almost certainly that the works of Aristotle were unknown, except perhaps by hearsay, to Palissy.

Arnold of Villanova (pp. 234–35) is mentioned but Palissy does not say he has read him, nor does the context indicate that he has.

Pierre Belon is mentioned (p. 342) as if he had written jointly with Rondelet (q.v.), an indication that Palissy had read the works of neither of them, but knew of them by hearsay from his friends.

The Bible, especially the Psalms, is referred to throughout Palissy's works. He was probably familiar with a French translation, quite possibly the translation printed and sold by Philibert Hamelin, whom he mentions (p. 133).

Jérôme Cardan (Cardanus). Palissy (p. 330) says in so many

words that he has seen Cardan's *De Subtilitate* but probably in a translation which was available in Palissy's day.

Fra Francesco Colonna's novel, the *Dream of Polyphilus,* originally titled *Hypnerotomachia Poliphili,* was published in Venice in 1499 and 1545. There was a French translation by Jean Martin, published in 1546, 1553, and 1600.

Dioscorides is alluded to briefly (p. 74). The little that Palissy says of him may have been gleaned from quotations in other authors or from hearsay. It does not prove that Palissy had read Dioscorides in the original or in translations.

Du Cerceau. A passage in the *Recepte véritable* (p. 145) shows that Palissy was familiar with Du Cerceau's work. He had seen and studied his plans of fortresses.

Gébert is mentioned with Arnold of Villanova (q.v.) and the same observations apply to both of them. There were several pseudo-Géberts in French in Palissy's time.

Philibert Hamelin. Palissy mentions that he sold Bibles printed by him, and Palissy probably owned one of them.

Raymond Lulle is cited (p. 164) and the context indicates that Palissy had read his book, probably a pirated and adulterated edition in French.

Paracelsus is mentioned incidentally (pp. 278–80) but there is no indication that Palissy had read his works.

Ambroise Paré attended Palissy's lectures and was a fellow Huguenot. Palissy undoubtedly knew of his works, some of them published in French in 1545, 1561, 1564, 1568, 1572, 1573, and 1575, long before the appearance of the *Discours Admirables,* yet Palissy makes no mention of them.

Pliny the Elder. His *Natural History* is quoted by Palissy with such care, "Thirtieth book, chapter 16" that Palissy must have had access to a translation, at least.

Plutarch was also known to him, again quite possibly in translation.

The *Roman de la Rose,* mentioned in the same sentence as Arnold of Villanova and Gébert (q.v.) may have been familiar to Palissy but undoubtedly in French.

Sebastiane, i.e., Sebastiano Serlio (1475–1552), wrote *Rules of Architecture* in Italian. There was a French translation as early as 1547. Palissy may well have been familiar with this book, which he mentions briefly (p. 85).

Jean Sleidan. The context (p. 174) seems to indicate that

Palissy had read Sleidan's works. There was a French translation, published in 1561.

Leonardo da Vinci. Palissy may have known something of da Vinci's ideas through Cardan, who is said to have borrowed freely from Leonardo, or through pirated versions of Leonardo's notebooks which existed in Italy and France during Palissy's lifetime (Thompson, 1954, quoting Duhem).

Vitruvius is mentioned several times (e.g., pp. 53, 85, 145, 213) and the context indicates that Palissy had read his works. There was a French translation by 1547.

Ysidore, that is, Isidore of Seville (died 636), is mentioned briefly, almost in passing (p. 74). Palissy may have known him only by hearsay. There may have been French translations of the Lapidary, but I do not know of any.

His biographers have not been consistent in reporting what authors Palissy had quoted. For example, Thompson (1954, p. 164) seems to have been the first to include Plutarch and Pliny in the list. There is no point in comparing each author's catalogue with the others' although the completeness of the catalogue and the knowledge of French translations may have affected a particular author's opinion concerning Palissy's originality and knowledge of Latin. From the above list it will appear that of the works read by or possibly known to Palissy, most, if not all, had been translated into French before 1580, the date of publication of the *Discours Admirables;* in fact, some of them had been translated before 1563, when the *Recepte véritable* was printed.

Of equal importance in evaluating Palissy's originality are the works that he does not mention. He was, of course, under no obligation to give a complete list of his sources, as scientific writers try to do today. Thorndike (1941, quoted by Thompson, 1954) cannot believe that Palissy did not know the works of von Megenberg (*Das Buch der Natur,* 1475), Douglas (*De naturae mirabilibus opusculum,* 1524), Savonarola (*Compendium totius philosophiae,* 1542), Copernicus (*De revolutionibus orbium coelestium,* 1543) and Agricola (*De natura fossilium,* 1546; *De re metallica,* 1556). That should not be surprising, for these books were not translated into French, so far as I know, during Palissy's lifetime. For Agricola's works the Hoovers (1912) and the Bandys (1955) show that there was no French translation in print in Palissy's day. Palissy's ignorance of these books seems consistent with his statement that he could read neither Latin nor Greek.

We must note also that Palissy acquired much information from his friends. At Saintes, before 1563 and the printing of the *Recepte véritable,* he was befriended by Antoine de Ponts, who had traveled in Italy and was a patron of the arts. He was a protégé of the constable Anne de Montmorency, who built him a shop and gave him many important commissions. His friends also included lawyers, physicians, druggists, and wealthy merchants from whom he acquired specimens and, almost certainly, a great deal of information on all sorts of subjects.

In Paris, his circle of friends was much larger and included influential men through whom Palissy could have had access to many books but, more important, to the ideas in these books through discussion with his friends.

Was Palissy a shameless plagiarist who appropriated the ideas of others without giving credit where it was due? Thorndike (quoted by Thompson, 1954, pp. 162 ff.) thought so and cited especially the remarkable similarities between Palissy's treatise on fountains and a small book by Jacques Besson (1569) which Palissy could easily have seen. Still, there is a possibility that Besson, who was at court at the same time as Palissy and probably knew him, borrowed from Palissy's *Recepte véritable* and added some of his own ideas. If so, Palissy returned the compliment in his *Discours Admirables.* Such borrowing without credit seems alien to Palissy's character and especially to the scrupulous honesty which emanates from his two books. The writer prefers to think that Besson and Palissy were acquainted; that they discussed the subject of fountains repeatedly; and that they published their ideas independently, each thinking that he had originated ideas developed by both of them.

Among Frenchmen of his century, Palissy stands out by his attitudes toward scientific matters. He makes it quite clear that he rejects, nay defies, established authority and that he intends to base his scientific work on his own observation and not on the writings of his predecessors. Scathing denunciations of the fashionable authorities of his day appear throughout his book. They begin on the fourth page, in the dedication to Antoine de Ponts, and in terms that leave the reader in no doubt at all concerning Palissy's contempt for those who, under the cloak of beautiful Latin and polished language, broadcast what he considered and intended to prove to be falsehood. In his forthright way, he immediately names Geber, the author of the Romance of the Rose, Raymond Lule, and the disciples of Paracelsus. Later, he derides others, among them some of the most revered authorities of his time. Sweeping rejections of this sort would not be surprising in a later age—for example, in the time of Voltaire or during the French Revolution—but two centuries earlier, when timid questioning of the authority of medieval science was just beginning, such an attitude struck the learned doctors of the University of Paris like a thunderbolt. Many a gray beard waggled in indignation at such irreverence and many a professor of philosophy fulminated *ex cathedra* at this impious and uncultured iconoclast. There is no doubt that Palissy's approach to science struck his contemporaries as original. Most of them considered it sacrilegious and untenable as well—all except the faithful few who had listened intently to his lectures, observed his demonstrations, and convinced themselves of their truth. Foremost among these was Antoine de Ponts, Palissy's patron and friend, and the handful of discriminating thinkers whom Palissy names in his book (1580, p. 209).

Why this wholesale rejection? Why this suspicion of established authority? The reasons are fairly obvious. Palissy had become a Protestant fairly early in life and as such had been thoroughly imbued with the necessity of examining the Scriptures and of making his own conclusions on religious matters. If the established Church could be wrong on theological points, why should its philosophers be infallible in scientific matters? When their dicta conflicted with his own observations, why should he bow to their superior authority? As a Protestant, he would be suspicious of anything written in Latin by philosophers who had the approval of the Church. All the more so since he was not bound to current philosophical thought by ties of affection and regard for a particularly honored teacher. Palissy was self-taught and had no sentimental attachment to the University.

He might have let matters rest at this point, as did many others of his day, doubting or rejecting without logical evidence everything that had been published before him. Another facet of his character, the compulsion to pass on his knowledge, would not allow him to be silent and he undertook to set down everything he knew, taking literally, as he himself says (1580, p. iv), the Bible's injunction not to bury his talent in the ground. In his book he revealed the full measure of his originality, pitting his observations and conclusions point by point and argument by

argument against those of his predecessors. He shows us the
working of his mind, unhampered by preconceived ideas derived
from books. By great good fortune rather than planned design,
observation almost always comes first with him, deduction and
explanation second. In this approach to natural phenomena lies
Palissy's greatest claim to originality. Others had observed before him but few, if any, had arrived, as he had, at such correct
conclusions on so many natural phenomena.

Another claim to originality may be made for Palissy on the
basis of his methods. Others before him had lectured and written
on natural phenomena, but none had so intimately connected
arguments with specimens, available for inspection and study. If
the advocates of visual aids in teaching need a patron saint, they
could not find a better one than Palissy, for, as he says himself,
he satisfies sight, hearing, and touch.

Palissy summarized his ideas at the end of the *Discours Admirables* (1580, pp. 362–77) in a series of "maxims" related to
the text. A perusal of these theses, for that is what they are,
gives us an idea of the scope of Palissy's originality. Some of
the ideas expressed may have been derived from earlier writers
but it is equally probable that he originated them independently.
They deal with an impressive variety of subjects: philosophy,
geology, paleontology, botany, zoölogy, engineering, hydrology,
chemistry, physics, medicine, alchemy, metallurgy, agriculture,
mineralogy, embalming, toxicology, meteorology, and ceramics.
It would be difficult, if not impossible, to check all of his contemporaries and predecessors and to assess the absolute originality
of each idea. Yet, in justice to Palissy, attention should be
called to a few of his ideas which appear to be original or which
he seems to have originated independently. It is no discredit to
his genius that he should have had an idea previously expressed but generally unknown to his contemporaries. We tread
on uncertain ground here and must keep in mind that we do not
know for certain just what Palissy had or had not read. With
these strictures in mind, let us examine a few of his ideas.

The first and longest chapter of the *Discours Admirables* is on
water. It is both theoretical and practical, containing side by
side ideas on the origin of groundwater and detailed instruc-
tions for building reservoirs. Palissy may have borrowed ideas
from Besson, as alleged by Thorndike (see above, p. 13). If the
ideas expressed here are indeed Palissy's, we can credit him with

giving the first correct explanation of artesian wells. His description of pump mechanisms (1580, p. 4) may be the earliest on record in French. He correctly explained the relationship between wells and rivers (1580, p. 8) and his statement on recharge from rivers is as clear and definite as one could wish, if the words bed or aquifer are substituted for "veins." So, likewise, is his statement of the hydrologic cycle (1580, pp. 42–43) and the lag in change of water levels (1580, p. 67). The passage (1580, p. 48) on the movement of water underground is a good explanation of contact springs, perhaps the first to be published. His plan for making "fountains," more exactly reservoirs, seems plausible but may be purely theoretical. Nothing in the works of any of Palissy's biographers and commentators indicates that his ideas were ever put into practice.

Palissy was fascinated by fossils and he mentions them repeatedly throughout the book. He does not call them fossils because he used that term in a much wider sense, clearly explained in his glossary (1580, p. 380), to include all mineral materials buried in the earth. This usage of the term was general until the third decade of the nineteenth century and it persisted much later in certain quarters. The summary of his views (1580, pp. 362 ff.) contains four theses concerning fossils in the contemporary meaning of the term. These four theses and the passages in which they are discussed at length show that Palissy understood the nature of fossils as the remains of animals and plants and not as curiously shaped rocks. He was not the first to discover this fact; the idea goes back at least as far as Xenophanes of Colophon but was not generally accepted in Palissy's time. He may have arrived at his conclusion independently but he certainly knew that it had been published before, among others by Cardan whom he criticizes at length (1580, p. 211).

Palissy emphatically denies that fossils are due to the biblical Flood (1580, pp. 211 ff.; 370). In this he specifically contradicts Cardan, because he has read his works, but also he contradicts indirectly many thinkers of the Middle Ages and later who held the same opinion. His explanation of the presence of fossils far inland is ingenious. First he insists (1580, p. 216) that they were born on the very spot where they are found; and secondly that they lived in a large lake (1580, pp. 216, 217, 230) which has since congealed. The entire context indicates that Palissy meant a freshwater lake but he is also aware that the process can be carried out in sea water (1580, p. 218). He recognized that some of the fossils in rocks far from the sea are identical with marine forms (1580, pp. 222 ff.) but he explained this by thinking that they lived in lakes whose waters "are salty, not as much so as those of the sea: but they are salty enough to produce all kinds of shellfish" (1580, p. 223). He came very close to concluding that wherever marine fossils are found in the rocks the sea had once been present but the fact is that he did not, although some writers had done so in Antiquity. This is additional evidence that he was speaking the truth when he said that he had not read them.

He is quite explicit on the relation of fossil shells to living forms. For example he recognized the similarity between living mussels in the Meuse River and those in the mountains nearby (1580, p. 222); between the oysters of the sea and those of the Ardennes rocks (1580, p. 222). He is even more specific for Venteul where he collected purple shells and whelks (1580, p. 224). He enumerates eleven different kinds of fossils (1580, p. 225), most of which are recognizable.

He also recognizes that some fossil forms are now extinct (1580, pp. 225–26) but, most surprisingly, that some extinct forms are related to species of ". . . the Indies and Guinea." He specifies that these are "certain purple shells, whelks and other large snails" which makes it almost certain that he was dealing with Tertiary forms from the Paris Basin, some of which are, in fact, related to tropical forms not now represented on the Atlantic coast of France.

His observations on the preservation of fossils are among his most acute and most original. They are briefly stated in three maxims (1580, pp. 363, 367, 377). In the first of these (p. 363) he states that all plants and animals, including man, can be reduced to rock by the action of congelative water. In the second (p. 367) he states that they can be changed to metal, a clear statement, perhaps the first in print, of the process of replacement. In the third (p. 377) he insists on the widespread occurrence of "lapified shells" far from the sea, "even in the highest parts of the Ardennes." The text of his book is clearer concerning the process which, in his opinion, is responsible for petrifaction. As we read his account (1580, pp. 129–32) of petrifaction, we are tempted to substitute "mineral solutions" for "metallic waters" and "generative water"; if we do so, this account becomes thoroughly similar to present-day explanations of replacement. He is just as lucid in a later passage (1580, pp. 203–207) in which replacement by nonmetallic materials is discussed. He recognizes also that some fossils are unaltered (1580, p. 226) because they have not been exposed to the action of "congelative waters."

Palissy (1580, p. 228) categorically asserts that all crystal forms originate in water and cannot originate elsewhere. This generalization, which makes him a Neptunist before Werner's time, led him to some brilliant conclusions and some understandable errors. The crucial experiment which started him along this train of thought is described on p. 109 of the 1580 edition. He dissolved saltpeter in water and when it cooled he observed that it had formed "long icicles of quadrangular form." Next he observed that rock crystal from Spain had the same form. From this he concluded that all minerals with geometric forms have crystallized in water. It was particularly unfortunate that he should use "marcasites" (really pyrite) in slate as an example, but how can we expect him to know about metamorphism in the late sixteenth century?

He came close to discovering the constancy of crystal angles, for he recognized that crystal forms are triangular, quadrangular, or pentagonal (1580, p. 364) and noted that this was an essential characteristic of crystals, just as "roses and gooseberries form prickly spines."

One original discovery that seems to be uniquely his is the soil auger which he describes in such clear detail (1580, p. 320) that his specifications could be used for making and operating such a tool even now. The important conclusion here is that ". . . thus, with several handles of various lengths, one could know what the deeper earths were. . . ." What more was needed for the geologic exploration of the subsurface except longer "handles" powered by means undreamed of by Palissy and harder, differently shaped drill bits?

His account of the development of sedimentary rocks (1580, pp. 197–99) contains the germ of the law of superposition. Rocks are formed one layer at a time and accumulate in horizontal layers. The materials are carried downward by water "until they have found a bottom that stops them . . ." and the congelation did not happen all at one time. The necessary data are in place; all that is lacking is the conclusion: therefore the bottom layers are older than the upper ones. Palissy did not make that conclusion but his original observation provided all the bases for it.

Palissy's skepticism in an age of gullibility is most refreshing and could be called original. He displays complete distrust in medicinal baths and devotes a whole section of his book to the castigation of mithridate, a complex medicine made up of three hundred improbable and useless, if not downright harmful, ingredients. Another section is devoted to exploding the virtues of "drinkable" gold which, as he demonstrates, is neither drinkable nor beneficial. He has true regard for honest physicians but he is merciless in his contempt for quacks and pseudoscientists such as those who claimed to be able to transmute base metals into gold.

In agricultural science he is also an original thinker. The use of marl as a fertilizer was known in Antiquity but Palissy was apparently the first to propose a theory of mineral nutrition of plants (1580, p. 164) when he wrote ". . . no vegetative thing could vegetate without the action of salts, which is in seeds. . . ." His immediate successors, among them Olivier de Serres, knew nothing of his work in this respect, or if they did, they neglected to use it.

Many more examples of original thought might be cited but these will suffice to show that Palissy's thinking was highly original for his time. Other curious instances are noted as they appear in the text.

Finally, it must be recognized that Palissy was far from being always right. He contradicts himself from time to time, he accepts as fact old wives' tales which are unworthy of him, and he gives explanations of natural phenomena that are ludicrously wrong. In spite of this, he has much to say that is still worthwhile after more than three and a half centuries. His story is best told in the *Discours Admirables*, the work of his old age, the final product of his great mind.

ADMIRABLE DISCOURSES [2]

on the nature of waters and fountains,
either natural or artificial,
on metals, salts and salines,
on rocks, earths, fire and enamels.
With many other wonderful secrets about Nature.
Plus a treatise on marl, very useful and
necessary, for those who practice agriculture.
The whole arranged as dialogues, in which are
included theory and practice.

[2] The title pages of other editions have minor variations from this one, which is translated as faithfully as possible from the 1580 edition. The title *Discours Admirables* may seem pompous to us but it may have been a bookseller's device to promote the sale of the book by assuring the reader of its value at the start. Changes of title for the purpose of promoting sales are not unknown even now. The word *fonteines* might be translated as "springs" but I have used "fountains" which is closer to the original both in sound and meaning, as the context will show. *Salines* may mean either saline substances or salt flats. The text makes it clear that salt flats are meant. The word *pierres* may be rendered either as "stones" or "rocks." If Palissy were writing today he would probably use rocks, in the geological sense, and not stones. The word *terres* may mean lands, farms, or earths; it seems clear that earths was meant here, as in "fuller's earth." It is tempting to render the expression *se mellent de l'agriculture* by "who dabble in agriculture." Perhaps that is what Palissy had in mind, i.e., those who are not born to the soil and therefore could not understand his advice, but noblemen and burghers who play at being gentlemen farmers. I am not sure that "potteries" is the right word for *figulines,* but that seems to be as close as the idea can be approximated in English. The king at the time of publication of Palissy's book was Henry III (1574–89) and the Queen Mother was Catherine de Medicis (1519–89), daughter of the noble merchant banker family of Florence who had married Henry II of France. The word *sieur* is an abbreviation of *monseigneur.* Perhaps the word "Lord" might be used here but it has too many other meanings to be acceptable. The English title "Sir" may not be quite appropriate here, but it corresponds fairly well with *le Sire* of the original.

By M. Bernard Palissy, inventor of rustic potteries
to the King and the Queen his mother.
To the Most High and Most Mighty Seignior, Sir
Anthoine de Ponts, Knight of the Orders of the
King, Captain of the hundred gentlemen, and most
faithful counselor of His Majesty.

Paris

Martin le Ieune, at the sign of the Serpent,
across from the College of Cambrai

1580

With Privilege of the King. [ii]

EXTRACT FROM THE PRIVILEGE [3]

By the grace and privilege of the King, Martin le Ieune, bookseller and printer in the University of Paris, is permitted to print or cause to be printed a book entitled, *Admirable discourses on the nature of waters and fountains, either natural or artificial, on metals, salts and salines, on rocks, earths, fire and enamels, etc.*[4] Forbidding all booksellers, printers or others, of whatever class,[5] quality or condition they may be, to print or cause to be printed, sell or distribute others than those which the said le Ieune shall have printed or caused to be printed, on pain of confiscation of the books otherwise printed, and of arbitrary fine. And this until the time and end of eight years finished and complete, on this given at Paris, the eighth of July 1580.

Signed by the council,

De L'Estoille.[6] [iii]

[3] This page does not appear in the 1880 edition. In the 1580 edition it is the first of 15 unnumbered pages after the title page, all of which have been given Roman numerals in this translation. There are 23 unnumbered pages after p. 361 which have been numbered consecutively. All page numbers supplied by the translator are enclosed in brackets; the original page numbers are in parentheses. The disjointed verbiage of this extract indicates that the actual "Privilege" was much longer and probably even more verbose.

[4] The title is considerably abbreviated, but the essentials for recognition are given.

[5] *Estat* may mean profession or trade as well as class.

[6] Pierre de l'Estoille, *grana audiencier de la Chancellerie* who knew and esteemed Palissy, and whose account of Palissy's death has been preserved.

*To the Most High and Most Mighty Seignior
Sir Antoine* [7] *de Ponts, knight of the orders
of the King, Captain of the hundred gentlemen
and most faithful counselor of His Majesty.*

My age [8] has incited me to be so bold as to say to you that one day I was considering the color of my beard, which caused me to think about the little time that is left me,[9] to finish my life: and that led me to admire the lilies and the wheat of the countryside,[10] and many kinds of plants, which change their green color to white when they are ready to yield [iv] their fruits. Thus many trees hasten to blossom when they feel that their natural vegetative power is waning. These thoughts reminded me that it is written that we should take care not to abuse the gifts of God nor to hide talent in the ground.[11] It is also written that the dolt concealing his foolishness is better than the sage hiding his knowledge. It is therefore reasonable and just that everyone try to multiply the talent he has received from God, according to his commandment. Therefore I have tried to bring to light the things which it has pleased God to make me understand according to the measure in which he has been pleased to endow me, in order to benefit posterity. And because many men, under beautiful Latin, or other well polished language have left [v] many

[7] Note the variant in spelling, *Anthoine* on the title page, *Antoine* here. The editor of this book, if there was any other than the printer, was not such a stickler for uniformity as his present-day counterparts.

[8] In 1580, Palissy was at least 70 years old, an advanced age in a century when life expectancy was not as great as it is today.

[9] Palissy had ten more years to live, half of them in prison.

[10] The comparison is probably biblical, i.e., the lilies of the field that toil not, neither do they spin, but Palissy gives it a new twist; they turn white, like his beard, when they are about to yield their fruit.

[11] The allusion is obviously biblical and it is only one of innumerable ones throughout the book.

23

pernicious talents to delude youth and waste its time: thus a
Geber,[12] a Romance of the Rose, and a Raymond Lule, and
some disciples of Paracelsus, and many other alchemists have left
books in the study of which many have lost both their time and
wealth. Such pernicious books have led me to scratch the earth,
during forty years, and to search its bowels, in order to know the
things it produces within itself, and by these means I have found
grace before God, who has revealed to me secrets which until now
have remained unknown to men, even the most learned, as may
be ascertained by my writings, contained in this book. I well
know that some will scoff, [vi] saying that it is impossible that a
man without Latin [13] could have knowledge of Nature; and
they will say that it is very bold of me to write against the opinion
of so many famous and ancient philosophers, who have written
on natural things, and filled the whole earth with wisdom. I
know also that others will judge by appearances, saying that I
am but a poor workman: and by such statements will try to
make my writings appear harmful. In truth, there are things in
my book which it will be hard for ignorant people to believe.
Notwithstanding all these considerations, I have not ceased to
pursue my undertaking, and to counter all calumnies and snares.
I have set up a cabinet in which I have placed many [vii] and
strange things which I have drawn from the bowels of the earth,
and which give reliable evidence of what I say, and no one will
be found who will not be forced to admit them to be true, after
he has seen the things which I have prepared in my cabinet, in
order to convince all those who otherwise would not wish to
believe my writings. If perchance there should come some swelled
head who would wish to ignore the proofs placed in my cabinet, I
should ask for no judgment other than your own, which is sufficient to overcome and refute all the opinions of those who would
wish to contradict them. I say it truly and without any flattery:
for much as I had good evidence of the excellence of your mind
as early as the time [viii] when you returned from Ferrara to your
castle of Ponts, (that opinion was confirmed) when lately it
pleased you to speak to me of various sciences, namely philosophy,
astrology, and other arts drawn from mathematics. This, I say,

[12] For Palissy's knowledge of Geber and other authors, see Introduction,
p. 10.
[13] See the discussion of Palissy's claim that he knew no Latin, Introduction,
pp. 4, 10.

has made me doubly sure of the competence of your marvelous mind, and although age dims the memory of many, yet I have found yours more increased than diminished. This I have learned through your statements to me. And for these reasons I have thought that there is no nobleman in the world to whom my work might better be dedicated than to you, knowing well that though it may be esteemed by some as a fable full of lies, by you [ix] it will be prized and esteemed a rare thing. And if there is anything poorly finished or badly organized, you will easily draw the substance from the matter, and excuse the too rude language of the author, and in this hope, I shall beg you very humbly to do me the honor of accepting it as from the hand of one of your very humble servants. [x]

WARNING TO THE READER

Friend reader, my wish that you should profit by reading this book has led me to warn you to take care not to dull your mind with sciences written in the study by an imaginative or biased theory or taken from some book written from imagination by those who have practiced nothing, and to be wary of believing the opinions of those who say and maintain that theory begat practice. Those who teach such a doctrine argue wrongly, saying that the thing that one wants to do must be imagined and pictured in one's mind, before laying hand to one's task. If man could carry out his [xi] imaginings I should adopt their party and opinion: but far from it, if the things conceived by the mind could be carried out, the amateur alchemists would do wonderful things and would not amuse themselves seeking for fifty years, as many have done; if the theory imagined by war leaders could be carried out, they would never lose a battle. I dare say, to the confusion of those who hold such opinion, that they could not make a shoe, not even the heel of a boot, even if they had all the theory in the world. I would ask those who hold such opinion whether they, having studied fifty years in books on cosmography and navigation on the sea, and having maps of all regions and the chronometer, the compass and [xii] astronomical instruments, would undertake to sail a ship to all countries: as will a man who is expert and practical. They dare not place themselves in such danger, whatever theory they may have learned: and when they have long debated, they will be forced to admit that practice has begotten theory. I have advanced this proposal to silence those who ask how it is possible for a man to know something and to speak of natural things without having seen the Latin books of the philosophers? Such a statement could be made about me, since in many instances I prove by practice that the theory of several philosophers is false, even that of the most renowned and most ancient, as anyone can see and hear in less than two hours, providing he will take the trouble to [xiii] come and see my cabinet, in which will be seen marvelous things which are placed there as witness and proof of my writings, arranged in order on shelves, with labels below them: in order that one may learn by himself: I can assure you, reader, that in a very few hours, even during the first day, you will learn more natural philosophy about the things contained in this book, than you could learn in fifty years by reading the theories and opinions of the ancient philosophers. Enemies of science will scoff at the astrologers: [14] saying, where is the ladder on which they have climbed to heaven, to know the foundation of the stars? But in this respect I am exempt from such scoffing; for in proving my written reasons, I satisfy sight, hearing, and touch: [xiv] for this reason, defamers will have no power over me: as you will see when you come to see me in my little Academy.

Good luck to you. [xv]

Since printing of the book has started, many noblemen have asked me to read it, so that they might understand the difficult things, which has induced me to write the following: to wit, that if after the printing of this book, someone should not be satisfied with having seen the things in writing by himself, and should wish to have a detailed interpretation, let him seek out the printer and he will tell him where I live, where he will always find me ready to give readings and demonstrations of the things contained in it.

Also, if someone should wish to build a fountain, according to the design therein contained, and if he should be unable to understand clearly the intent of the author, I shall make him a model, by which he will be able to understand the above easily. [xvi]

[14] Palissy uses the word with the present-day meaning of "astronomer," as the context shows.

THE MAIN POINTS TREATED IN THIS BOOK

[15] These are the pages of the original edition; they are not given in the 1880 edition whose pages do not correspond to those of the original edition.

ON WATERS AND FOUNTAINS [16]

Theory begins.

Lately, going through the fields, I found myself very thirsty, and passing through a certain village, I asked where I could find some good fountain, in order to refresh myself and slake my thirst, to which I got answer that there was none in this place, and that their wells were all dry, because of the drought, and that there was only a little muddy water at the bottom of their wells. Which caused me great disappointment, and I was much astonished at the plight of the inhabitants of the village, because of the scarcity of water. And then I remembered a promise that you made me long ago to show me how to make fountains in places most barren of water. Therefore, since we are not busy, I pray you, according to your promise, to teach me this knowledge, which will be most useful to me: For I have a property [17] on which there are no fountains and there is only a well which is subject to drying up, like others. (2) [18]

Practice

I shall gladly do so: but before talking of the fountains of my invention, I wish to make you a little speech on the cause of good or harmful waters, and on the rashness of certain modern fountain-makers. Also, on the source of natural springs. And in order

[16] Palissy here does not mean fountains in the present-day sense but, as the context will show, natural springs and springs made to flow by digging into the earth. The word "fountains" has been retained in the title to keep it as close as possible to the French wording.

[17] The original is *héritage* which means strictly a legacy, but the term was used loosely to designate a plot of land or a house and the land on which it was built.

[18] The page number of the 1580 edition is indicated in two ways. A new 1580 page begins after the page number in parentheses if it actually appeared in the 1580 edition, or in brackets if the page is unnumbered in the 1580 edition. This page is the first numbered page in the 1580 edition.

to do so, we must look to modern invention to understand its usefulness and long duration. Many of these [19] moderns, having no means of finding natural springs or fountains, have dug into the ground to make wells, and to avoid the great labor of drawing water, they have observed the pumps of ships, and even though they were invented by the ancients, certain artisans [20] (wishing to gain and to increase [21] their renown) have advised many noblemen and others to attach pumps to their wells; not as an old invention, but as the first inventors, and have thereby increased their prestige, and many have spent much on these pumps, which are still very much in fashion. However, I know for certain, either by practice or theory, that these pumps will not last long, because of the violence of their movements, which they suffer either by the subtleness of the waters or by the winds that funnel into the pipes. And it must be concluded that all violent things cannot last. (3)

Theory

How dare you sneer at such an ingenious and useful device, since you yourself admit that it was invented by the ancients, and it has at all times been used for the safety of ships: for without these pumps they would often perish: also, it is well known that in many metal mines these pumps are used: for otherwise the waters would flood them all the time.

Practice

I do not despise the invention of pumps: but on the contrary I esteem it greatly: and whoever invented them was very clever and has not failed to observe human anatomy. For I well know that the water that has climbed up the tubes has climbed by no other means than the drawing of breath caused by the valve,

---

[19] Palissy is fond of the expression *le dit* and its related forms, just as present-day lawyers are fond of its English equivalent "the said" which adds nothing to clarity in English. *Le dit* and its variants are translated here as "this" or "these," accord'ng to the context, or simply as "the" where nothing more is necessary for a clear translation.

[20] The term *artisans* seems roughly equal to "engineers" in the present-day sense.

[21] At this point in the text occurs the first of many marginal headings. They have not been reproduced here as their use is inconsistent and erratic. The editor of the 1880 edition likewise omitted them, probably for the same reason.

which having caused aspiration, or sucking of wind which is brought about by the piston of the pump, and that by the attraction and raising both of the valve and piston, a quantity of water having entered the pipe, this valve being put back into its place, encloses the water and the air, which are enclosed in the pump, being left and pushed by the movement of the piston, which forces the water to rise, and this can be done without much violence: As you see that a man cannot spit without first drawing in his breath or air, and this cannot be done unless the valve of the throat (4) of man (which surgeons call the epiglottis) acts like that of pumps.[22] And although I esteem the invention of these pumps marvelously much, and I know that they will always be in demand, and useful both in ships and mines, still, for domestic wells they will be of very little use: for workers must always be at them, because of the breaks caused by violence: and because there are very few men who know how to repair them. That is why I speak boldly, being sure that many in Paris and elsewhere have had such pumps made at great cost, who in the end have abandoned them because of the repairs which must often be made. Also, I know that there has lived in our time a French architect who had himself called almost a god of the masons or architects: and inasmuch as he held twenty thousand in grants and that he knew himself to be favorably known at court, it happened that he boasted of making water rise as high as he wished, by means of pumps or machines, and by such boasting caused a great lord to want to raise the water of a river to a high garden which he had near the river. He ordered that money should be paid for the costs: which being done, the architect had a quantity of lead pipes made and certain wheels in the river, to cause the movement of the (5) hammers that move the valves, but when the time came to raise the water, every pipe burst; because of the violence of the air enclosed with the water: seeing by this that the lead was too weak, the architect ordered that brass pipes be cast quickly, for which a great many founders were hired, so many that the cost was so great that it was found from the accountant's papers, that it amounted to 40,000 francs; even if the project never came to anything: And talking about this, I have seen many pumps which

[22] A very clear statement of the mechanism of pumps, all the more remarkable because of the date of publication.

have brought up such a huge quantity of sand by the action of
the valves that it was necessary to break open the pipes, to take
out the sand that was in them.

Theory

I don't know how what you say can be true: for I have seen
a thousand models of pumps, which poured out water as naturally
as if they had been springs.

Practice

You are wrong in quoting me models: for they have fooled a
million men, either models of buildings or platforms, batteries,
bridges, or moving of river beds, levees or causeways [23] and particularly in the raising of waters. For many, having approved the
raising or emptying of waters by models of pumps, have made
great works, to base pillars in rivers, believing that after the
water was dammed back (6) around the spot destined for the
foundation of the pillars, it would be easy to empty it out with
pumps, have had great pumps made according to the models
which they had found correct, in which they have been disappointed, and have ruined themselves: since they were unable
to do on a large scale that which they did on a small one. The
same thing has happened to many others with the changing of
the course of rivers. If enquiry were made about these things,
evidence would be found at Toulouse, in the building of a bridge
across the Garonne, from which we must conclude that pumps
are useful and necessary in ships, and in some mines: but to use
them in wells, one is soon tired of them, for the reasons that I
have given above: hence I shall not tell you more of them.

Theory

And as for well water, what do you think of it? Do you find it
good or harmful?

Practice

I can say nothing more concerning well waters than that all
of them are cold and stagnant, the ones more, the others less,
and you must not think that well waters come from some spring:

---

[23] *Paissières* is the word of the original. It does not appear in modern
dictionaries but Cotgrave gives "A bank, or causey, held up, or in, by stakes,"
It seems to be related to the verb *paître*, to graze.

for if it were from some constant source, wells would suddenly fill up: therefore it must be noted that they come from no great distance and are only the result of rains that fall around the wells: and those that are inside (7) cities are subject to receiving much urine, and if there are privies around it cannot be doubted that the water of these wells will be affected: and we cannot conclude otherwise than that wells are the continual outflow [24] of the rains, which slowly descend little by little into the earth. And this means that some wells are better than others, and for no other reason than that the surrounding lands are clean of all minerals, saltpeter and other substances which the waters could pick up in passing through the earth. However, after the waters have entered the well, they stagnate, and are easy to poison since they do not run. If you had read the history of John Sleidan,[25] you would know that the waters of wells and cisterns are subject to poisons. He says that during the war that the Emperor Charles V waged against the Protestants many wells and still waters were poisoned, and that a man was caught who confessed having come from a distant country, especially to do this foul deed, this by order of two great noblemen whom I do not wish to name. At the great market of Meaux, in Brie, in the house of the Gillets, they wanted to clean out a well, and the first man who went down it to do so died suddenly at the bottom of the well, and another man was sent down to find out why, and he died, like the other: still another man was sent down who (8) went down half way: but once there, he started to shout to be pulled up quickly, which was done, and when he was outside, he was so sick that he had trouble saving his life.[26]

Still another story tells that there was once a doctor who, finding himself without money or patients, bethought him of throwing some drugs into the wells of the city where he lived, which caused all those who drank the water to have a flux of the stomach, which tormented them wondrously and caused them

[24] The word translated here as outflow is *égoûts* which means sewers, but that word would not fit the context. Here Palissy seems to use the word in its literal sense, "to flow drop by drop out of."

[25] John Sleidan is the author of memoirs in Latin entitled *De statu religionis et reipublicae Carolo Quinto Caesare Commentarii*. A French translation was published at Geneva in 1561 with the title *Histoire entière déduite depuis le déluge jusqu'au temps présent* and consists of 29 "books" or chapters.

[26] The men sent down into the well were probably killed by carbon monoxide or other noxious gases accumulated at the bottom of the well. Palissy gives no reason for their death but realizes that the well was "poisoned."

to run after the doctor who, rejoicing over the effect of this medicine, boldly comforted the sick, and feigning to give them very expensive medicine, he gave them good wine to drink, forbidding them to drink water, and by this means, the malice of the water passed away, and the nourishment of the wine remained, and the doctor earned much. There are also wells near rivers, in which the water comes only from the nearby river: [27] and that is all the more certain since when the rivers are high there is much water in these wells, and when the rivers are low so is the water in these wells: and this shows us that there are certain veins which go from the wells to the rivers, by which the waters come to these wells. Some of those who have worked at the congelation of salt, which is done in Lorraine, have assured me that the water, from (9) which they make the salt, is caught in wells: and when the rivers are high, fresh water enters these wells, which causes them to stop until the rivers have returned to their beds. From which I conclude that some wells are fed by the waters of nearby rivers.

Theory

Since we are talking about waters, what do you think of the waters of ponds which people in many countries are forced to use, both for their own use and that of their animals?

Practice

There are many kinds of ponds: many call them claunes: [28] in some places these are only a shallow trench, dug on a slope, so that the rain water flows into the trench or pool, and oxen, cows and other cattle may easily enter or leave to drink in it, and these are dug only on the hanging [29] side. In truth, such waters cannot be good either for men or beasts. For they are warmed by the air and the sun and by this means generate and produce many kinds of animals. And since a great quantity of

[27] This statement on the recharge of wells is correct and may constitute another first for Palissy. The statement could not be any clearer and it is in full agreement with what is known of wells at present; most large yielding wells are fed from rivers.

[28] *Claune* or *clône:* a colloquial term used in Saintonge for a small body of water or a pond.

[29] Palissy's meaning here is not quite clear. From the context it would seem that he means that these trenches are dug only at or near the base of a slope.

frogs, serpents, asps [30] and vipers always gather around these claunes in order to feed on the frogs. There are often also leeches in them (10) so that if the oxen and cows remain some time within these pools, they cannot avoid being bitten by the leeches. I have many times seen aspics and serpents, lying curled up at the bottom of these ponds: therefore I say that these waters, thus aerated and heated cannot be good; and very often oxen, cows and other cattle die from sickness caught in drinking places so infected. If those who will look at the teachings which I shall give below would believe me, they would always have pure and clean watcr both for themselves and for their animals.

Theory

What do you say about the pools which are lower,[31] which are used in many parts of Normandy and other regions, for domestic use?

Practice

What can I say except that it is stagnant water? but since it is cooler it can produce no animal, since there is never produced any generation, either animal or vegetable, without heated humor. But if, on top of these waters, there is only green slime, it is the sign of putrefaction and the beginning of the generation of something: and the more putrefaction appears to be generated in them, the more their use is pernicious. (11)

Theory

Tell me, what think you of the cisterns which our ancestors have used, as we see so well, either by their vestiges or by the testimony of Scripture.

Practice

The waters of cisterns come from the rain, like those of claunes: but since they are enclosed, shut, well masoned, and paved underneath, they are undoubtedly better than the waters of pools: for they can produce nothing because of their coldness

[30] "Serpents, asps and vipers" seems unduly repetitive since they all imply venomous snakes but each name may have had special meaning to Palissy and his contemporaries.

[31] Apparently "lower" as compared with *claunes* which are dug on slopes.

and the little air that they have: however, all these waters are not naturally good, like those which I intend to show you later. I shall therefore refrain from talking now of putrid waters, and shall talk of those of natural springs, which we now use.

Theory

And what would you say of natural springs? Since they are natural you could not find fault with them, as you have with pools and pumps and wells: if you should dare to speak against natural springs you would speak against God, who made them.

Practice

You correct me before I have spoken; I well know that the sources of natural springs are (12) made by the hand of God: therefore I could not find fault with them, for the errors are made in conducting the waters from their natural sources: but still the fountain-makers who bring springs through pipes, canals, and aqueducts from the source to houses, cities, and castles can commit great errors. That is what I intend to talk about and since man's life is so short that it is impossible for a man to know the properties of waters in so few years, and not knowing them, it is impossible to carry and bring them a long way, without making some mistake, and if it is brought two or three leagues away, enclosed and shut in by pipes, it will last for a very short time, and it will need constant attention. That is why I want to tell you emphatically that water and fire joined with air have such an irresistible and vehement effect that never has man known it directly, as you will understand when I shall speak of earthquakes: and if you wish to consider a little the vestiges and antiquities of our ancestors, you will find many ancient pyramids, built either by the Roman emperors or the kings of Egypt; you will also find many triumphal arches built in the time of the Caesars, as you have seen in the city of Xaintes,[32] two triumphal arches which, although their foundations are in water, nevertheless still stand, (13) and it cannot be denied that they are of the time of the Caesars, the writings on them prove it. I have put this thought before you to show you that although our ancestors also spent much on aqueducts, pipes, and the adornment of fountains, still you could not show me a single ancient fountain, like the buildings of triumphal arches, palaces, and amphi-

[32] Ancient spelling of Saintes; likewise Xaintonge for Saintonge.

theaters: and one must not think nevertheless that our ancient predecessors did not study and work at great expense on fountains as well as on other buildings, and nevertheless someone has assured me having seen in Italy aqueducts of 50 leagues in length (an incredible thing, still) which were built to bring water from one place to another. Our ancestors show thereby that they knew well that waters carried by aqueducts flowed more freely than those carried enclosed in pipes. It is certain that at Xaintes (which is an ancient city, where are still found the vestiges of an amphitheater, and many antiquities, likewise great quantities of the coins of the Emperors) there was an aqueduct, whose vestiges still exist, by which they brought water two long leagues from the city, even though it has fallen into ruins so that now there are very few men who know of this aqueduct. (14) That is why I have said that although the ancients built better than the moderns, that they cared less about expense, still we find no ancient fountains. I don't say, however, that the springs are lost: for it is well known that the ancient spring of the city of Xaintes is still in the spot whence it comes: in order to see it, chancellor de l'Hôpital turned aside (returning from his Bayonne voyage) to see the excellence of this spring. There are still, in certain valleys between the city and the spring, a few arches over which the waters of this spring were made to pass: however, the reason for these arches is unknown to the common people. And if you want to know why I set before you these arches in the valleys, it is to show you the ignorance of the moderns. For if the ancients had brought the pipes for their fountains underground they would have had to go up and down and then up again as many times as there are mountains and valleys, and to arrange the pipes according to all these variations; and as I have told you many times, water that is thus enclosed, together with the subtle gases mixed with it, causes such a strain that no man has ever understood perfectly the violence of these waters. It is one of the wonders of confined waters; few are the men who are willing to believe (15) that water which fills and occupies a pipe two inches in diameter, when it is violently pushed by winds or other water, will contract in such a way as to pass through a duct an inch in diameter: and since the air which is enclosed in these pipes or ducts occupies as much space as the water, the fountain-makers are often unsuccessful in their undertakings likewise with pipes buried underground: for sometimes these pipes are occupied by roots which originate and grow within them, having some root ends between the joints: others are occupied and blocked by congelative waters that lapify inside these pipes. That is why the ancients made open-air aqueducts at great expense, in order to carry the water without violence, and avoid all these accidents. However, I am certain that when the waters congeal, into crystals or otherwise, they are forced to shrink in their congelation, and no congelation takes place without compression. The same thing is found in the violence of fire, which, being enclosed in the mountains, generates an aqueous vapor and a wind so impetuous that it causes the earth to quake and the mountains to tumble, and very often also cities and villages; that is the reason why the ancients carried their springs by means of aqueducts, and to give proper slope to their waters they made (16) arches in the valleys, to conform to the mountains. I ask for no better witness than the Pont du Gua [33] which is in Languedoc, and was made expressly to carry the aqueduct that crossed the valley between two mountains: in order to bring water from ten leagues away from the city of Nîmes: and this to avoid the compressions and violences that the waters would have generated if they had been made to follow the mountains and valleys. This bridge is an admirable structure; for to reach from the base of the mountains to their summit, it was necessary to build three rows of arches one on top of the other, and these arches are of extraordinary height, and built of stones of marvelous size. From this we can conclude that Nîmes (an ancient city, of which evidence is found both in the amphitheater and other vestiges) was a city on which the ancient Roman Emperors and their proconsuls had spent much and lavishly, to embellish it and enrich it, and had employed there men of science, the best in the Roman Empire, as the work still demonstrates. If you had been to Rome you could easily judge how far the moderns are behind our predecessors in the matter of fountains, for there are few good houses in Rome in which there are no fountains coming from the aqueducts built (17) high in the air, and to prove this, look a while at the picture [34] of this city of Rome lately printed; you will see high in the air a water reservoir of a rather impressive

[33] The Pont-du-Gard, which still stands.
[34] The word translated here as picture is *pourtraict* (portrait in modern French) in the original. In Palissy's usage, this may mean a portrait, picture, or plan.

size, which contains such a large quantity of water that it supplies the greater part of Rome, for this reservoir has several aqueducts, divided into branches, going along from street to street, to supply the palaces and great houses of the city, and these aqueducts are carried along certain arches rather close to each other yet as high as the houses of the city. And you must note that there is a great main aqueduct coming from very far away that supplies the great reservoir from which all the other aqueducts lead away. Now, if the fountains of the ancient fountain-makers, built at such great cost, could not last until now, how much less duration can we expect of those which modern fountain-makers cause to pass by hill and dale with soldered lead pipes hidden 3 or 4 feet underground: if the Queen's architect, who had traveled in Italy, and had won authority and command over all the artisans of this Lady, had had even a little plain natural philosophy, without any letters,[35] he would have built some sort of wall or arcade in the valley of St-Cloud, and thence brought in the waters easily from the bridge of St-Cloud to the walls of the park, (18) and then reinforced this wall around the park in order to carry the water over it, and at the angle and corner of this park made certain arches, diminishing little by little to the inside; then the fountain could have lasted and would not have needed so much attention.

Theory

Since you find so many faults in the waters of ponds, wells, and ducts or pipes of fountains, I now want to make a request of you, namely, why is it that the sources of certain natural fountains are better than others?

Practice

A man who is familiar with mines, ditches and trenches, and who has examined the diverse kinds of clay soils, and who has wished to know the various kinds of salts and other fossil things, can easily judge the cause of the goodness or badness of waters coming from their natural sources. And to give sure judgment of them, we must first consider that there is no part of the earth that is not full of some kind of salt, that causes the generation of many things, either stone, slate, or some kind of metal or mineral; and it is certain that the internal parts of the earth are no less

[35] In the sense of knowledge of literature.

active than the external ones, which daily produce trees, bushes, brambles, thorns, and all sorts of plants. It must therefore be concluded that it is impossible for the flow of (19) fountains to pass through the veins of the earth without carrying along some kind of salt, which, when dissolved in the water, is unknown to and outside the judgment of men: and if the salt is poisonous, it will render the water poisonous: like those that pass through copper mines; they bring with them a salt of vitriol or copperas which is very harmful. Those that pass through aluminous or salpetrous veins can bring nothing but the salsitive substance through which they pass; and if a spring goes through rotten wood or trunks within the earth, it cannot be bad, for the salt of rotten wood is not poisonous, like that of copperas. I do not say that there may not be some tree, and therefore some plants, whose salt could be poisonous: and we must not think that all drinkable waters are free of poison: but a little poison in a large quantity of water has no power to activate its evil nature: just as the waters that pass through veins containing common salt cannot be bad. Those that pass through the channels of rocks can bring nothing else but the kind of salt that has caused the congelation of these rocks: and this salt is present in the calcination extracted from the rocks; and when such stones are calcined one finds by taste of tongue the bite and sharpness of this salt, which, when it is in the water, can just as easily congeal (20) stones in a man's body as it does in the ground, except for the reason which I have given above, that the great quantity of water counteracts the power of a little poison. It is certain that some fountains give the fever to those who drink from them. Never have I seen a stranger come to the Bigorre region to live than soon after he contracted fever. One sees in this region a great number of men and women whose throat is as large as two fists: and it is certain that the waters give them this sickness, either because of the coldness of the waters or the minerals through which they have passed.[36] Pliny tells, in the thirtieth book of his Natural History, chapter 16, that there is a fountain in Arcadia whose waters are so harmful that it dissolves all vessels in which it is placed: and no vessel can be found which can hold it. Concerning this, I shall tell what Plutarch writes

---

[36] Palissy missed the cause of goitre, as well he might, because of the ignorance prevalent at the time concerning the medicinal properties of iodine. Nevertheless, he laid the blame on the water, not on some occult cause.

about it in the life of Alexander the Great, namely that some have thought that Aristotle had shown Antipater how to collect this water, namely in the hoof of a donkey and that in this way Alexander was poisoned. It is quite certain that just as there are various kinds of salts in the earth, there are also various oils, for example oil of petroleum, which issues from the rocks: and one must believe that bitumen is nothing more than oil before it is congealed. And just as subterranean waters bring with them some (21) kinds of salts through which they pass, similarly if they encounter oils they will carry them along and in drinking such waters we often drink oil and salt. Have you not read some historians who say there is a river and a few fountains from which issue large quantities of bitumen, which is gathered up by the inhabitants of the country, who make great trade of it, carrying it to foreign countries? And as proof and evidence of what I have said, that oils and salts can render waters harmful and noxious, those who have written about fountains and rivers give testimony that such waters are noxious, and that even birds die from their odor. The springs that pass through mines of clayey earth cannot but carry some harmful saltiness: the more so since there are few clayey earths that do not contain some sulphurous marcasites and beginnings of metals: also that there are few clayey earths that are not of diverse colors, such as white, red, yellow, black or gray, mixed with the above colors which are caused by the sulphurous minerals that are in them as we know in truth that iron, lead, silver, antimony, and several other minerals have in them a yellow dye, whose color yellow earths have assumed. Here then is incontrovertible evidence that (22) the waters that pass through clayey earths bring with them salts similar to those contained in these earths: which earths could never harden, bake, collect, nor be fixed were it not for the virtue of the salt that is in these earths, and by means of this salt they are very good for making bricks, tiles, and all kinds of vessels for the use of man, as I shall explain more clearly when speaking of clayey earths and stones: and shall finish with the goodness or harmfulness of waters, if what I have said about them has satisfied you.

Theory

I am more than satisfied with what you have said to me about them: however, until now, I have heard nothing from you about the cause of hot waters which are in many countries, and even in France, at Cauterets, Bavières,[37] and in many other places.

Practice

I can assert that nothing more can cause the hotness of waters, than the four materials named above, that is sulphur, coal, clods of earth, and bitumen: but none of these substances can heat the waters unless first fire is ignited within one of these four substances. You will say, who is it who has lighted a fire underground to burn these things. To this I answer that it needs (23) only for a stone to fall or lean against another to produce certain sparks, which will be sufficient to light some sulphurous vein: and thence the fire will be able to follow one of these four substances in such a way that the fire will never go out, as long as there is material to nourish it: and when one of these four is lighted, the waters, enclosed in the rocks, descending continually from level to level, until they reach these burning materials, cannot pass without being heated, and this cannot be done without producing a marvelous conflict between fire and water: And whatever the philosophers may have said concerning earthquakes, I shall never admit that an earthquake can be produced without fire: I shall concede them that waters alone with the enclosed winds in them, can damage castles, cities, and mountains, as much by the action of the wind, enclosed in caverns, as by the compression of overflowing waters, which by their subtlety and vehemence can push, demolish and ruin the above: and this by carrying away the earth on which these things are built, and when they have dug away under the foundations, these things can fall into this abyss, without any aid from igneous action. But earthquakes cannot be produced unless there be (24) first fire, water and air joined together. Some historians say that in certain countries there are earthquakes, which have lasted for two years (an easy thing to believe) and this can be produced by no other means than that which I have stated above. Before the earth quakes, great quantities of one of these materials must be lighted and while burning it must have found in its way some reservoirs of water in the rocks, and the fire must be so great as to be able to cause the waters enclosed in the rocks to boil, and then, by the fire, the waters, and the enclosed air, there will be generated a vapor which by its power

[37] This does not mean Bavaria but appears to be a misspelling of Bagnères, in France, as noted in the 1880 edition.

will lift up the rocks, lands, and houses, above it. And if the violence of the fire, the water and the air cannot throw aside so great a mass, it will cause it to quake, and in the quaking some subtle openings will be formed which will give a little air to the fire, water and winds, and by such means the violence is pacified which otherwise would have upset everything; if the three substances that cause the quaking did not take in a little air in producing their action, there is never so powerful a mountain but would be quickly thrown down, as has happened in many places, where many mountains have been transformed into valleys, by earthquakes, and many valleys into mountains by the same (25) action. And when these earthquakes have thrown down cities, castles and mountains, it is then that these three substances, in their great struggle, could get no air. Now it must necessarily be, either that the things which were above these three elements should prevail and choke out the elements, or that the elements joined together in their superb grandeur should vanquish, giving themselves an opening in order to live.[38] Do you want me to tell you in what book of the Philosophers I have learned these fine secrets? It was only a kettle half full of water, which in boiling, when the water was a little hard pressed by the heat in the bottom of the kettle, it rose up over the brim of this cauldron: and this could not be done unless some gas was generated in the water by the virtue of the fire since the kettle was only half full of water when it was cold and full when it was hot. The kilns in which I bake my work have taught me much concerning the violence of fire: but among the other things which have made me know the strength of the elements, which generate earthquakes, I have observed a brass ball with only a small hole in it; when it is heated over coals, it will exhale a very strong wind which will cause wood to burn on the fire even if it was cut on the same day. (26)

Theory

Now you are trapped by your own words: for you have just said that waters and air, pushed and roiled up by fire, which is their opposite, could not subsist together, which caused earth-

---

[38] This account of the cause of earthquakes is similar to others current in Palissy's time and before it. If Palissy is to be accused of having read more books than he admits, then this passage would "convict" him of having read Galesius, *de Terraemotu Liber*, Bologna, 1571, discussed by Adams (1938, p. 405 ff.) rather than von Megenberg's *Buch der Natur*, quoted by Adams (1938, p. 404), but in this writer's opinion such evidence is extremely tenuous.

quakes, and the downfall of cities and castles, as would many casks of lighted gunpowder. And now I prove the contrary by picking up your words. For you say that hot waters (from which are made the baths, either at Aigues-caudes, Cauterets, Bavières, or at Aix in Germany, Savoy and Provence and elsewhere) are heated up by fire which continually burns underground, or by sulphur, coal and clods of earth, or by bitumen. And yet I know nevertheless that these hot springs have lasted a long time and still exist in the same state, so long a time, in fact, that memory of it has been lost. And if it were as you say, would not the fire, air, and water long since have mixed and cut up and blown away to right and left the channels and vaults through which these waters pass or at least have generated (according to you) a continual earthquake?

Practice

You have very badly misunderstood me: when I told you about earthquakes, I said that in trembling by the force of the three elements (27) enclosed below, that many subtle openings were made through which came out a part of the force and breath of the vapor of these elements, and that otherwise, these elements would turn upside down all the vaults over the channels where the movement happens, and since you have told me that this should happen inside the vaults, through which the waters of the baths are heated up, by the same effect as those which cause earthquakes, to this I answer that the cause, why the earth cannot be weakened nor shaken by these fires is because there is a duct through which the waters pass and come out, which appeases the violence of these elements. For they breathe and take in through the duct through which the water comes out. And just as a man could not live with his neck tightened and the air enclosed in his body, so fire could not live without air. And just as a man or an animal whose breathing openings were stopped up would struggle hard to escape, so fire, finding itself filled with too much air, which it has itself caused, fleeing from humidity, finding itself oppressed, and not wishing to die, then it overturns mountains, to draw breath, trying to live. And this conclusion is so certain that no Philosopher was able to impugn it with legitimate reasons, so I shall reserve the rest until we talk about Alchemy. (28)

Theory

Since we are talking about hot waters, tell me why so many people go to bathe in these waters, in France as well as in Germany. Do you think they can serve to cure all sicknesses? If you have some knowledge of it, pray tell me about it.

Practice

All that I know about these things is that just as fish, pork and other meats are fortified and hardened by the action of salt, it may be that the salts that are mixed with the hot waters could harden some loose putrefied humors in the body of those who bathe: but to assure you that they cure all ills, I am very far from such an opinion. I have lived some years at Tarbes, the main city of Bigorre, and I have seen many sick people go to the baths who came back just as sick as they were before. On the other hand, if the fire this year is in a place where there is some kind of mineral, and it should have the power to cure some sickness, possibly next year the fire will find another mineral, whose salt will not be able to do the same thing as the first. That is why I say that things are uncertain, since the waters come from unknown places. (29)

Theory

What of the waters of Spa in the Liège region, do you mean to say that its cure is uncertain? Do not sick people suffering from various diseases go every day to stay there some time, to drink this water, and feel better for it? Even barren women go there, in order to conceive.

Practice

Your request is not to the point: for the waters of Spa are not hot: however, in order to reply to your question, I tell you that if the waters of Spa could cause a woman to conceive, they would make fine miracles. I know well that many have gone there to drink of this water, who would have done better to drink wine. I do not say that this water is not useful for gravel: [39] because many have felt better for it: and the reason for that is that it moves one to urinate: and not staying long in the usual parts, the matters that cause the stone do not have time to assemble in order to harden and lapify. Some doctors and others firmly believe that these waters pass through iron mines, and draw this argument from the fact that the mouth of the spring is dyed yellow. The argument is well founded, as you will understand by the proofs which I will give you later. There are in many villages of the Liège region fountains that (30) have the same virtue: but the

[39] That is, for the disease of that name.

inhabitants of Spa have publicized theirs first: from which they draw great profit. If it is true that the iron mine has such powers, there will be found in the Ardennes region numerous fountains as good as these: for the earth of the country is full of iron mines, the yellow clay earths there are a witness of it.

Theory

You have lately given me to understand that if the baths of Bavière, Cauterets, Argelais and Aix have some power to heal sicknesses, that this was done by virtue of the salts, and now you say that the iron mine causes the power of the Spa water.

Practice

When you have thoroughly understood all my discourse, you will understand that iron is generated by nothing else but salt. But because this topic will be more in its place in proving that there is salt in everything, I will keep it until then.

Theory

If that is so, we should not eat fresh butter. I never saw anyone so insistent on these salts. But do you think you will make me believe that there is salt underground and that the waters can bring it up to cause the effects of medicine?

Practice

You are scarcely wise to make such a request; have you not heard those who come from Poland say that (31) the salt mine is wondrously deep in the earth? have you not heard also that there are salt wells in Lorraine? It seems to me I said so above. Do we not know that in Béarn there are salt springs, from which is made the salt that supplies this region and Bigorre? This is not yet enough: for even if there were no common salt in the earths and ducts where fire is burning, through which the hot waters pass, there will be some of many other kinds: for if the fire that is burning in subterranean parts encounters marble or some other kind of rock whose humor is not fixed, the fire will calcine them, and being reduced to lime, the waters that pass through this lime will dissolve the salt that was in the marble and other imperfect rocks. I call imperfect rocks those that are subject to be calcined. The perfect ones are never calcined; some of them are vitrified. Thus if the fire that is kindled and that has caused the warmth of the water has attacked clods of earth that are full of little roots,[40] which makes them burn, the clods and roots having burned, will leave behind the salt that is in them, and having left it in the ashes, and the waters passing through them, will not fail to carry away the salt dissolved in them: the same will happen to the ashes of sulphur and of coal. And even if the waters cannot be salted by the means I have said (which cannot be otherwise) (32) still they would be salted by the salt that drips continually with the waters that pass through the earth to get to the place where these fires are burning. It must therefore be concluded that in these hot waters there may be many and diverse kinds of salts at the same time: common salt, salt of vitriol, of alum, and of copperas, and of all kinds of minerals. And besides these there may be many kinds of salts that will be mixed with sand or pebbles, so that the violence of fire will force them to vitrify just as this happened by accident to those who first invented glass. Some say that the children of Israel, having set fire to some woods, the fire was so great that it heated niter with the sand until it flowed and distilled among the mountains, and that henceforth they searched for a way of making artificially that which had happened accidentally, to make glass. Others say that the idea originated on the sea shore, where some pirates had landed and wishing to boil water and having no andirons or *landiers* [41] they took stones of niter, on which they put great logs and much wood, which caused such a large fire that these stones came to liquefy, and when liquid, flowed on the sand, which caused this sand, when mixed with the niter, to be vitrified like the niter, the whole making a diaphanous and vitreous substance. (33) Therefore I tell you that whoever could see the place where the fires burn under the lands and mountains would find many vitrified substances of various colors. Also molten gold and silver and other metals and minerals; for just as I have said before, that the outside of the earth is full of various plants, so the interior exerts itself daily to produce various things. And because I have said above that the fires enclosed below ground cannot produce earthquakes, except when they can draw breath, and the air is confined. As evidence of this

[40] Palissy here may mean peat.
[41] Cotgrave translates the word as andiron but there is a difference between *chenêt* (andiron) and *landiers*. Bescherelle describes the latter as a large andiron with an upright to which rings are attached on which kitchen utensils may be hung.

I have been told by trustworthy people, that in places where there are sulphurous earths one sees a great many small holes in the ground, through which come flames proceeding from the sulphur which is burning underground and they say that these holes are no larger than worm holes and around the mouth of these holes one finds sulphur which the flames have raised from underground, and these fires appear only at night. You can learn from this that the fires, breathing through these holes, burn without any violence or quaking of the ground. The same is true of the fire that warms the baths; because it breathes through the ducts of these waters. Until now I have endeavored to show you the cause of the goodness (34) or harmfulness of waters either of natural springs, or of wells, ponds and other reservoirs, and all this in order that you might understand better the goodness of the waters of fountains, which I want to teach you to make in places quite barren of water. I shall therefore lay aside all other topics to come to the cause of natural springs: All the more so because it is impossible to imitate Nature in anything whatsoever, without first studying their effects, taking Nature as a pattern and example for nothing in this world is perfect save the works of the Lord. Following the examples of this beautiful formulary which he has left us, we shall manage to imitate them.

When I had long and closely examined the source of the springs of natural fountains, and the place whence they could come, I finally understood that they could not come from or be produced by anything but rains. That is what has moved me to undertake to collect the rain, in imitation of and nearest to nature, as possible, and following the formulary of the Sovereign fountain-maker, I am quite sure that I shall be able to make fountains whose waters will be as good, pure and clean as those of natural ones.

Theory

After hearing your argument, I am forced (35) to say that you are a great dolt. Do you think I am so ignorant as to believe more what you say than many philosophers who say that all waters come from the sea and return to it? Even old wives say the same thing, and we have always so believed. It is very presumptuous of you to want us to believe an entirely new doctrine, as if you were the ablest of philosophers.

Practice

If I were not so sure of my opinion you would shame me greatly: but I am surprised neither by your insults nor by your fine language: for I am quite certain I shall win out against you and all those who are of your opinion, even Aristotle and all the most excellent philosophers of all time: for I am quite sure that my opinion is correct.

Theory

Let us come to the proof: give me some reasons which will show me that there is some semblance of truth in your opinion.

Practice

My reason is this, that God has set the limits of the sea, which it shall not exceed: as it is written by the prophets. We see by the effects that this is true for although the sea (36) in many places is higher than the land, still it maintains some height in the middle, but at the extremities it maintains a mean by God's command-ment, so that it should not submerge the land. We have good evidence of this, and among the works of God this one is very marvelous, for if you had studied the terrible effects of the sea you would say that it seems to come twice every twenty-four hours to give battle to the land, to vanquish and submerge it. And its coming resembles that of a great army which would come against the land to battle with it: and the point, like the point of a battle, hurls itself impetuously against the cliffs and limits of the land, making such a furious noise, that it seems to want to destroy everything. And because there are certain inlets near the edge of the sea in the neighboring lands, people have built mills on these inlets in which there are many gates to allow the water to enter when the tide comes in: so that in coming in it should cause these mills to grind and when it tries to enter the inlet, it finds the gates shut and finding no better servant than itself, it opens the gate and causes the mill to grind in return for its wel-come. And when it wishes to go back, like a good servant it closes the gate of the inlet, to leave it full of water, which water (37) is then led through a spillway so as to cause the mill to grind continuously. And if it were as you say, according to the opinion of the philosophers, that the springs of fountains should come from the sea, it would follow that their waters would be salty, like those of the sea, and moreover that the sea should be higher than the highest mountains, which is not true.

Thus, just as the water which has entered the inlets and caused the mills to grind, and which brings ships into many and diverse channels, to load salt, wood and other things near the sea, is bound to follow the great army of the sea which has come to fight with the land. In this case, I say that the fountains, rivers and brooks should return with it: and also they should be dry while the sea is away, just as the inlets are filled by the coming of the sea and go dry in its absence: Now see if your fine philosophers have some valid reason to overcome mine. It is certain that when it has gone [i.e., at low tide] the sea in many places lays bare more than two whole leagues of sand where one can walk dry shod. And one must believe that when it goes away the fishes flee with it. There are certain shell-bearing fish, such as mussels, cockles, scallops, hard-shell clams,[42] oysters and many kinds of snails [43] that (38) have the form of slugs,[44] which deign not to follow the sea, but trusting in their armor, those with a single shell cling to the rocks and the others with two remain on the sand. Some kinds of these, which have the form of a knife handle about half a foot long,[45] hide quite far down in the sand, and then the fishermen go fetch them. It is a marvelous thing that the oysters, when they are brought ten or twelve leagues from the sea, feel the hour when it returns and comes near the places where they used to live, and open up of their own accord, to receive food from the sea as if they were still in it. And because they still have this instinct, the crab, well knowing that they will open their doors when the sea returns to its limits, stays near their dwellings, and when the oyster has both shells open, this crab, to fool the oyster, takes a little stone which it places between the two shells, so that they may not close, and this done, he is able to feed on the oysters.

[42] The original is *availlons*, a colloquial term for *Venus borealis* according to Bescherelle. Clam is too general a term to apply here, so I have borrowed a term used in North America for *Venus mercenaria*, a distant relative of *V. borealis*. In both of these, the shell is thicker than in other kinds of clams.

[43] The original has *burgaus*, a name applied to many kinds of gastropods or snails.

[44] That is, whose animal is like a slug. This interpretation assumes that Palissy distinguished between *limace*, a slug, and *limaçon*, a snail; however, this is not at all certain. If he did not make the distinction, perhaps he simply meant that *burgaus* (sea snails) were like *limaces* (land snails).

[45] By Palissy's description, razor clams.

But mice have not learned why oysters have two shells: for it has happened in many places far from the sea, that when the oysters felt the hour of the tide, as I have said above, the mice, finding them open, wished to eat them, and the oyster, (39) feeling the pain of the bite, closed and tightened its two shells: and thus many mice have been caught: for they had not put stones between the two shells, like the crab. As for the large fishes, the fishermen of the islands of Xaintonge have invented a fine thing to fool them; for they have planted in certain places in the sea many large and stout poles, and on them have placed pulleys to which they attach cords from their nets and when the sea has gone out, they allow their nets to fall on the sand, but leave both ends of the ropes tied to the pulleys. And when the sea returns, the fishes come with it, and seek food here and there, without heeding the nets on the sand, because they swim above them: and when the fishermen see that the sea is ready to leave, they raise their nets as high as the level of the water, and having tied them to the poles, the bottom of these nets is held down by many stones, by lead, which keeps them straight to the bottom. The mariners, having stretched and raised their nets in this way, wait until the sea has gone, and as the sea leaves the fishes try to follow it, as they are used to doing: but they are unable to do so because the nets stop them and in this way they are caught by the fishermen when the sea is out. (40)

And in order not to leave our topic I shall give you another example. It is certain that the sea is just as high in summer as in winter, and if I should say more, I should not lie: for the highest tides are in the full moon of March and of July: at which time they cover more land in the maritime regions of the Xaintonge islands than in any other season. If the springs of fountains came from the sea, how could they dry out in summer? since the sea is no lower than in winter; take this into account and you will learn that if the sea gave milk from its breasts to the fountains of the universe, they could never go dry in July, August and September, at which time an infinite number of wells dry up. I must argue further with you and your Latin philosophers: because you find nothing good unless it comes from the Latins. I give you as a general and certain rule that waters never rise higher than the springs whence they come. Don't you know that there are more fountains in the mountains than in the valleys: and even if the sea were as high as the highest mountain, still it would be impossible for mountain springs to come from the sea: the reason is, that to bring water from a high place to make it climb to another (41) just as high, the pipe through which the water flows must necessarily be well enclosed, so that nothing leaks through it: otherwise the water, having come down into the valley, would never go up again to high places: but would come out at the first hole it would find. Now, then, I wish to conclude that even if the sea were as high as the mountains, its waters could not get to the heights of the mountains whence springs originate. For the land in many places is full of holes, cracks and abysses, through which the water coming from the sea would come out on the plain, through the first holes, springs, or abysses it would find, and before it should climb to the tops of the mountains, all the plains would be drowned and covered with water: and even if the land were not pierced, the continual fires, which come out of the depths, bring with them sulphurous vapors, which are evidence of the fire, and it would take but a single hole, or a single crack, to submerge all the plains. Now fetch your Latin philosophers to give me a contrary argument that would be as easy to grasp as the one I put forward.[46]

Theory

You say that if the waters of fountains came from the sea, that their waters would be salt, like those of the sea, and yet it is general and common opinion that waters are desalted in passing (42) through the veins of the earth.

Practice

Those who hold such an opinion know nothing about the matter: because it should rather be believed that the salt of the sea comes from the land, being carried by the rivers that empty into it, than by the impetuous waves that strike violently against salty rocks and lands. For it must be noted that in many countries there are salty cliffs. Some author has written that there is a country where the houses are made with blocks of salt: considering which, you must find better arguments to make me believe that the waters of fountains and rivers come from the sea.

[46] Palissy's indignant insistence on his denial that waters flow from the sea to the mountains seems overdone to the present-day reader. There was good reason to drive home the point in the late sixteenth century, as one may understand after reading Adams' account of the subject (1938, pp. 426–60, especially pp. 426–45).

Theory

And I pray you, do make me understand your opinion clearly, and whence you believe that they come, if not from the sea.

Practice

You must firmly believe that all the waters that are, will be, and have been, have been created right at the beginning of the world: and God not wishing to leave anything in idleness, commands them to come and go and produce; which they do without rest, as I have said that the sea does not cease to come and go. Likewise, rain water that falls in the winter goes up in summer, to come again in winter, and the waters and the action of the sun and dry winds, striking the land, cause great (43) quantities of water to rise: which, being gathered in the air and formed into clouds, have gone in all directions like heralds sent by God. And when the winds push these vapors the waters fall on all parts of the land, and when it pleases God that these clouds (which are nothing more than a mass of water) should dissolve, these vapors are turned into rain that falls on the ground.[47]

Theory

Truly I know now that you are a great liar, and if the waters of the sea were raised into the air and fell later on the ground, they would be salt waters. You are therefore trapped by your own words.

Practice

Your theory on this is very bad: do you believe that you have caught me unawares on this point? You are far from correct. If you had studied the method of making common salt, you would not have advanced such an argument, and if it were as you say, salt could never be made. But you must understand that the salt-makers put sea water in their pans, to cause it to congeal by the heat of the sun and wind, which raises up the fresh water, which is mixed in with the salt water. And when the fresh water is taken out, the salt water begins to cream and to congeal. That is how I prove that (44) the clouds raised up from sea water are not salty. For if the sun and wind took the salt water out of the

[47] An excellent statement of the hydrologic cycle. Except for the archaic language, it expresses the views held at present.

sea they could also take out the one from which salt is made, and thus it would be impossible to make salt. Now your arguments are refuted.

Theory

And what then will become of the theory of so many philosophers who say that fountains, streams or rivers are generated by a thick air, which comes out from under mountains, from certain caverns that are in these mountains, and say that this air begins to thicken, and some time later dissolves and becomes water, which is the source of fountains and rivers?

Practice

Do you fully understand what you are saying? That it is an air that thickens against the vaults of caverns, cliffs, and that it finally dissolves into water? Suppose that is so: still it seems to me that this way of speaking is not correct. You say that it is a thickened air, and then that it dissolves into water: then it was water just like that which I say is raised, which we call clouds, the which, coming near the ground, darken the air by a compression which they cause, and cause this air to be so much moved by compression of the waters gathered in the form of clouds. And be that as it may, watch when these (45) clouds are dissolved and turned into rain, you will see that the winds are nothing more than a compression of the air, produced by the fall of waters: since when the waters have fallen, the winds are suddenly appeased, hence the proverb, small rain quiets great wind. Thus, then, the rain had caused these winds, which, being appeased by the falling of the rain, thereafter the air, which was darkened, begins to get lighter. This will show you that I do not deny that the waters enclosed in caverns and chasms of mountains can be exhaled against the rocks and vaults that are under these chasms: but I deny that this is the sole cause of springs and fountains, far from it: for if you will consider that since the creation of the world, fountains, rivers, and brooks have been flowing continuously from these mountains, you will understand that it is impossible for these caverns to furnish enough water for a year, nay for a month, so many rivers flow daily. We must therefore conclude that the waters that flow from these caverns come neither from the sea nor from the chasms: for I am sure that from these rocky depths there flows a marvelous quantity of water: and in many mountains we see it coming forth as a great thick smoke, which in rising darkens the air as it dilates in it on all sides, (46) and when the vapor dissolves it is nothing more than rain. I have often seen such thick vapors issuing forth in the Ardennes region, and those who saw them with me would say that shortly it would rain, being very sure that these vapors would dissolve into water. In the Pyrenees I have many times seen such vapors issuing forth which, rising up, congealed into snow, and soon afterwards these snows covered all the ground. I do not deny, therefore, that the aqueous vapors of underground caverns may contain great quantities of water: but it must of necessity have been put and carried there by the post and messengers of God, to wit: winds, rains, storms and tempests, as it is written that they are the heralds of the justice of God. Well then, the waters of caverns have been put there by rains produced either by the waters rising from the sea, or the land, or all humid things, which in drying out the aqueous vapors are raised up to fall later. That is how the waters ceaselessly rise and fall, for as the sun and moon have in them no rest, so the waters never cease to work at generating, producing, coming and going, as God has ordered them to do.

Theory

You have lately concluded, as by a final decree, (47) that all the sources of fountains and rivers proceed from nothing but rain water, something quite different from all common opinion; I pray you give me some reason which has the semblance of truth, to make me believe that your assertion is founded on some legitimate proof.

Practice

Before coming to reasons, you must consider the cause of mountains, and consequently of valleys, and having examined these things very closely, you will understand directly the reason why in certain regions one can find no source of water, not even underground, to make wells. And when you understand these things, it will be easy for you to believe that all fountains proceed only from springs produced by rain. Let us then come to the knowledge of mountains, why it is that they are higher than the ground; there is no other reason than that of the form of man: just as man is held up in his height and size because of his bones, and without these man would be as flat as a cow terd. In the same

way, if it were not for rocks and minerals which are the bones of
the form of mountains, they would suddenly be changed into
valleys, or at least all countries would be flat and level, by the
effects of waters, which would go down with them from the lands
and mountains straight down into the valleys. Remembering such
things, (48) you will be able to know the reason why there are
many more fountains and rivers flowing from the mountains than
from the rest of the earth, which is nothing more than that cliffs
and mountains retain rain water as a bronze vessel would. And
these waters, falling on these mountains through the ground and
cracks, always descend and do not stop until they find some region
blocked by stones or rock very close-set and condensed: And then
they rest on such a bottom and having found some channel or
other opening, they flow out as fountains or brooks or rivers,
according to the size of the opening and receptacles; and since
such a spring cannot throw itself (against nature) on the mountains, it descends into the valleys. And even though the beginnings
of such springs coming from the mountains are not very large,
they receive aid from all sides, to enlarge and augment them: and
particularly from the lands and mountains to the right and left
of these springs. Here is in a few words the cause of springs and
fountains, rivers and brooks: and you need seek no other reason
but this one. If the philosophers have written that springs are
produced by thickened air issuing from the foot of mountains,
and that this air, dissolving into water caused the springs, then it
was water before that, coming from rains (49) that fell before
they rose up.

Let us come now to the reason why there are no springs in flat
country as there are in the mountains. You must understand that
if the whole earth were sandy, loose or spongy, like arable lands,
no springs would be found anywhere. For the rain waters that fall
on these lands would always go down as far as the center, and
could never stop to produce wells and fountains. The reason then
why waters are found either in springs or in wells, is none other
than that they have found a rocky bottom or one of earth or clay
which can hold water as well as the rock; and if someone seeks
water in sandy ground he will never find any unless there is underneath some clayey earth, stone or slate, or mineral, which retain
rain waters after they have passed through the ground. You may
point out that you have seen many springs flowing out of sandy
ground, even from sand itself; to which I answer, as above, that

there is under it some layer of rock, and that if the water rises higher than the sand, it also comes from higher up: And do not stick blindly to your opinion alone: for you will never find more certain reasons than that which I have given you in many places in this discourse. And if you do not wish to believe me it would be very (50) foolish of me to tell you more, so I shall finish with the cause of springs and fountains.

Theory

In truth we have been a long time on this topic and I am much disappointed: because right at the beginning you promised to show me how to make fountains in places barren of water, and wherever I wished: but up to now you have not said a word about that.

Practice

You are not very wise. Don't you believe that the careful physician, will not prescribe a medicine for a patient, if first he does not know the cause of his sickness? In the same way, before teaching you how to make fountains, should I not show you the cause of those that are made naturally? Do you not know that I promised you right from the start to teach you to make fountains in imitation of those of the sovereign fountain-maker? And how can this be done without first observing nature? That is why I have wanted to urge you to undertake such an observation. And although up till now I have talked to you much about the essence of springs, still I want you to understand that it is impossible that they should proceed from the sea, for a reason that I forgot to tell you before, which is that there is no void under the sun, and that when the sea goes out from the inlets, concavities, (51) holes or ducts, into which it entered when it was high [48] the waters have barely left these holes or inlets empty than they are filled with air, and if the water, returning from the sea should enclose and trap the air that in its absence has taken possession of these holes, the air will be an obstacle for the water unless there is some subtle vent to draw it out. And if this happens in a glass vial, large or small, how much more can you believe that this can happen more certainly in a water pipe which would go from the sea to the mountains of Auvergne? If you say that between the mountains and the sea there can be subtle vents through which the air can

[48] That is, at high tide; I have preferred to retain Palissy's phraseology here.

escape before the water, I answer that if the air passes through it so will the water: and it is certain that sea water travels so fast that even if there should be a well-enclosed pipe between the sea and the mountains, and that it should be as high as the mountains, still this water could not get to the mountains without causing the pipe to burst because of the great distance and the air enclosed with it. And as I have said before, if that could be done, the rivers, fountains and springs of the mountains would dry up when the sea has gone, which is a rule just as reliable as that which I have given above, to wit that if the fountains and rivers came from the sea their waters would be salty. I have still another curious example, (52) the last one on this topic, which is that in the country and islands of Xaintonge near the sea, there are in many boroughs and villages fresh-water wells and salt-water wells. This shows clearly that the wells whose waters are salty are fed by the waters of the sea, and that the fresh-water wells, which are near the salty ones, and also near the sea, are fed by the run-off [49] of rains which come from the parts opposite the sea. And what is more, and to be noted well, there are many little islands, near to and surrounded by sea water, even a few containing not an *arpent* [50] of dry land on which there are fresh-water wells. This gives us clearly to understand that these fresh waters come neither from springs nor from the sea: but from the run-off of rains, penetrating the ground until they find bottom, as I have already told you. Once I knew without any doubt that the waters of natural fountains were caused and produced by rains, I have thought that it was stupid for those who possess lands barren of water not to learn ways of making fountains, seeing that God sends waters on sandy lands as well as on others, and that it takes very little science to know how to catch it. If the ancients had not otherwise studied the works of God, they would have lived on the pasturage of animals, they would only have (53) taken the fruits of the fields as they came, without work: but they wisely decided to plant, sow and cultivate, to aid nature. That is why the first inventors of some good thing, to help nature, have been so honored by our predecessors, that they have thought them to

[49] The original is *esgouts* translated as outflow in another context; see footnote 24.

[50] An ancient French measure of land area, still in use in French Canada. It contained a hundred square perches, varying with the value of the perch from about an acre and a quarter to about five-sixths of an acre, according to the *Shorter Oxford English Dictionary*.

be participants of the spirit of God. Ceres, who thought of sowing and cultivating wheat, has been called a goddess; Bacchus, a good man (not a drunkard as the painters picture him) was exalted because he thought of planting and cultivating the grape: Priapus, in the same way, for having invented the division of lands so that each man should tend his own share: Neptune, for having invented navigation; and hence all inventors of useful things, have been thought to partake of the gifts of God, even if Bacchus had found wild grapes, Ceres wild wheat: But this did not suffice to feed them enjoyably, as when these things were transplanted. We know by this that God wishes us to work, to help nature, just as all transplanted things are much more enjoyable than the wild ones: and since God sends us pure and clean water, even to our doors, which costs nothing except for a place to catch it in: is it not great sloth for us, after seeing a good invention to catch the waters that God sends us, (54) to rot in our idleness, without deigning to receive such a blessing? Therefore I shall do my duty, according to the promise I gave you, protesting that if you despise it you are unworthy of ever enjoying the benefit of fountain waters, providing you have some land where you can catch the waters, as I shall explain to you.

Theory

Pray do not keep me waiting longer, but show me promptly how to go about it.

Practice

I cannot wisely instruct you before you tell me whether the place where you want to make your fountain is hilly or flat: because the thing must be planned according to the nature of the place: otherwise one would work in vain.

Theory

I have a country place near which there is a fairly steep mountain, and my house is near the foot of this mountain.

Practice

If that is so, it is easy for you to build your fountain at little cost, and I'll tell you how: there is no mountain that does not have a rock bottom, as I have told you many times. You can thus be sure that if you make certain that there is no hole or crack along the mountain, you can catch a great quantity of water, and bring it down near your house. (55) Take care, then, that there is no opening through which your water might be lost, and if there is one, close it with rocks and earth, then wall up the circumference to the right and left of the place where you wish to receive the rain water: And having thus made a wall like a roadway, all the water that will fall within your enclosure will come to the place you have prepared for it: And when this is done you will make two reservoirs, one above the other: the second will be lower than the first: so that the water of the first, being already purified, will flow into the second. And to purify these waters, they must pass through a quantity of sand, which you will have placed at the front of the first reservoir, and the stones of the first reservoir must be joined without mortar: so that the waters may pass into the second, or else make some sort of brass grid or a plate pierced with small holes; so that only water will come through, and thus, when it has passed through the sand and the first reservoir, it will be well cleaned when it flows into the second, and at the bottom of this one, because the first reservoir will be large, and open to the air like a pond, a third step lower than the other two must be made, from which will flow the waters for household use; if you wish to enrich the face of the reservoir on the side where you draw water, you can enrich it with such ornaments as you may wish, either (56) by stone carvings or otherwise; and also you can plant trees to right and left which you can arch down into an arbor or cabinet, to give beauty to your fountain.

Theory

But suppose my house were a castle, surrounded by a moat, I could not use that.

Practice

If that were the case, the water of the reservoir would have to be brought into the castle by means of pipes, just as you see in the fountains of Paris, and those of the Queen, which are led through the moat, inside certain pieces of wood, that are hollowed out for this purpose, and are covered above, and inside there is a leaden pipe through which the water of the fountains passes.

Theory

I see now that there is some semblance of truth in what you say: however, when I should have built all that you say, I should have built nothing but a cistern. I am quite sure that all those who would see my fountain would not call it otherwise.

Practice

How can you know the truth and weight of my words, if you do not remember what I have said before, about the cause of natural springs? It is quite certain that if you remember only a part of all I have told you, you will understand nothing. (57) But anyone who hears the fine examples and the particular proofs that I have already given you, will always admit that the fountain that I want to teach you how to make cannot be called a cistern: but with good reason it will be called a natural fountain; since the water that will flow from it comes from the same natural treasure as other fountains. And there is no difference between them save two points; the first is that we have helped to catch, or better receive, the wealth that is presented to us. But what am I saying? is there no work involved? and do we not spend money to bring natural springs into cities and castles? do we not need masonry also for these as for the one I am showing you how to build? and who is the one who can legitimately call it a cistern? seeing that it lacks nothing that natural fountains have. I have told you that it was quite similar to the natural ones, except for two points: the first is, as I have said, that we have helped nature: just as the sowing of wheat, the pruning and cultivation of the grape are nothing more than helping nature; the second is very important, and cannot be understood if you have not well remembered the beginning of my talk, and having understood it, you will be able to judge, by the proofs I have advanced, that no natural fountain could produce water that can be guaranteed to be good, as can the one I am teaching you to make. The reason is, as (58) you have been able to understand, that the whole earth is full of various kinds of salts and minerals, and that it is impossible for waters passing through the rocks and veins of the earth not to carry with them some noxious salt or mineral, which cannot happen in the fountain I am teaching you how to make. For you know well that as a general rule, the lightest waters are the best. I ask you, are there any lighter waters than rain water? I have told you before that they have risen up before coming down, and this was done by virtue of a warm exhalation: but the waters that have risen can bear with them very little terrestrial substance, and still less of mineral substance. And this water which has thus lightly risen by exhalation, comes down again on the land, which you well know is free of all minerals and other things that can make waters harmful. That is why I can conclude that the waters of fountains made according to my design will be more certainly good than natural ones, and must not be called anything else but natural fountains. And just as fruit trees cannot change their names because they have been grafted and transplanted, so my fountains cannot change their name because they are better than the others. If it were permissible to change their name, it (59) would be necessary to call natural springs wild as compared with those I show you: just as the fruit trees that grow naturally in the woods are called wild: and when transplanted, they are called domestic. And to show you that rain waters are the lightest, and therefore the best, ask the dyers and the sugar refiners, they will say that rain water is best for their work, and for many other things. If you don't want to believe all these fine proofs, which I have given you, I refer you to the great Vitruvius, who, of all those who have spoken of waters, is the one who treats them most correctly: he proves in his book, by satisfactory reasons, that rain water is the best and the most healthful.[51]

Theory

I know now that what you say is quite easy to do, and that the waters of such fountains are certainly good: But I fear a difficulty, which is that when it rains hard during storms, the waters that descend violently from the mountains would bring down large quantities of earth, sand, and other things, which would prevent the flow of the fountain or of the waters that would come to it. (60)

Practice

Really, I can see by this that you do not lack judgment, and because I see that you are attentive to my words, I shall draw you later a suitable picture or plan for the place you have described to me, to make your fountain. And to guard against the damage

---

[51] Vitruvius (fl. 35 B.C.), the great Roman architect, wrote *De Architectura*, the book referred to here by Palissy, whose regard for the great Roman is not misplaced. Perhaps Palissy was influenced by the passage from Vitruvius

of high waters which could assemble in a few hours because of a storm, you must, after having chosen your park to receive the waters, put large stones across the deeper channels that come into your park. And by these means the violence of the waters and ravines will be lessened, and your water will flow quietly into your reservoirs.

Theory

I ask you, if there are trees along the mountain that I wish to choose for the park, should they be cut down?

Practice

Good Lord, no! don't do that: for these trees will be very useful to you in this matter. There are in many parts of France, and particularly at Nantes, wooden bridges, where, to break the violence of water and ice against the pillars of these bridges, great quantities of upright posts have been placed in front of the pillars, for otherwise they would not last long. In the same way, trees planted (61) along the mountain, where you wish to make your park, will serve much to reduce the violence of the waters, and far from advising you to cut them down, I would advise you to plant some if there were none: for they would serve to prevent the waters from excavating the ground, and by such means grass will be preserved, and along this grass the waters will flow quietly straight down to your reservoir:[52] And you must note a particular point which is known to few people, which is that tree leaves falling into your park and the grasses growing under it, and particularly the fruits if the trees have any, when they are putrefied, the waters of the park will draw out the salts of these fruits, leaves, and grasses, which will make the water of your fountains much better. When we talk about salts you will be able to understand this point more clearly: so I shall not tell you more about it now.

Theory

I have another country house: but the mountain is a good half quarter-league from my house: would there be some way of

quoted by Adams (1938, pp. 431–32) in forming his opinions on ground water and the hydrologic cycle.

[52] This may be the earliest printed statement concerning the benefits of tree planting in preventing soil erosion. Palissy's ideas are entirely in accord with present-day principles of soil conservation.

bringing the fountain to it? for when the waters come down they fall into a meadow rather far from my house.

Practice

Is there not some way of damming up the waters at the foot (62) of the mountain, and of leading them to your place? and when you have brought them to the plain, toward your house, you will have to bring them the rest of the way in leaden, earthen, or wooden pipes: you can do that; it's easy.

Theory

And if I wished to build a fountain in some country place, where the ground is flat, as often happens in the country, would there be a way of doing so?

Practice

Certainly: but it will cost more than in the mountains: since where the ground is flat it must be given a slope with manpower.

Theory

How is it possible to give it a slope, if there is none naturally?

Practice

That is not the worst of it: for it is very easy to make a slope by manpower: but the worst is that being raised to one side and lowered on the other, it must absolutely be paved, for otherwise the whole thing would be worthless.

Theory

It must be concluded right away that it can't be done: so we mustn't talk more about it.

Practice

Not so, and it is very easy, providing time and money can be found.

Theory

I pray you tell me how you would wish to proceed. (63)

Practice

First I would choose a field very near the house and according to the size of my family I would make my park, and having stretched my lines [53] I would have a number of laborers whom I would get to remove the earth from the end near the house where I would want to make the reservoirs, and have them carry it to the other end of my park, and by this means, as soon as the part near the house was lowered by two feet, the other part would be higher by four feet, which would be a height sufficient to bring all the rain water that would fall into my park. The cost of this is not so great as to be questioned. But as for the cost of paving, it might be more or less, according to the nearness of materials to the place.

Theory

And what's the need for paving this park?

Practice

Because you have told me that the country is flat, and that you have tried to dig wells in it, for which your predecessors and you have spent much. And if you have been unable to find water, I have told you before that if all ground were sandy and spongy, rain water would sink into it as soon as it fell; and if all ground were thus, there could never be springs for fountains, and fountains are caused only because the ground is paved with stone, or some mineral; (64) for these reasons, even if you had had the earth carried from one end of your park to the other, and it were all prepared to receive the rain, that would avail you nothing: because the rain would find nothing that could stop it. That is why I have told you that you absolutely must have your park paved in order to hold water. I don't mean that it should be a pavement of cut or hard stone, like that of cities, nor based on sand, if there is none on the spot, but laid at all angles, merely with earth. That is how I understand it: so that you won't think the cost so great; and if flat stones can be found, as they can in many regions, they must be laid flat; so that they will occupy more space. Provided they can prevent the ground from soaking up the water, it doesn't matter how they are placed.

Theory

And if I want to build my fountain in some spot where there is no stone?

[53] Palissy the surveyor speaks here. He stretches out lines or cords between pegs to indicate the place from which earth is to be removed.

Practice

If there is no stone, floor it with brick.

Theory

And if there is neither stone nor brick?

Practice

Floor it with clayey soil.

Theory

But how? won't clayey soil soak up (65) water like other soil?

Practice

No, for if waters could pass through clayey soil salt could not be made by the heat of the sun. Because that is so, the fields and parks of salt pans are floored with clayey soil, and by this means, sea water, which is enclosed in these parks, is kept in them to be congealed and reduced to salt. But you must note that the clayey soils used to keep in these waters must be waterproofed [54] and I shall tell you the method the islanders use to waterproof it. First they have a number of horses tied one behind the other, in a row, and on the first horse, to lead them, is a man who holds the bridle in one hand, and with the other suddenly hits them with a whip, making them walk all along the place, until it is well tamped: afterwards they level it and put it in such shape that it can serve them to hold the waters. And for this reason I have told you that you could floor your park with clayey soil, for lack of stone, or brick; I will tell you more about this in talking about common salt.

Theory

And if my park were paved with stone or brick or with clayey soil, I could not use it (66) except to receive the waters and that would be a great loss for a poor man, who would have only a little land, to use it only as a fountain.

[54] Palissy uses the verb *conroyer*. Bescherelle's dictionary has *conroy* and says that this is the name of waterproof soils in Limousin. Hence we can understand here that the verb means to waterproof or render watertight. George W. White suggests that the waterproof soil may be bentonite or montmorillonite and adds that the method is used by the Soil Conservation Service for making farm ponds in porous soils. *Sub sole nihil novum!*

Practice

If you will believe me, this park will bring you great profit and use; that is, by planting in it many fruit trees of all kinds, and planting them in straight lines, and then pave your park and at every tree, leave 3 or 4 inches of soil unpaved, so that this paving will not prevent the growth of the trees. And when that is done, you can have earth put over this pavement, up to a foot high and more: later you can sow whatever kind of vegetables you may wish, and in this way the trees will grow and the land will bear, and yield you many fruits, and even wood to warm you, and no piece of land will yield so much income: because it will serve for so many purposes. First for fountains, secondly for fruit, thirdly for wood, fourthly for the things you will sow in this park: if you do not to wish to sow anything I have mentioned, sow it with hay, which will serve for pasture: and finally, it will be a very delightful place to walk in. Therefore, here is a piece of land that will have five fine uses.[55]

Theory (67)

Yes, but if I cover this paved park with earth and sow something on top, the waters in passing will submerge the seeds I have sown there.

Practice

You have very badly remembered what I have told you many times, that spongy and tilled ground cannot hold water, from which you must understand that the rains that will fall into your park will sink through the ground to the pavement, and when they are on this pavement, and find its slope, they will go down to the sand that adjoins the reservoirs, and continuing, will pass through the sand to go to the first reservoir. This must make you consider well that rain water that falls on mountains, lands, and all places that slope toward rivers or fountains, do not get to them so very quickly. For if it were so, all fountains would go dry in summer: but because the waters that fell on the land in winter cannot flow quickly, but sink little by little until they

[55] To my knowledge no one has ever stated in print that a reservoir according to Palissy's plan was ever built. It is a rather elaborate construction and it would be interesting to know if it would fulfil its inventor's predictions for it.

have found the ground floored by something, and when they have found rock they follow its slope, going into the rivers. From this it follows that under these rivers there are many continual springs, and in this way, not being able to flow except little by little, all springs are fed from the end of one winter to the next.[56] (68)

Theory

You have given me the plan for three fountains, two in the mountains and one in flat country: but since the one in flat country cannot be built without expense, and everyone is not near mountains, could you not give me some device which farmers could use in flat country without being forced to pave the ground? Because everyone cannot afford to have paving: there are even many country places where neither stone nor brick nor clayey soil could be found.

Practice

If I were a villager and my house were in open country, I should hope to find a way of building some sort of fountain for the use of my family.

Theory

I pray you tell me how you would do that.

Practice

I would choose a piece of land near my house, and having raised it at one end, as I have said before, I should want some wooden mallets, and would beat the ground very level; and being thus beaten and well prepared, I would make the two reservoirs I have described above, and would look about, in meadows or woods, for some ground thick with grass and from it I would make such a large quantity of sods that I would have (69) enough to line the whole inside of my park, and so that the roots of the grass should enter from one sod into the other, I would fill all the joints with fine earth. By this means the roots of the sods would pass from one to the other, and then it would be a meadow pavement that would bring the waters into the reservoir by means of my slope.

---

[56] A correct and very modern explanation of the lag in change of water levels. No earlier account of this phenomenon is known to me.

Theory

And do you believe that rain water could not pass through these sods, or better, that the ground would soak it up without letting it flow to the reservoir?

Practice

And do you think that I give you such advice without first having studied natural meadows? I have seen more than a thousand with less than three feet of slope, where still the rain water flowed into the lower part of the meadow and remained there a long time before the ground soaked it up. For the quantity of grass and roots prevents the ground from soaking up the water as does plowed land. I do not say that the cracks that open up in summer because of drought cannot soak up part of these waters, when the ground is dry: but the inclination or slope of the park causes the greater part of the water that falls to flow quickly through the sands above the first reservoir. If you had simply bordered your park with many kinds (54, err. pro 70) of trees, this would shade the park: so that the sun would not split these sods. Therefore I should like to let the grass of these sods grow, not cutting it, and the rains descending from the top of the park to the bottom, would lay the grass flat and then it would serve as cover for the cracks in the ground. And when these grasses rotted, their salt would be brought by the water into the reservoir, which would cause a goodness in this water, as I have said.[57]

Theory

You have given me so many reasons that I am forced to confess that natural fountains proceed solely from rain water: still, I have seen such great springs that they turned mills, and others that were the beginnings of rivers and that cannot be done unless there is some source other than rain.

Practice

You are wrong: because you do not understand that those of the great springs come from very far, because they find much continuous rock, and having found a natural channel which the

[57] Just what benefit decaying vegetation would confer on water in Palissy's reservoir is not clear. Perhaps he was reasoning by analogy with acid swamp water but this is far from certain.

waters themselves have made over a long period of time, just as you see that into great rivers many small rivers flow: which is done in this case within the womb of the mountains: for there are in them main channels that bring about the springs, into which many others flow. (71) This happens just as well inside the mountains as it does visibly in all rivers. And do not seek further the reason for the largeness or smallness of springs: for you will find no one who can give you a truer one.

Theory

And if the field that I have made into a park to catch the waters for my fountain should not suffice for the whole year, and if they should dry up in the warmest weather, by what means could I replace the lack of these waters?

Practice

The means are very easy, and it does not take much brains to know it. If your park is insufficient, add another piece of field to it: and pave it in this case as I have said: and by this means you will never lack water.

Theory

I do not yet understand one main point, that is if this fountain will flow continuously or if the water must be drawn with a faucet.

Practice

I have told you before that in the face of your fountain you would put such beauty or adornment as you wished, and that you would need a faucet in this face.

Theory

And if that is so, I must draw water like wine from a cask, and for this reason it cannot be called (72) a fountain. For natural fountains flow continuously.

Practice

If I had never seen a fountain, you would make me believe many things: and is it not well known that those of Paris and a thousand others are tapped by faucets?

Theory

True, but you have told me that the fountains you are teaching me to make will be used by both me and my animals; do you want them to go and stick their mouths under the faucet?

Practice

I don't know how you dare make such a request. Could you not build some receptacle on the side, off the way to your fountain, to draw the water for your cattle? I would make a separate faucet, on the corner of the reservoir, and when the time came to water the cattle, it should be opened and allowed to flow into the drinking trough, and then your animals would drink fresh, pure and clean water.

Theory

Yes, but it would be a pity to use so much land solely for a fountain.

Practice

I never knew a man with so little brains. Do you prize so little the utility of fountains? Is there anything more necessary in this world? Do you not know that water is one of the elements, (73) nay, the first of them all, without which nothing could have a beginning? I say no living thing, nor plant, nor mineral, nor even rocks, as I shall make you understand in talking of these.

Therefore, I have told you that you can plant all kinds of trees in the park: and if so, do you consider a field useless that produces fruit trees or others? I must now make you a long speech on your ignorance, and that of a hundred thousand others, which ignorance I cannot detest enough, and my mind cannot cry out enough against such ignorance. First, consider what I have told you: that neither man nor beast could live without water. Also, I have said that they could not live without fire. That is why I say that even though your park should serve only to yield wood, it would be the finest thing for you to have on your property. I have told you above that you would be able to gather wood, fruits, and all sorts of pasturage in your park, without spoiling its waters at all. Do you believe that is little for a prudent man, who will consider the usefulness of the wood, and who will try to have some of everything on his property? What could you do without wood? Will you cook your dinner by the sun? I pray you, consider a little if you will find anyone, of whatever rank he may be, who can do without it. See how few artisans (74) earn their living without wood. If you wish to build houses, wood is needed for beams, joists, and chevrons, to burn lime, to make masonry. If there is need to make tools and instruments to work in whatever trade it may be, charcoal is needed to forge them. If there is need to navigate to trade in foreign countries, wood is needed to build ships; if defensive weapons are needed, they must be mounted in wood. Wood is needed to make wagons and carts; blacksmiths, locksmiths and goldsmiths, and all those who work with coal, what trade will they take up in order to do without wood? In short, to make mills, to tan leather, to make dyes, to make barrels for wine and other things, which we cannot do without, for all these things wood is necessary. As for fruits, such as pears, apples, cherries, chestnuts, plums, and other kinds: where shall we get them from if we do not plant trees? If I wanted to put in writing how great is the necessity of wood, and how impossible it is to do without it, I should never be finished. (75)

WARNING TO THE GOVERNOR AND INHABITANTS OF JACQUES PAULY, OTHERWISE KNOWN AS BROUAGE [58]

Following the discourse on fountains I think it well to advise through this book the governor of Brouage, of the fine means and usefulness, that exist in this place, of making a fountain according to my design, and at little cost. Since in this place there are already timbers for pumps, already pierced, and there is only need to fit them together, from the wood of Yers [59] to the place of Jacques Pauly, otherwise Brouage. The slope of this place is so convenient that one could cause a fountain to piss more than lance high at this place of Jacques Pauly, and I say this because I have heard of the great lack of water that occurred in this place during a siege which was laid during our time before this city. (74, err. pro 76)

[58] Now Hiers-Brouage, not far from Saintes.
[59] Ancient spelling of Hiers.

ON THE TIDAL BORE WHICH IS GENERATED
IN THE DORDOGNE RIVER IN GUIENNE

Theory

You have just given me a very long speech on the effects of waters, of fires, and of earthquakes, but you have said nothing about the cause of the essence of the tidal bore.

Practice

And what is it you call a tidal bore? For I have never heard tell of a tidal bore, nor do I know what it is, unless you tell me.

Theory

One calls tidal bore a great mountain of water which is built up in the Dordogne River, in the region of Libourne, and this mountain forms only in summer. Even in the quietest times, and when the waters are most calm, and all in an instant, at an unknown time, the mountain of water forms in a moment and runs along the water, sometimes far, sometimes a short distance. And when the mountain runs, it overturns all the boats it finds along its way. Hence the people who live near the river, when they see (77) the tidal bore forming, begin to shout everywhere, "watch out for the bore, watch out for the bore," and the boatmen who are on the river flee to the banks to save their lives, which otherwise would be in danger.

Practice

And what do the people of the country where it forms have to say about this tidal bore?

Theory

They are not all of the same opinion. For some say one thing and others something else. However, the men of Bordeaux and

Libourne and Guitres hold it as certain that the cause of this is none other than the rising tide which encounters the current of the river, and wish to conclude from this that the struggle of the two waters causes this great mountain to form. Here is the most likely and common opinion of the people of the region.

Practice

And what do you think is the cause of this effect?

Theory

I am of the opinion of the others.

Practice

Neither you nor they understand a thing about it. For if the rising tide and the current of the Dordogne caused the tidal bore, it would form just as well in the Garonne as in the Dordogne, even in the Charente and in the River (78) Loire, even, in a word, in all the rivers that flow into the sea, and yet we have never heard that in the autumn months and on quiet days there is a tidal bore, save in this Dordogne River. Therefore, we must seek some other cause for it, to get to know this effect.

Theory

I pray you, tell me what can be the cause of it.

Practice

I cannot think that it is anything else but air enclosed in some channel underground, going from the Garonne to the Dordogne, and this is quite credible, since this cannot be done except by air enclosed under the waters. However, the air could not do it because of its weakness if it were not pushed by accident; it must therefore be thought and believed that when the tide is low the Garonne is low because of the absence of the sea; that then there are some empty channels that fill up with air, from the Dordogne to the Garonne, and when thus filled with water, when the sea returns it causes the Garonne to swell and become larger, and being thus swollen it gets into the channels that it had left empty in its going down and from that it follows that the air in the channels, finding itself enclosed between the two rivers, and being strongly compressed by (63, err. pro 79) the waters of the Garonne, it flees before these waters and in fleeing finds itself shut in under

the Dordogne River, and being enclosed it raises up the waters
like a mountain and being unable to pierce them right away,
it carries them along in their height, without changing shape or
falling apart, until by some movement the waters thus raised
become weaker in some places, and then the enclosed air manages
to burst them in the weaker parts and having burst them this
air escapes and the waters go down suddenly and the river returns
to its original quiet. And you must not seek another reason for
the cause of the tidal bore.[60]

Theory

I find in your words an opinion contrary to the truth: for we
know that waves usually form in the sea quite as high as mountains, and even in the straits of Maumusson, which are so high
that ships cannot go through them without danger of shipwreck,
and may are lost in these straits.

Practice [61]

This does not affect what I say. For the waves of the sea are
formed only by the action of winds which thus causes the waters
of the sea to rise: and the reason why they are more swollen and
higher in the straits of Maumusson is because there are rocks
against which the waters of the sea, being pushed by the winds,
come and strike impetuously, which causes great elevation of the
waters, I say (80) an elevation so great that the noise of it is heard
more than seven leagues away. And when the sea is thus worked
up, ships refrain from passing through it because the waves would
throw them against the rocks and they would be crushed in an
instant. However, this does not contradict in any way what I have
to say about the tidal bore. For I tell you that the bore forms in
autumn, on the quietest days, and when the waters of rivers are
low, and if the bore was caused by the winds, like the waves of
the sea, it would appear and form oftener in winter than in
summer. But never has man seen it in winter, and I well know
that the land that divides the Dordogne from the Garonne makes
a point between Bordeaux and Blaye, where the two rivers meet,

[60] Palissy's explanation is fanciful, to say the least, and for once Theory
is right and Practice is wrong. His most sincere admirer must admit that
Jove nodded here or even went to sleep altogether.

[61] This heading is missing in the 1580 edition; it has been inserted in the
1880 edition and is used here also as the words clearly belong to "Practice"
and not to "Theory."

which point opposite Bourg is called the bec d'Ambez. I have sometimes been on this point, where there are several houses or tenant farms [62] which are built on the ground because if they were to dig for foundations, they would find water, which would prevent them from building, and one must not doubt that there is a great part of this point which is underlain by water at one end, and at the other end it is stopped by dry lands toward the higher ground. This I have found out because, shaking myself on these lands, I caused everything to quake around me as if I had been on a floor: I also saw that in (81) the months of August and September the ground of this point is split by such great cracks that very often the leg of a man could lodge in them. This leads me to believe and assure that the tidal bore is caused by nothing but the enclosed air, of which I have known by other examples, that of the rains that fall from the roofs of houses into brooks and form by the winds a round blister (bladder) which bursts when the wind comes out of it. I have also many times observed natural springs, which in such case bring up winds enclosed in the form of globes, which hold their round shape until the air bursts them. Since you see that the air, pushed by the might of the waters, has the power to raise up such great quantity of water, you can know by this that such things or similar ones can generate an earthquake, not so great as the three elements that I have treated of in the discourse written in this book, on the facts of the causes of earthquakes. (82)

[62] *Métairies* in the original. The word has persisted in France and in Louisiana, where a suburb of New Orleans is still known by that name.

TO THE READER

Friend reader, the great number of my days and the diversity of men have made me know the various indescribable affectations and opinions that exist in the universe among which I have found an opinion on the multiplication, generation and growth of metals: more ingrained in the mind of many men than any other opinion. And I know that many seek this knowledge without thought of fraud or malice but only to make sure that the thing is possible. This has caused me to protest by these writings that I wish to blame in no way three kinds of persons. To wit, the noblemen who, to occupy their minds and by way of recreation, without being influenced by love of illegitimate gain. The second are all kinds of physicians of whom it is required to know natures. The third are those who have the power, and who believe the thing is possible, and who would at no price abuse of it. And because I have undertaken to speak against a thousand others who are unworthy of such a science, and totally incapable because of their ignorance and lack of experience. (83) Also because they are unable to bear the losses caused by their mistakes, they are forced to resort to external dyes and sophistications of metals. For these reasons I have undertaken to speak sharply, with invincible proofs. I say invincible to those of whom I speak, and if there is someone who has worked so hard as to touch the charity of God to reveal him such a secret, I do not intend to speak of such a person. But on the contrary, inasmuch as the capacity of my mind cannot resign itself to believe that such a thing can be done, when I shall see the contrary, and that truth will confute me, I shall confess that there is nothing more inimical to science than the ignorant, among whom I shall have no shame in placing myself in the first rank, in that which concerns the generation of metals. And if there be someone to whom God has granted this gift, may he excuse my ignorance: for according to what I believe of it, I shall take up my pen to pursue what I think of it, or better, what I have learned about it with much labor, and not in a few days, nor by reading various books, but in dissecting the womb of the earth, as one can see by my discourse which follows. (84)

TREATISE ON METALS AND ALCHEMY

Theory

It seems to me that you have talked enough about fountains. According to your promise, I would like you to give me some knowledge of the facts concerning metals. For I know that a great many people in France labor every day on works of alchemy, and many make great profit at it, having found fine secrets, as much to increase gold or silver as other effects: things which I would very much like to know and hear.

Practice

By this you can know how much the insatiable avarice of men does harm in this base century. There is no abuse among men which causes more stealing and deceit than avarice, as it is written that avarice is the root of all evil. It is certain that many, wishing to be rich, have given themselves much pain: accordingly I cannot better understand that you wish to join the ranks of the misers than by your wishing to know how to make or increase gold or silver. (85) For many avaricious acts can be concealed by hypocrisy. But as for those who wish to make gold and silver, their avarice cannot be concealed.[63] And their intentions cannot be classed elsewhere than with the envious and lazy-bellies, who to avoid working at some useful and just art would want to know how to make gold and silver: in order to live in ease and make themselves great with little labor: and being ruled by such greed, not succeeding in making what they seek, they use what they can, just or unjust. Here is a point that no man of good will

[63] Palissy is thoroughly convinced that the transmutation of metals is an impossibility and he parries every thrust of Theory's in favor of it with an account of the tricks and devices used by the charlatans and the utter worthlessness of their methods. In this Palissy is far ahead of his time and the point is very much to his credit.

could deny for me. Therefore, if you will believe me, you will never place your affections in these things.

Theory

You give me here a terrible character, you almost wish to accuse me of evil which I have not yet done: on the other hand, do you want to make me believe that it is evil to take oil of antimony or oil of gold, and with these oils, by philosophic art to be able to dye silver the color of gold? Is it wrong to convert silver into gold? If I take fine copper and am able to take away its phlegm, or red color, and can reduce it to the color of silver, in such a way that it will bear the crucible test and other tests, what harm is there if I can do it, providing it is good silver? (86)

Practice

Whatever you do, work as much as you wish, and use up your days and your wealth as many others have done, you will never achieve it.

Theory

And don't I know that many others before me have achieved what I say? Do we not have many books which they have left us in writing: among others Gebert, Arnold of Villanova, the Romance of the Rose, and so many others, even that some of our ancients have made long ago a philosopher's stone, when they placed a certain pitch in the gold it increased it a thousand-fold, and that is what many seek today, well knowing that this has been done long ago, and this is called the great work.

Practice

Good God! Are you still so ignorant as to believe that? Do you think that the men of olden times could not lie, that they did not know how to attract silver by falsehood, as well as those of today? Do you not know what David says of his times: Lord help us: for we are quite devoid of honest men. Men (he says) are all full of flattery, and speak the opposite of their thoughts. And Solomon says that iniquity is so great that there is no artisan but is envious of his fellow. Do you think I want (87) to believe a Gebert, an Arnold of Villanova, or a Romance of the Rose, in what they have said against God's works? And do you think me so little learned, that I do not well know that gold and silver and all other metals are a divine work, and that it is a rash undertaking against the glory of God to wish to usurp that which is of his estate. Now, all that is given to man to be able to do to metals is to draw the impurities from them, and to purify and examine them, and to make of them such vessels or money as he may wish, and that is like harvesting and sowing of seeds. For it is man's sole privilege to separate the grain from the straw, the husks from the flour, and with the flour to make bread, and to press the grapes to make wine: But it is God's privilege to give them growth, flavor and color: I say that just as man can do none of this, so he cannot do the same with metals.

Theory

How so? You speak here of sowing: as if the metals came from seeds, like wheat and other plants.

Practice

I have not taken up such a topic, or advanced such an argument without reason. Don't I know that all these coveters of wealth, who try to learn how to make gold and silver, when (88) they are told they have been at it a long time, and we see no results, they say that just as the ploughman waits patiently for the time and season of harvest after having sown, so must they wait, and that this cannot be done save with the generation which they have decided to make in their vessels, which they have destined to work at and serve for a womb for the generation of metals. And they say this has been well studied and proved by the ancient philosophers: for just as we scatter the seed of the wheat to cause it to increase in the second generation, so, they say, after separating by calcinations, distillations, or by other means, the materials from each other, they put them to hatching or generating, according to their plans, by weight and measure, as they have planned, and this done, they put these things over a very slow fire, wishing to imitate the womb of woman or beast: well knowing that generation is achieved by slow heat: and in order always to have a continual fire and of even strength, they have thought of making a lamp with a wick all of even size, and when their materials are in the womb, they warm them with the heat of the lamp, and wait as long as it takes to hatch eggs: I say some have waited many years, as witness the splendid Maigret, a wise man and one experienced in these things, (89) who although he could not achieve his designs, boasted that if wars had not extinguished his lamp before the time he would have succeeded.[64] Others make ovens whose fire is of an intensity rather far removed from that at which eggs are hatched: but in order to keep it at slow and measured heat, they make a few iron doors, which they open according to the intensity they wish to give their fire. Such people sleep little, and have many thoughts in mind, and torment of spirit, languishing for the time to visit their hatching eggs. That is one of the points by which I prove that the alchemists misuse this word seed and other terms. It is not without reason that I have said that it is the work of God to sow the matter of metals and give them their growth, and of men to gather them, purify and examine them, melt and hammer, to put them into such form as they may wish, for their use.

Theory

That is a rather long speech, and yet I cannot understand it: the more so as I know that man is allowed to sow all kinds of seeds, and yet you call the metals divine seed, and wish to prevent me from sowing them.

Practice

You have spoken much better than you thought, (90) in saying that the matter of minerals is divine seeds, I say so divine that they are unknown to man, even invisible, and this we must not doubt, and believe me, if I strive to prove it to you, I shall teach it to you so clearly that you will be forced to approve my methods and conclusions.

Theory

I pray you then to give me your discourse in full, that I may judge if what you say is true.

Practice

You must then be sure that all the waters in the world, which have been and are, were all created in one and the same day, and if that is true of the waters, I say to you that the seeds of metals

[64] In the original *qu'il avoit trouvé la fève;* i.e., literally "he would have found the bean." This colloquialism may be an allusion to a curious custom. At Epiphany, January 6, the "feast of kings," a cake is baked with a bean in it. He who finds the bean in his piece of the cake becomes the king of the party. Hence, "finding the bean" may mean to be lucky, or to succeed.

and all minerals and all stones were also created in one day; the same is true of the earth, of the air and fire, for the sovereign Creator has left nothing void, and since he is perfect, he has left nothing imperfect. But (as I have told you so many times in talking about fountains) he has commanded nature to work, produce and conceive, consume and dissipate; as you see that fire consumes many things, so it feeds and sustains many things; flood waters dissipate and spoil many things, and yet, without them, nothing could say—I am. And just as water and fire (91) dissipate on the one hand, they generate and produce on the other. According to which, I can say nothing else of metals, save that their matter is a salt dissolved and liquefied in common waters, which salt is unknown to men: the more so as it is intermixed with the waters, of the same color as the liquid, diaphanous or transparent waters, it is indistinguishable and unknown to all: having no apparent sign by which men can distinguish it from common waters. Here is a peculiar feature, which (I think) is hidden from and unknown to many men who think they are good philosophers: and remember this point and keep it, to use against all those who will try to make you believe that the generation of metals can be accomplished by hand work. For even if you had but this single point, it will suffice you to overcome all the opinions of the alchemists.

Theory

So! but how can I vanquish them with this point? I don't see that they can be defeated by that.

Practice

I'm beating out my brains for nothing. I ask you, tell me how the alchemists work on the generation, multiplication or increase of metals? And when you have told me that, (92) I will show you that you have not understood very well the principle I have given you.

Theory

The Alchemists work with fires of reverberation, calcination, distillation, putrefaction, and infusion.

Practice

And why do they use so many kinds of fires?

Theory

Because they use some to destroy copper, gold, and silver and other metals: and when they have destroyed, calcined, and pulverized them, they make a heap of many of these substances: And because quicksilver, which they like to use, would evaporate in a hot fire, they must use low fires, and having enclosed the quicksilver, which they call Mercury, in well corked and enclosed vessels, they try to fix it little by little and capture it over a low fire to compel it to congeal; so that later it can endure hotter fire. That is why they have many kinds of vessels and various kinds of ovens.

Practice

I ask you for no other proof than that which you put forth to show you, by your own admission, that even though all the alchemists in France seek the generation of metals by fire, yet I have told you, as a certain rule and sure method, (93) that metals are generated by a kind of water, to wit salt water, or better a dissolved salt, and if that is so (and it is the truth) all the alchemists are seeking to build by means of the destroyer. Fire is the destroyer of water, and wherever it enters it must expel the water, or if it does not, the water will kill it: therefore, since fire and water are opposites, it is pure folly to wish to generate metals by fire: since it is their enemy and destroyer.

Theory

I understand perfectly that you have told me that metals are generated from a liquefied salt. But that does not contradict what I say: quite the contrary, it supports me. The reason is this, that the salt which is dissolved in sea water is unknown, as are metallic salts: and yet they congeal and separate from the waters by fire.

Practice

You are mistaken. All congelations caused by cold are dissolved by heat; and all congelations caused by heat are dissolved by moisture: like the salt you mention, it congeals through heat and dissolves through moisture. Now all the metals dissolve through heat, therefore it follows that they are generated and congealed by moisture. You are now deprived of your rhetorical arguments. (94)

Theory

That's a fine one, trying to make me believe that metals are generated or congealed by moisture.

Practice

If you don't believe it, go and see the mines from which are taken gold, silver and other metals, and you will find that from most of them water must be drained night and day to get the metal that is in them. Once Anthony, king of Navarre, ordered that the vein of certain silver mines in the Pyrenees should be followed. But when a certain amount of it had been taken from them, the waters in them forced the mine foremen to give up everything. And it is well known that many mines have been abandoned for this reason. You will therefore find it very strange, when I shall prove to you later, that no stone can be congealed or formed without water, and if there is water, then it is through moisture, which is directly contrary to those who seek the generation of metals by fire. I could give you many valid proofs to bear out what I say: but since they belong more properly to my talk about the essence, matter and congelation of all stones, I shall keep the rest of my proofs until then.

Theory

Say what you will: but I have seen a (95) philosopher who increased a coin [65] before me: and so that there should be no deception, he made me do it myself.

Practice

And how?

Theory

He made me weigh a coin and as much quicksilver, and made me place the whole thing into a crucible, and when it had been put in the fire, he gave me a powder to mix, which had the power to fix the quicksilver. Then he made me blow until everything was melted together, and when it was melted it was found to have the weight of two coins of good silver: for the quicksilver

[65] The word is *teston* which Cotgrave translates as "a Testoone; a piece of silver coyn worth xviij d sterling."

had been fixed by virtue of the powder he had given me, and I had myself done the whole thing: therefore, there was no trickery.

Practice

Tell me a bit how you did it.

Theory

While the materials were melting, I stirred them with a stick.

Practice

Where did you get that stick?

Theory

In a corner, the first that I found handy.

Practice

I knew you had been tricked. Because this master philosopher had put this stick near you, (96) well knowing that he would make you use it to stir the materials: and that is how he deceived you, for he had put silver at the end of the stick and while you were stirring the materials in the crucible, the wax, with which he had sealed the silver into the end of the stick, melted away, and the silver fell into the crucible, and the quicksilver and the powder went up in smoke. And thus nothing remained in the crucible save the silver of the lump and the same weight of silver which he had put into the end of the stick: that is how he increased your lump by half.

Theory

Is it possible that he fooled me in that way?

Practice

Why, my friend, that is the least of the tricks with which they deceive people. If I should tell you about all the tricks they know and of which I have been informed, I should never have done. If he had not placed the silver in the crucible in that way, he would have given you a silver powder unknown to you and would have made you believe that this powder had fixed the quicksilver: and this powder would have weighed as much as he would have wanted to make the increase: or if he had not put in the increase in this way, he would have put in the silver unknown to you, in a large piece of coal, which he would have made you use to cover your crucible, and the coal and silver would have fallen into your crucible: thus you could not escape (97) being fooled. Tell me, pray, did he show you how to multiply silver?

Theory

No.

Practice

And why was he doing this in your presence?

Theory

Because he wanted to show it to me for money.

Practice

Haven't I told you it was nothing but deceit? For if the science were real he would never have shown it to you: but he was spreading his nets to catch your money. And even if you had been tricked, you would never have boasted about it. For nothing would have come of it except that you would have been jeered at; I well know that there are in France more than two thousand people who have been tricked in this way, but not one has sued to recover his money.

Theory

Then you think that there are many who make a practice of fooling people in this way?

Practice

I say not only in this way: for I know that they have a thousand other more subtle ways with which they fool the most knowing ones, and even the ones who think they are the most careful. The sieur (98) de Courlanges, the king's personal servant, knew many such tricks, if he had wanted to use them. For, one day, arguing about these things before King Charles IX, he boasted facetiously that he would teach the king to make gold and silver, to test which the king ordered Courlange to work quickly: which was done, and on the day of the test, Courlange brought two vials full of water clear as fountain water, which were so well contrived that when a needle or other piece of iron was put into one of these

Theory

vials it suddenly turned a golden color, and when the iron was
put into the other vial it turned silvery: then quicksilver was put
into the vials and it suddenly congealed: in the one vial to a
golden color, in the other silvery: and the king, taking the two
ingots, went to his mother and boasted that he had learned to
make gold and silver. And yet it was a trick, as the same Courlange
has told me himself. That is why I have told you that the trick
the other wanted to fool you with was one of the coarsest.

Say what you will: but I know that several alchemists have
found how to make a "medium of silver" [66] and a *tiercelet* [67] of
gold, which they (99) do commonly: for I am quite sure of it.

Practice

As for me, I am quite sure that if their medium of silver and
tiercelet of gold were put to the test, nothing good would be
found in them except the natural things that were put there,
and the surplus of what had been added would be known to be
false: and I well know that all the additions and sophistications
that they know how to make have started off a thousand counterfeiters: for they cannot get rid of their goods except as money,
because if they sold it in ingots its falsity would be found out in
melting. But they easily pass off money to all sorts of people. That
is why, when they have worked hard and cannot recoup their
losses, they are forced to turn to money. A Bearnese counterfeiter
was caught in the diocese of Xaintonge who had on him four
hundred pieces ready for stamping which, if they had been
stamped, no goldsmith or other would have turned them down.
For they passed the *mail,* [68] the *touche,*[69] melting and tone: quite
like the good ones. But when they were put into the crucible, their
falsity was discovered. In those days, there was at Xaintes a
provost named Grimaut who assured me that in prosecuting a
counterfeiter, the latter gave him the names and surnames of
eight score men who practiced (100) his trade, as well as their

[66] A "corne-measure, containing almost two of our bushels" (Cotgrave).
[67] A coin used in Milan in the twelfth century; or the name of a good alloy
in the language of the counterfeiters of the seventeenth century (Bescherelle).
[68] Literally, "the hammer."
[69] A test for gold by means of touchstone, a variety of blackish, siliceous
schist (Bescherelle). See the section on this subject in the translation of Lazarus
Ercker (p. 64).

age, rank, and addresses, and other reliable information. And when I asked this provost why he did not arrest the counterfeiters named on his list, he replied that he would not dare attempt it: for among them were many judges and magistrates of the Bordelais, Périgord, and Limousin; and that if he should undertake to antagonize them, they would find a way to kill him. When iniquity exists among the great and those who are supposed to punish others, it is like a great fire which men cannot extinguish. If I wanted to talk about all the abuses committed under cover of just labor, I should never have done. I have given you only this example, so that you may never be tempted to seek for the generation, increase or congelation of metals: because also it is something that is done by God's command, invisibly and by such most occult nature that it was never given to man to know it.

Theory

Preach as you will, for I know that many good men and great personages seek for these things daily who would not for the world be attached to money: also they are well able to do without it. (101)

Practice

I admit that there are many nobles, good men and great personages, who practice alchemy, and depend much on it. Let them be: this protects them from a greater vice: and their income permits them to test these things. As for the physicians, in seeking alchemy they will learn to know natures: and that will serve them in their art: and at the same time they will learn the impossibility of the thing. I have collected certain stones, transparent as crystal, with neither color nor blemish, yet by examination it can be shown that there is metal in these stones, even though they are as clear, transparent and clean as if they were still water.

Theory

You are always saying that it is impossible: and your opinion wishes to overcome that of many thousands of men who are incomparably more learned than you are, who would make you blush if you undertook to argue against them: For you have few reasons, and they would give you a thousand, which you could not contradict.

Practice

If it were only a matter of reasons, I have a great many of which the least will suffice to overcome all those which they could bring up. (102)

Theory

I pray you then, give me one of these fine reasons you talk about.

Practice

When the alchemists wish to make gold or silver, they calcine and pulverize their metals, and having pulverized them by calcination, they endeavor to regenerate these substances. But, if in this way they can make a new generation of metals outside the womb where they were made originally, it would be much easier for them to regenerate a nut, a pear or an apple that they would have pulverized. Do tell the bravest among them to pound a nut, I mean the shell and the kernel, and having pulverized it, let him put it into his alchemist's kettle and if he can reassemble the materials of a nut, or of a crushed chestnut, putting them into the same state as they were previously, then I shall say that they can make gold or silver; but wait, I am mistaken, for although they could reassemble and regenerate a nut or a chestnut, still that would not be multiplying and increasing it a hundredfold, as they say that if they had found the philosopher's stone, the weight of these (that is, gold and silver) would be increased a hundredfold. Well, I know that they can do the one as well as the other.

Theory

Why do you bring up nuts, (103) chestnuts and other fruits? Because these are vegetative spirits, that cannot be formed except after a long time, and they must first have come from seeds. But as for the metals, there is no reason for comparing them with fruits: since their body and their effects are imperceptible.

Practice

To this I reply that it is much easier to imitate something visible than something invisible; fruits are formed visibly, and yet it is impossible to imitate them: but still it is easier to do so than for metals. And as for what you say, that fruits are formed by vegetative action and that metals are dead and insensible bodies, on this I want to tell you a secret you do not know about. Know then that as soon as God created the earth, he put into it all the substances that are and will be in it: for otherwise nothing could vegetate or take form: and we must believe that the trees planted and sown have taken growth from the beginning of their nature by God's command, and since then (as I have said in talking of fountains) men who had wild seeds have sown, cultivated and transplanted them. But these seeds could not grow if the material for growth were not in the earth. We must therefore conclude (104) that as soon as the earth was created, with it were created all vegetative matters, all sweetness and bitterness, all colors, odors and virtues, and thence comes the fact that when each of these seeds is thrown into the earth, it attracts to itself odors and virtues. Some attract noxious and pernicious matters, drawing all these things from the earth.

Theory

All that you have said has no effect on my opinion.

Practice

But it does: for just as I have told you that the seeds or matters of all vegetative things were created at the very beginning of the world along with the earth: also I have told you that all mineral matters (which you call inert bodies) were also created like the vegetative ones, and exert themselves to produce seeds to generate others. Also, the mineral ones are not so inert that they do not generate and produce from one degree to another, more excellent things, and to make you understand it better, the mineral substances are intermixed and hidden among the waters, in the womb of the earth, just as every human and brute creature is conceived as water in its formation: and being intermixed among the waters, there is some supreme substance which attracts others of its nature to form itself. And we must not (105) think that before their formation and congelation, their color was known among the waters. But just as you see that chestnuts are white at first and black when ripe: apples black at first and red when ripe: grapes green at first, red when ripe: so the metals in their first form have no color but that of water: and this I have found out with great labor; protesting that I have done nothing of it to pretend that I was doing alchemy. For I have always thought the thing impossible: I say so impossible that no man can give me legitimate reasons why it can be done. When I have contemplated the various works and beautiful order that God has made in the earth, I have been astonished at the presumption of man: for I see that there are many shellfish that have such beautiful luster that no pearl in the world is so beautiful. Among others, there is one in M. Rasce's cabinet which has such a luster that it looks like a carbuncle, because of its fine polish, and seeing such things I say to myself, why is it that those who say they can make gold do not powder some of these shells and make a paste to fashion a fine cup? I am sure that a cup, well made of such materials, would be (106) more precious than gold. Or else, why do they not find out what the fish has used to make this fine house, and take such materials to make a fine vessel. The fish that makes his shell is not as glorious as man, it is an animal with very little form, and yet it can do what man could not. In a part of the Ocean Sea are found a great number of fishes, each carrying a shell on its back, which attaches to the rock, and because it is covered with its shell, it makes six holes in it, in order to breathe, or to obtain food; and as it enlarges its shell it makes a new hole and closes another. The largest of these shells is the color of pearl, and more beautiful: for it is like the rainbow, like the stone called opal: the top of this shell is rather rough and displeasing, because of the waters of the sea that beat on it: But when its crust is removed, the top is as beautiful as the inside. This fish has no form, and yet it can do what the alchemists could not.[70] There is an island in which there is such a quantity of this fish that the islanders fatten their pigs with it, and to take them out of their shells, they boil them, and burn these shells to (107) make lime.

Theory

Why do you give me such a long speech about a shell, seeing that our subject is alchemy?

Practice

It is to overcome your error and that of all those who are of your opinion, that I have put forward the most malformed fish

[70] The mollusk described here can be easily identified. It is a very low-spired gastropod, *Haliotis tuberculata*, the ormer in the British Isles, the *oreille-de-mer* or *ormier* in France. The description is correct in every respect and Americans familiar with the abalone of the West Coast of North America, which belongs to the same genus, will have no trouble recognizing it from the description.

that could be found in the sea, which can make a painted house of such beauty that all the alchemists in the world could not make one like it. I have often admired the colors of these shells and have been unable to understand their cause: yet in the end, I have thought that the cause of the rainbow was nothing more than that the sun passes directly through the rain which is opposite the face of the sun: [71] for no one ever saw a rainbow unless the sun was directly opposite to it; also, the rainbow is never seen unless the rain is falling toward the region where it forms: following which I have thought that when this fish builds its house, it climbs up on some rock where the sea water is not very deep and while the fish is building its house, the sun shines through the water and produces the colors of the rainbow in the water, and the materials of these shells being aqueous and liquid, during their formation (108) and congelation, retain the colors produced by the reflection of the sun through the water. That is why there is a time and a season for both man and animals; the plants, which have no feeling, teach us these things. I have often seen the snails working at the building of their houses; but never has anyone seen them doing so in winter. Nor do the bees or honey-flies and other animals do so, from which it is easy to conclude that the metals and all minerals have some season for their formation which is unknown to us. We can see by these things the folly of those who want to generate gold and silver outside the womb of the earth, and worse, want to generate them without knowing the materials peculiar to their essence: and still worse, wish to make with fire that which is naturally done with water. And, as I have said before, the materials of metals are hidden in such a way that it is impossible for man to know them before they are congealed, no more than water in which salt has been dissolved could be known as such unless tasted with the tongue.

Theory

And how do you know that, and what is your basis for undertaking to contradict so many learned philosophers who have written such fine books on alchemy? you who know neither Greek (109) nor Latin, nor scarcely good French.

---

[71] An accurate description of the cause of the rainbow. The first correct explanation, according to Leroux (1927, p. 103) is generally attributed to archbishop Antonio Dominis of Spalatro (1611). Palissy anticipates him by thirty-one years.

Practice

I'll tell you that. Once I happened to dissolve a pound of saltpeter in a caldron full of water, then I put it to cool, and when it was cold, I found that the saltpeter in congealing had attached itself to the caldron in long icicles of quadrangular form. Some time later I bought some crystal which had been brought from Spain which was formed like the saltpeter that I had dissolved. I knew then that even if metals are inert bodies (as you have said) still the crystal is not so dead that it cannot separate from the other waters, and among them to form into angles and diamond points: and just as it is possible for crystal, saltpeter and common salt to congeal and form a body apart in common water, so mineral matters can do the same, as I prove by a slate which you see here, in which many marcasites have formed. And not for nothing have I shown you this slate: for it has made me know the conclusion on what I have alleged before. You see that the metallic marcasites in it are square [72] like the faces of a die. If I ask you which of the two was formed first, the slate or the marcasite, you could not (110) answer me; I shall therefore be priest Martin,[73] I shall answer myself, taking for argument the shells which I prove to have been formed in the water and have since been petrified, and the waters and muds in which they lived. And just as the shells were formed before they were petrified, and the place where they lived: similarly, the marcasites in this slate were formed before the slate, and it is certain that when they were forming they were covered with water mixed with earth, which has since been reduced to slate, and the marcasites have kept their own form, encased in the slate, as the shells are encased in the rock.[74] Conclude then that these marcasites were formed by a material which (before its formation) was hidden in the waters, and by an order which God has put in nature, the materials which formerly were wandering, have been formed in such a way that men should greatly marvel at the works of God, and know that it is great folly to think of imitating him in such things. Some time after I became aware of the above, I was walk-

[72] The "square faces" show that in this instance and perhaps in all others, Palissy's marcasites are pyrite.

[73] There is an allusion here to some anecdote which I have been unable to trace.

[74] The reasoning is clever but it led Palissy to a wrong conclusion. See Introduction, p. 18 for discussion of this point.

ing in the fields, head down, to contemplate the works of nature: when I found certain laborers who were mining iron, fairly deep in the earth, and this ore was in stones of about the size (111) of an egg, I specify the size because in the Ardennes the iron ore is very small. But the ore that these laborers were mining had no shape, some of the stones were long and others round, twisted, according to the place where the material had stopped at the time of its congelation. Some time later I found some large stones of it, whose surface was shaped into diamond points; I was many years thinking over what could be the cause of the form of these points, and being unable to understand it, I put it aside for a while, not thinking about it any more. And at another time I was seeking the cause of the formation of all stones, which on the one hand were shaped into diamond points which were pure, clean, spotless and transparent as crystal, and on the other hand were cloudy, rough and displeasing. But since they had been congealed in this same spot, I knew that the diaphanous part was formed by pure water, and the cloudy part by a muddy water mixed with earth: But as for the diamond points I did not yet understand their cause. It happened that one day someone showed me some tin ore which was thus shaped into points, another time some silver ore still in the rock was shown to me, in which the materials of the silver had been congealed, (112) which ore was also shaped into diamond points. When I had pondered all these things, I understood that all rocks and kinds of salts, marcasites and other minerals whose congelation takes place in water, carry in them some triangular, quadrangular or pentagonal form,[75] and the side which is in the earth and against the rock, can have no other form than that of the shape of the place where it was lying at the time of its congelation. That will suffice to overthrow the opinions of all those who seek gold and silver by its opposite. For since there are diamond point shapes in gold, silver, lead, and tin ores and those of other metals, you may be sure that the main material of these is nothing more than a dissolved salt, which exists with the other waters and separates from

[75] That three forms are peculiar to crystals formed in water is a generalization that brought Palissy close to a realization of the laws that govern their formation. Lazarus Ercker, whose book on assaying was published in 1580, the same year as Palissy's *Discours Admirables*, has almost nothing to say about crystals. Agricola, in the translation by Bandy and Bandy (1955) and Hoover and Hoover (1912), has much to say about rock crystal but nothing as to laws of formation. Steno (1669) was the first to state these laws clearly.

them, attracting to itself the things it likes, to congeal them and reduce them to metals. And even if all the philosophers have concluded that gold is made of sulphur and mercury, I maintain that the sulphur that we see could not be mixed with mineral matters or their seeds: I freely admit that among the waters there is some kind of oil, which when mixed with water and mineral salt, helps in the generation of metals, and the metals having reached their perfect decoction, the oil is then congealed in the metal and is called sulphur. There are secrets so well concealed (113) and unknown in all natures that the more a man knows of philosophy, the more he will fear the hazards that ordinarily beset experiments on fusion, metals, and vulcanism. Is it not a strange and wonderful thing that at Montpelier there are certain waters in which copper is reduced to verdigris, and right next to them, there are other waters in which this cannot be done? Are there not also waters that are good for dyeing and for boiling vegetables and others quite near them that are no good for this? I have seen, in the time when the glaziers were much in demand,[76] because they made designs in the windows of churches, that those who painted these designs dared not eat garlic or onions. For if they had, the paint would not have stuck to the glass. I knew one called Jean de Connet, because his breath stank, all the painting he did on glass never stuck, although he was well trained in his work. The historians say that if a palm tree is planted on the bank of a river and another on the other bank, their roots will go from one to the other under the river, because of the love or affinity they have for each other. It is also certain that women in milk, when away from their sleeping children, feel in their breasts when they wake up and cry. I have seen a modest, wise and honorable woman who, when (114) her husband was in the fields, felt by some secret movement, the day when her husband was to return. Such movements exist not only in the human and brute creatures, but also in vegetable and metallic ones. And just as living matter uses food, and having extracted from it the nutritive substance, rejects the remainder as excrement, so the metals produce some useless excrements after their formation. I consider therefore that sulphur is a colophane or excrement which has

[76] A reference to his early years when he himself had practiced the trade of glass making. Whether it is true or not that garlic breath prevented the paint from sticking to glass is not known, but Palissy spoke from first-hand knowledge here and he was probably right.

served in generation, and once it is finished, the excrements are no longer useful, and if this happens with humans and animals, it does also in all plants. And if you doubt this, you see nuts and chestnuts which have an excremental husk and as soon as they reach perfection, they throw off their husk as useless excrement. Thus all seeds and vegetative plants produce something to help and serve them for a time only. Similarly, those who refine the ores of metals separate the sulphur from the metal, as being useless, just as the farmer separates the grain from the straw. That is why I tell you that common sulphur is not as it was when it generated metals, and that formerly it could be nothing else but an unknown oil; just as you see that gum (115) is but a water when it is inside the tree; and when it has come out of it and flows along the tree it dries out and hardens and then it is called a gum. Turpentine is an oil distilled from pines, and when it is cooked it hardens and is then called *poix raisine*.[77] This is how you must understand that the generation of metals is accomplished by matters and powers unknown to man. And do not think that quicksilver is anything more than the beginning of a metal, made or begun by an aqueous and salty material. I do not mean common salt, for I know that the number of kinds of salts is infinite to our knowledge as I shall explain to you later in talking about salts.

Theory

You are terribly prompt to ridicule the philosophers and philosophy is the finest thing in the world, for through it are made distillations more useful to medicine than anything one could find: even through philosophy, all odors, virtues, and flavors are drawn from spices and all fragrant things.

Practice

You are making fun of me when you say I hate philosophy, and you know very well that I prize it more than anything else and search for it every day, and what I say about it is not against living philosophers worthy (116) of the name. But I speak against those who deserve to be called antiphilosophers rather than philosophers. For I praise greatly the distillers and drawers of

---

[77] Cotgrave translates this as "rosen" (i.e., rosin) but Bescherelle explains: "a gummy, yellowish liquid that flows from incisions in resinous trees and which is still in a natural state."

essences and esteem this science highly useful and profitable. I wish to speak only against those who wish to usurp (to live in luxury) a secret which God has reserved for himself, such as the power to cause all plants and things to vegetate and grow. For it is God himself who has sown the seed of metals in the earth. And they want to attempt to do something that is done secretly in the earth, of which they know neither the means nor the materials, not by what power or how, nor in how much time the thing can reach its perfection. We have some knowledge of the time it takes for grain and other seeds to mature: but as for the seed of metals, they have no knowledge of it, nor knowledge of the power through which the materials combine and congeal. I know very well that these things have some power to attract each other, as the magnet draws iron. Also I well know that I have sometimes taken a rock of fusible matter, that after pounding and grinding it as fine as smoke, and having thus pulverized it, I mixed it with clay, and a few days later when I wished to work with this clay, I found that the rock had begun to gather together, even though it was (117) so thoroughly mixed with the clay that no one could have found a piece of it as large as the little motes that are seen in the sun's rays when they come into a room, which I thought was a marvelously admirable thing. That must make you believe that the materials of metals gather together and congeal admirably, according to the admirable order and power that God has ordained for them.

Theory

However much you speak against alchemy, still I have seen many philosophers who gave me good reasons for the fact of the generation of gold and other metals.

Practice

I suspect that those whom you call philosophers are the greatest enemies of philosophy. For if you knew what philosophy is, you would know that those who seek to make gold and silver do not deserve this title. Because philosopher means lover of knowledge. But God is knowledge: one cannot therefore love knowledge without loving God. And I marvel at how a bunch of counterfeiters, who work only at deceit and evil, are not ashamed to rank themselves as philosophers. So, as I said at the very beginning, avarice is the root of all evil, and those who seek to make gold and silver

cannot escape being called miserly, and being miserly, cannot be
called (118) philosophers nor included with those who love
knowledge. I have pointed this out because all those who seek to
make gold and silver are forever using this word, and because
the secret of knowing how to make metals belongs to no one save
the children of philosophy, and not only do they say it, but write
it in printed books. For example a book on drinkable gold was
printed at Lyon at the time when King Henry III was there on
his way back from Poland, in which book it is clearly written that
alchemy must be revealed only to the children of philosophy. If
they are children of philosophy, they are children of knowledge,
and consequently children of God. If that were so, it would be
well for all of us to belong to the religion of the alchemists.

Theory

You have just brought up chestnuts, nuts and other fruits: but
this has no weight against me, for metals are one thing and fruits
another.

Practice

I am ashamed that this topic should last so long: still, because
of your stubbornness, I'll talk about it more. Why don't you think
about the magnet which has a peculiar power to attract iron:
though it has no vegetative soul: and if this happens outside the
womb of the earth, how much greater power do you think it
has (119) in the earth, when it is still liquid? The magnet is not
alone in having power to attract the things it likes. Do you not
see jet and amber, which attract lint? Likewise, oil thrown into
water gathers itself apart from the water; do you want better
proof than common salt, saltpeter, alum, copperas, and all kinds
of salts which, when dissolved in water, can separate from it and
form a distinct and separate body? And to confirm what I
have said above, I tell you again that the seed of the metals is
liquid and hidden from man: And just as I have told you
that the seed of liquid salt can separate itself from ordinary
water, to congeal, so it is with metallic matters. And here you
must reason still more closely: observe the seeds, when they
are thrown into the ground; they have but a single color; when
they come to their growth and maturity, they take on many
colors: the flowers, the branches, the leaves, and the buds will
all be of various colors, and even in a single flower there will be

various colors. Similarly, you will find snakes, caterpillars, and butterflies which will be of many beautiful colors. Let us now reason even farther; you will admit that since all these things draw nourishment from the earth, their color comes also from the earth: And I shall tell you how, (120) and what is the cause of it. If you can extract from the earth, by alchemic art, the various colors, as these little animals do, I shall grant you that you can also attract metallic matters and gather them together to make gold and silver. But (as I have told you so many times) you go about it in a way quite opposite to that of nature. You have understood by my arguments that all metallic matters are aqueous and form in water, and yet you want to make them by fire, its opposite. Have I not shown you clearly by a slate full of marcasites that, while metallic matters are still fluid in water, they attract each other to become a body: and as I have always said, they are hidden and indistinguishable from other waters, until they congeal.

Theory

I find it very strange that you say that metallic matters are hidden within the waters, and yet we see the contrary, for all philosophers say that all metals are made up of sulphur and quicksilver. If that is so, why should I believe that they cannot be seen in water? For I am certain that if there were any in water I should be very well able to see them.

Practice

And why don't you remember what I have told you about common salt and others to (121) make you understand that just as salt has no color, when it is liquid in water, so also the metallic matters have no color until they congeal. But they take it on while gathering and congealing: just as all kinds of fruits change color during growth and maturity. If I wished to examine human and animal seeds, would they have any color before their formation? No, no more than the metals. I have told you before, that you have never seen sulphur or quicksilver unless it was congealed and that previously they were not of the color they now have, and that they were hidden, just as salt is hidden in sea water. I thought I would have done with the topic of alchemy long ago, judging that as I talked about rocks you would see the truth of my proofs. But because I find you stubborn and too set in your opinion, I am forced to close the subject, to tell you that nothing can be understood about metals except what human, animal, and plant natures give me to understand: which is, that when a chestnut, a nut, and all other fruits are sown into the earth, in them are contained the roots, the branches, the leaves, and all the parts, powers, odors, and colors that the tree can produce when it is born. Also that in the seed of human and animal natures, the bones, the flesh, blood (122) and all other parts are contained in this seed. And just as you see that none of these things retains its original color: but in their growth change color; and in one thing are many colors: Therefore, you must believe that the seeds of metals (which are liquid and aqueous matters) change color, weight and hardness. The first knowledge I had of these things was in the clay pit of a tile factory near St-Sorlain de Marennes in the islands of Xaintonge, where I found in the clay a large number of marcasites of various sizes and weights, all of which were formed in such a way that the material of their formation was liquid and that it had fallen down from above at the time of its congelation, just as if molten wax had been allowed to fall little by little to make it congeal.[78]

Theory

I quite understand your reasons. But would it not be very good for France if five or six men had been able to succeed in the matter of the ancient philosophers' stone? For I have heard it said by many alchemists that if they had succeeded, they would make enough gold to wage war against all enemies, even the Turks. (123)

Practice

Of all the things you have said until now, not one is so unwise as the one you have just said: But I say on the contrary, that it would be better to have a plague, a war, and a famine in France, than six men who could make gold in such great abundance as you say. For once it would be certain that the thing can be done, everybody would despise the tilling of the soil, and would strive to make gold, and thus the land would lie fallow, and all the forests in France could not supply all the alchemists with coal for six years. Those who have read history say that a king, having found a few gold mines in his kingdom, employed most of his

[78] His "marcasites of various sizes and weights" may have been concretions.

subjects in digging out and refining the gold, with the result that the lands lay fallow and famine began in the realm. But the Queen (who was wise and loved her subjects) in secret had capons, chickens, pigeons and other meats made of pure gold, and when the king wished to dine, she had these meats served to him, which pleased him, for he did not understand what the Queen was up to: but seeing that no other meats were brought to him, he began to be angry; when she saw this, the Queen begged him to realize that gold was not food, and that it was better to employ (124) his subjects in tilling the soil than in seeking gold mines. If this fine example is not enough for you, think a little, and be assured that if there were six men in France, as you say, who knew how to make gold, they would make such a great quantity of it that the least among them would want to make himself king, and they would make war on each other, and after the method was revealed, such a great quantity of gold would be made that it would be so despised that no one would want to exchange it for bread or wine. I do not say that it is not right for rulers to send people into the mines, even convicted criminals, to take out the ore, for their use in commerce and for necessary instruments which are made from these metals.

Theory

You have given me above many arguments against those who wish to generate metals by fire and you have even boasted that you would prove that there is a fifth element. Of these things I cannot be satisfied unless I have a more certain conclusion.

Practice

I can come to no other conclusion concerning metals except the one I have given above: that all metallic matters are liquid, fluid and diaphanous, and concealed in ordinary water, until their congelation, and as for the fifth element, I can give no other (125) proof of it except that which I have given publicly before my hearers, when you were present, which is proved by the rock that you see here.

Don't you remember that while explaining this rock, I said that all rocks having triangular, or pentagonal, quadrangular or diamond-point shapes were formed in water and that otherwise they could not assume these shapes? Having thus established such an argument, I showed them this rock which was made up of

three different materials, to wit, the top of the rock is of clean,
pure crystal terminating at the top in diamond points, and the
next layer down is of silver ore: and the third layer is of common
stone which shows clearly that the one which I call common,
which some call tuff, similar to that of quarries, was formed first,
and after it was formed, the matter of silver, descending from
above before its congelation, was laid down on the quarry of the
said rock, and a little later was congealed into silver ore, and
later, the crystalline matter was laid down on the ore and congealed into diamond points, and this while the ordinary waters
were above these matters: for otherwise the crystal (126) would
never have formed into points. You know well that all those to
whom I gave this demonstration agreed with my arguments, without any contradiction. And to come to the proof of the fifth
element, the same stone also served me as proof: because I proved
to them that never was crystal formed nor other rock with points
or faces, unless they were in ordinary water and that is so true
that crystal, diamond, and all other diaphanous stones are formed
only from aqueous matters, and then that crystal and other
diaphanous stones form in ordinary water, wishing to have no
affinity with them in their congelation, no more than suet, fat,
oils, pitch and other such matters that separate from ordinary
water? It must be concluded, then, that the water from which
crystal is formed is of a different kind than ordinary water: and
if it is of another kind, we can then affirm that there are two
waters, the one exhalative, the other essencive, congelative, and
generative, which two waters are intermixed with each other, in
such a way that it is impossible to distinguish them before one
of the two is congealed.

Theory

If you put forward such an idea, you will be jeered at; because
the philosophers hold it as certain that there are only four elements: (127) and if there were two kinds of water, as you say,
there would be five elements.

Practice

I have explained it enough to you through crystal, which, when
it wishes to congeal, most often within snow, it separates from
the other waters, and the ordinary waters which have remained

as snow, dissolve, and the crystal cannot dissolve, neither by sun nor fire: which is a very certain argument that the ordinary waters merely come and go, up and down, as I have said while speaking of fountains, and I dare say further that congelative waters are also evaporative and exhalative, and their dwelling place is in ordinary water until they congeal.

Theory

Few men will believe what you say: for they will wish to side with the ancient philosophers.

Practice

Say what you will: but when you have thoroughly examined all things through the effects of fire, you will find that I am right, and admit to me that the beginning and origin of all natural things is water: the generative water of human and animal seed is not ordinary water; the water that causes the germination of all trees and plants is not ordinary water, and although no tree, or plant, (128) or human or animal nature could live without the aid of ordinary water, still, within it, there is another germinative, congelative water, without which no thing could say—I am; it is the one that germinates all trees and plants and which sustains and nourishes their formation until the end: and even when their end and destruction has taken place by fire, this water is found in the ashes, from which can be made glass similar to the water from which crystal is formed, and you must not think that corn and other dry plants can subsist otherwise: for the exhalative water, which was in them before their maturity, has evaporated by the attraction of the sun: But the congelative water has always sustained the form of the straw. In such a case, you must believe that although man drinks only water that is ordinary in appearance, nevertheless in drinking and eating he absorbs some of this generative water, which is in all nutritive materials: and according to the effect of nature, the hardness of bones is caused by the action of congelative water,[79] and for these reasons, there are several kinds of bones that will resist fire better than natural

---

[79] In the state of chemistry in his day, Palissy could not speak of minerals dissolved in water but he very cleverly suspected that the same agent that caused crystals to form also caused bones to acquire hardness. Here he has not quite grasped the truth but he has come very near to it.

rocks. It will be easier for you to burn a natural rock than the foot bones of a sheep or egg shells. Through this you can learn that the crystalline water that causes sight has some affinity with generative water, of which eyeglasses, crystal, and mirrors are made. (129)

Theory

It seems to me that you contradict yourself in talking about this generative water: for when you talk of salts you say there is salt in all things, and that without it nothing could exist.

Practice

You will find no contradiction in my ideas. Do you want me to call sea water a salt when it is mixed with ordinary water? I can call fluid, liquid or aqueous things nothing else but water while they are concealed in ordinary water. Not even the metals before their congelation: for I have told you that metallic matters have no color except that of water, until their congelation.

Theory

You have told me so many times that metallic matters were liquid like ordinary water before their congelation, yet I cannot understand how that can be true if you do not give me more intelligible proofs.

Practice

I could give you no more valid proofs than those I have explained clearly in your presence to my disciples, which is (as you know) a great many kinds of wood reduced to metal. Don't you remember that when I showed them this wood I told them how would it be possible (130) for the wood to be reduced to metal unless it had for a long time lain in metallic waters mixed with ordinary water? and if the metallic waters had not been as liquid and subtle as the ordinary ones, how could they have penetrated into the wood and soaked into all its parts, without in any way changing its original form? It is a point which all who consider it will be forced to agree with my opinion. And I shall give you still another more certain proof, to show you how subtle the metallic matters must be to work on and reduce to metal, without deforming them, the things of which I wish to tell you. First, there are many shellfish which, after having soaked some time in metallic waters, are reduced to metal without losing their form, of which I have seen quite a few in the cabinet of M. de Roisi. For myself, I have one which I have shown to the master mason of the fortifications of Brest, in lower Brittany, who has assured me that there are many such in that region. In the cabinet of M. Race, a famous surgeon of this city of Paris, there is a rock of brass ore in which is a fish of the same material. In the region of Mansfeld is found a great quantity of fishes reduced to metal,[80] and that seems very strange to those who live without philosophy, and can never attain to the (131) knowledge of the cause; although it is rather simple, as I shall explain later; but first I must anticipate on what I have to tell you about the cause of petrified shells and wood, which is that the shells are formed of a dense, non-porous, compact and very hard material: and yet, when these shells have soaked for a long time in ordinary water, they attract a crystalline, generative water, of which I have told you so much, which changes them from shell material to rock material, without changing anything of their form. I ask for no other witness of this than you, who were present when I showed my audience a great many shells of various kinds reduced to stone, and not only the shells, but also fishes: and also many pieces of wood. It is therefore easy to conclude that the fishes which are reduced to metal used to live in certain waters and ponds, with which were mingled other, metallic waters, that since have congealed into brass ore and have congealed the fish and the shell and the ordinary waters have evaporated as usual, as is their wont, as I have told you above; and if, when the waters congealed into metal, there was in them some dead body, of man or beast, it would also have been reduced to metal: and of this one must not doubt.[81] And just as you see that ordinary waters (132) in flowing carry with them many impurities, such as earth, sand and other débris, so the metallic waters, being impure during their congelation, congeal all things which are in them: thereby the refiners have much trouble separating the pure from the impure, as you will be able to see in my conclusion on the treatise on stones. You well know that the reason why I remind you of these things is none other

[80] Probably the fossilized fishes of what would now be called the Kupferschiefer.

[81] Except for the archaic language of the original, this passage could have been taken from a current textbook of paleontology which would give the same explanation, using "minerals in solution" instead of "crystalline generative water."

than to deter you from associating with those who want to generate metals. For through the teachings I have given you, you can easily understand that they are mistaken in wishing to make with fire that which is made with water. I can assure you I have known a great many of these searchers who are so ignorant that they think they can keep spirits enclosed in earthen vessels, which it is impossible for them to do.

Theory

And what is it that they call spirits?

Practice

They call spirits all exhalative materials, and particularly quicksilver which is a water that evaporates like ordinary water, when it is pressed by fire, and they think that if they could make vessels to heat the quicksilver enclosed in them, that it would congeal into silver and become (133) malleable. But these poor people are so clumsily mistaken that I am ashamed to say it. For even if the vessel were a hundred *toises* [82] thick, it would be impossible to prevent it from bursting, if it were completely closed, providing it contained the least bit of moisture: as I have explained to you in talking about earthquakes, that humid matters being touched by fire make strenuous efforts and cannot endure to be enclosed without air, as you have understood through a brass apple; and even eggs, chestnuts, apples and other fruits must burst when their humors are heated: and that is why one must break the skin of chestnuts, so that the heated humor will not make them burst: if these good people considered these effects, they would not seek for earthenware to contain spirits.

Theory

You have cited me chestnuts, nuts and other fruits against my opinion of alchemy: but that does not affect me: because metals are one thing and fruits are another.

Practice

I am greatly ashamed that this topic should last so long: still, because of your stubbornness I am forced to talk of it still. Are you such a great dolt that you attach no weight to the power of the magnet which, by a peculiar power, attracts iron to itself,

[82] An ancient French measure of length, about 6 feet or 2 meters long.

although it has no vegetative soul, and if that happens (134) outside the matrix of the earth, how much more power do you suppose it has in the earth, when it is still liquid? And do you think that the magnet is the only thing that has the power to attract the things it likes? Don't you see that jet and amber attract lint? More, don't you understand that oil thrown into water stays apart from the water? Must you have better proof than common salt, saltpeter, alum, copperas, and all kinds of salts which, when dissolved in water, can easily separate from it and form a separate mass, distinct and separate from the water? In confirming what I have told you, I tell you again that the seed of metals is liquid and concealed from man, just as the dissolved salt cannot be known in ordinary water until its perfect congelation: Also, to be sure, the seed of metals cannot be perceived when it is liquid matter mixed with water, before its congelation: And just as I have told you that the seed of liquid salt can separate from ordinary water to congeal, so it is with metallic materials. And here you must reason still more closely. Look at the seeds, when you throw them into the earth, they are all of the same color, and in coming to their growth and maturity, they form many colors, the flower, the leaves, the branches, the twigs and the buds will all be of (135) different colors, and even in a single flower there will be various colors. Similarly, you will find serpents, caterpillars, and butterflies which will be adorned with marvelous colors, nay, by such labor that no painter, no embroiderer could imitate their fine works. Let us now reason still farther: you will admit that inasmuch as these things take their food from the earth, so their color also comes from the earth: and shall I tell you how and who is the cause of it? If you give me clear proof of all this, and could draw from the earth, by your alchemical art, the various colors, as these little animals do, I would admit that you can also draw out metallic matters and combine them, to make gold and silver. But what? I have told you so many times that you proceed quite against nature, and you can see from my arguments that metallic matters are all aqueous and form within water, and you want to form them by fire which is its opposite. Have I not shown you clearly by a slate filled with marcasites, and other rocks, and minerals, that while the metallic matters were still fluid in the water, they attract each other to become metallic bodies and (as I have always said) they are concealed and indistinguishable from the other waters, until they congeal. (136)

Theory

I find it very strange that you say that metallic matters are concealed within the waters, and yet we see the contrary: for all philosophers say: "that all metals are made up of sulphur and quicksilver." If that is so, do you want me to believe that sulphur and quicksilver are concealed in water? I hold it as certain that if there were some sulphur and quicksilver in water, I would know it.

Practice

I am convinced that I am wasting my time. You are just as great a dolt today as yesterday. And don't you remember that I have put forth common salt and others: to make you understand that just as salt has no color while it is liquid in the water, so also metallic materials have no color until they congeal, but take on their color as they gather together and congeal: just as you see all kinds of fruits change color in their growth and maturity. If I wished to bring up the seeds of human and animal natures, would they have any color before their formation, any more than the metals? Haven't I told you that you could never say you have seen sulphur or quicksilver unless they were congealed? Do you think that the quicksilver and sulphur that you see were from the (137) beginning the same color as they are now? I know very well that they were not, and that formerly they were concealed, as salt is concealed in sea water. (138)

.   .   .   .

Since I have criticized, in the preceding discourse, alchemistic medicine on the effects of generation, increase and fixation, in the matter of metals: I have found it good and proper to criticize also the effects of drinkable gold which I consider to be inimical to the bodily nourishment of human beings.

TREATISE ON DRINKABLE GOLD [83]

Theory

Even if you gave me the best reasons in the world, still you would not make me despise alchemy: for I know that many men do wonderful things, and almost miracles by means of it, for example drinkable gold which the alchemists have invented: a very important and praiseworthy thing. For it almost resurrects the dead: it cures all diseases, maintains beauty, prolongs life, and keeps men happy: what can you say against this?

Practice

What now? are you still wrapped in these dreams? Have you not seen a little book [84] that I caused to be printed during the first troubles, by which I have sufficiently proved that gold cannot serve as a tonic, but rather as a poison, and that many doctors of medicine, after knowing my reasons, agreed with me? So much so that lately, a certain medical doctor and regent of the faculty of medicine in Paris, has confirmed my opinions from his chair, putting them before his (139) disciples as certain doctrine. Even if that were all, it would be enough to refute your arguments.

Theory

How dare you hold such an opinion? seeing that so many doctors have for a long time prescribed gold as a tonic for the sick, and even the Arab doctors, who were the best of all, used it.

[83] There was every reason for Palissy to thunder against drinkable gold. Its supposed virtues were highly regarded in his day and remained so, in France, until the early nineteenth century, according to Morley (1855, p. 458).

[84] The reference is to the *Recepte véritable* (Palissy, 1563). The passage on drinkable gold is quoted in translation by Morley (1855, pp. 396–99).

Practice

I grant you that an infinite number of doctors have boiled gold pieces inside capon stomachs and then have given the broth to their patients to drink and have said that the broth had retained some of the substance of the gold, because the coins were whitened a little on the surface by salt and fat: which was false, for if they had weighed these coins, after boiling them, they would have found them as heavy as before. Others had the gold coins filed and made their patients eat the filings with meat, which was worse than if they had eaten sand. Others used the gold leaf that painters use: but all this served as well one way as another.

Theory

Even if gold is useless to the sick in the form you mention, you can't deny that it does them good (140) when it is made drinkable, for the alchemists who make it drinkable, calcine it to a very fine powder, and when it is mixed with some kind of liquid, it dissolves just as easily as capon fat in broth. Here is how and by what means gold can serve as a cure and nourish the patient.

Practice

You don't understand what you are talking about. For you know very well that furnaces cannot consume pure gold; how, then, would it be possible for the stomach of a patient to digest it, since he is already so weak that he could not digest a baked apple?

Theory

And you are laughing at me: isn't the gold already digested when it is drinkable? The alchemist who has made it drinkable has made it as liquid as clear water.

Practice

You are mistaken and you understand nothing about what I am saying, or else you pretend you don't want to understand: For even though all the alchemists had made gold into a broth more subtle than the fine essence or quintessence of wine, still I would say that they have not made it fit to serve as food. It is true that if they could dissolve gold without any addition then I should agree with them, providing also that it could be dissolved (141) at a temperature at all similar to that of the stomach: For else of what use would a substance be to the stomach if its natural temperature is incapable of dissolving it, as with the meat which it is given as food? But no! they only adulterate, calcine, and pulverize and then add other liquids to make one drink it. Don't I know very well that all hard, dry, and parched things, when pulverized, can be drunk with other liquids? Still, that does not mean that they can serve as food: you may drink sand or other powders: can you then say that they serve you as food? It is well known that they don't.

Theory

It isn't the same thing: for gold is taken as a tonic, the most perfect of all foods, and it is said that a man who would feed on gold would be immortal, because gold cannot be consumed and lasts forever.

Practice

Really, you have spoken well this time: for if a man could feed on gold, what a fine idol he would be! I am surprised that you are not ashamed to put forth such an idea: the more so as this idea is enough to overcome all your arguments. You say that gold is eternal, according to the meaning of this century. But if it is eternal, the human stomach will not consume it, since neither time, (142) the earth, nor fire can do so; how then will it be consumed by the stomach? For the work of the human stomach is to cook and consume what it is given: and whatever is good for nourishment is distributed to all members, to increase the flesh and blood of all that is in man and the surplus is discarded as excrement. Now, I ask you, if a man is fed on gold without eating anything else, could he produce any excrement? If you say yes, then gold is not eternal: if you say no, privies will no longer be needed, nor chairs with holes, for those who would be fed with drinkable gold.

Theory

It is impossible to change your opinions: still, many have written that drinkable gold has wonderful powers. Have you not seen the book printed long ago, which says that Paracelsus, the German physician, has cured a number of lepers with drinkable gold? And you who are nothing but a laborer without knowledge of languages, except the one your mother taught you, do you really dare talk against such a personage, who has written more than fifty books on medicine, who is said to be unique, even a king amongst physicians?

Practice

Even if Paracelsus and all the physicians who ever lived had preached to me, I will always say (143) that if drinkable gold were put into a crucible and sealed in, the liquid that had been put in with the gold would evaporate, burn, and be consumed, the gold that was in the broth would form an ingot, and if the human stomach were as hot as a furnace, it would also form this drinkable gold into a mass or ingot: and if it were otherwise, gold could not be called fixed or eternal, as you say.

Theory

And what about what Paracelsus says, he who has cured so many lepers?

Practice

I suspect that Paracelsus is smarter than you or I. For perhaps after he had found some rare medicine, by means of the imperfect metals, marcasites or other simples, he pretended that it was drinkable gold, in order to make it seem better, and to be better paid for it. It is the smallest ruse that he could have thought of: I have seen smarter tricks in a little town of Poitou, where there was a physician less learned than any in the region, and yet by a single ruse, he became almost adored. He had a secret study very near the door of his house, and through a little hole he could watch the arrival of those who came to bring him urine samples, and when they had entered the yard, his well-trained wife came and sat on a bench near the study where there was a (144) shuttered window, and asked the patient where he was from, and said that her husband was in town, but that he would return soon, and asking them to sit beside her, she asked them when they took sick, and what part of the body was ailing, and consequently of all the effects and symptoms of the ailment; and while the messenger answered her questions, Master Physician listened to it all, and then went out the back door and came in by the front one, through which the messenger saw him come in; then the wife told him: here is my husband, talk to him. The bearer had no sooner presented his urine than Master Physician, looking at it wisely, gave him a speech on the ailment, according to what he had heard from his study: and when the messenger returned to the patient's home he spoke as if it were a miracle, about the great knowledge of this Physician who knew all about the ailment as soon as he had seen the urine, and in this way the physician's reputation increased daily. That is why I told you that perhaps Paracelsus pretended that his medicine was drinkable gold, and that he never had any.

Theory

I don't know what you mean: you just said that perhaps Paracelsus made some kind of medicine for leprosy from some metal or (145) other simples, and then pretended that it was drinkable gold, in order to get paid. Since medicine must be made from metals, why couldn't gold be used for medicine as well as the other metals?

Practice

You are mistaken: your desire to find your cause good prevents you from understanding what I say. For I did not say that Paracelsus used metals, but actually imperfect metals, or some marcasites, or other minerals, such as antimony, which many use in medicine.

Theory

You are trapped by your own words: for since you admit that antimony can be used in medicine, I say to you that gold can be used also, for antimony is a metal, therefore I have won the argument, and you must admit you have lost it.

Practice

You are just as wise as before, to say that antimony is a metal and that it is used in medicine. You know very well that our whole argument is about the tonic value, which is the same as saying the repair of nature: in the first place, you are very wrong when you say that antimony is a metal; for it is certain that it is only a sort of marcasite, or else the beginning of a metal: on the other hand, you tell me that I have said that it is used in medicine: it is, (146) but not as a tonic. For if it could serve as a tonic it could be eaten like other foods. But far from it: for the man who takes more than four or six grains of it is in danger of dying. Now, those who want to praise drinkable gold say that a patient can take some twice a day: hence antimony has nothing to do with proving the restorative effect of gold. For a perfect metal cannot be changed at the temperature of the stomach. But that is not true of antimony, for its action is poisonous, and by its poisonous nature it affects all parts of the stomach, the belly and the whole body, and that is done by an exhalation caused by it, because it is imperfect and has been taken out of the mine before its decoction was perfectly completed: likewise the perfect metals cannot cause any vapor in the stomach, as antimony does. That is how one must speak of these things, with solid proof based on evidence, not fetching celestial bodies, like those who, to prove the restorative power of gold climb into the heavens to fetch the sun, moon, Mercury, and the other planets to the number of seven, saying that they have powers over metals and human bodies: I know nothing of astrology, but I do know that the human body can be fed only with things subject to putrefaction. (147) And since gold cannot putrefy or be consumed in the human body, I say and maintain that it cannot be used as medicine nor as a tonic; and that all things whose taste the tongue cannot draw out cannot serve as food. For God has placed the tongue to feel out the things that are useful for the other parts of the body and it must be noted that when a man is very ill, he is given the tenderest of meats: if he is given fruit it is cooked so that it can putrefy sooner; otherwise his weak stomach could not absorb it to send the nourishing liquid to all parts of the body and the waste to the excreting organs. If a weak stomach has trouble digesting a cooked apple, how can you believe that it can absorb gold, seeing that the body can absorb nothing except those things from which the tongue can first draw some taste, before they can go further. How can it absorb gold? Feel gold as you will with your tongue, you can draw no taste from it. Do you want me to tell you a fine story before I finish my argument? If the tongue could draw some taste from a gold piece, I can assure you that it would lose weight, by as much as the tongue would have drawn from it. Also I tell you that whatever flower you smell, you diminish its power, by as much as you take away with your nose. And again, note this point: all things (148) which you present to the tongue, and draw some taste from it, this taste is nothing more than the salt that is in the thing you taste. For salt is of such nature that it dissolves in moisture and when the moisture is warm it dissolves more quickly. Now, the tongue bears in itself a warm humor which immediately attracts a little of the salt of the things it touches. That is why I say that if the tongue could draw some taste from gold, it would be salt, and the gold would decrease, since the tongue would have attracted some, and since it cannot draw any from it as it does from nourishing foods, it is easy to conclude that gold cannot serve as food.

ON MITHRIDATE OR THERIAC [85]

Now, having demolished an error of such long standing, about the golden tonic, I feel like talking about mithridate, before talking about salts. (149)

Theory

And do you have something to say against mithridate?

Practice

I certainly have: but in order not to displease the physicians, and prevent them from criticizing my works on that account, I shall talk about it only in the form of a debate, taking my argument from what some say, that it takes three hundred kinds of drugs to make it, which I find far beyond me, and I cannot think that so many kinds of simples can be together inside a stomach without harming each other.

Theory

If you put forth such an idea you will get yourself hated by many people. Do you really wish to contradict so many prominent physicians, who have diligently examined the question many times; and it has been debated many times in universities and medical schools? I know that in one German city, the magistrates ordered the physicians of the place to meet and to give their collective advice on some way of fighting the poison of the plague, which was then in the city. Following which, the physi-

[85] Mithridate is a medicine consisting of many ingredients and considered as an antidote against all poisons and infectious diseases. The recipe for it was supposed to have been one of the most prized possessions of King Mithridates, found in his tent by Pompey. The recipe had been absurdly enlarged, as Palissy points out, and in his day it was held in high repute, in spite of the very sensible arguments against it given by Palissy and others. The word theriac also denotes an antidote to poisons.

cians found nothing better than mithridate which they prescribed, and it was made from the number of simples above. That is why I tell you that if you speak against so many learned men, you will be (150) considered mad.

Practice

But isn't it possible that the physicians were mistaken in the composition of mithridate, just as they were mistaken in following the opinion of the Arabs about the golden tonic? For you have clearly understood above that it is a manifest abuse, the wise physicians will not dare find wrong what I say about it: because it is in the form of a debate, and that will urge them to wonder if there is some good in my arguments.

Theory

And what are your arguments?

Practice

They are weighty enough, and among others, I have three particular ones. The first is the consideration of a bouquet made up of many flowers; the perfume of this bouquet will never be as pleasing as if it were made up of one kind of flower only, and by this you will learn that mixed perfumes are so confusing that you cannot decide which one is the first and best of them. Next, if you take a capon, a grouse, a woodcock, a pigeon, and all sorts of meat, all well cooked and prepared, then put them into a mortar and mash them together before you eat them, they will be good; but will you find them as tasty as if you ate them separately; surely not. Next, if you take (151) blue, vermillion, yellow, and all other colors and mix them all together, making a mixture of them, you will find out that the least of them was more beautiful alone than all of them mixed together. That makes me think that so many simples together cannot help rubbing out and destroying each other's power: just like perfumes, flavors, and colors. I pray you also, consider what harmony there could be in a choir of three hundred musicians singing all together. A few days ago I saw a book that the druggists use in making their drugs, and when I asked the druggist to name me in French the drugs in mithridate, he did so willingly, and among others named gypsum and alabaster: which gives me confidence in speaking, for I know that both are indigestible. And when they are calcined, they are nothing more than plaster. I have seen an old book which says that plaster is fatal: because (it says) it blocks the ducts. From this I know that many people write things they do not understand. Because some time they saw holes in a wall filled up with plaster, they have thought that it could do the same in the human body, which is poorly reasoned, for plaster never hardens when it is made drinkable, and if too much water is added to it, it loses (152) all its strength. The argument is therefore poorly based to say that plaster blocks the ducts. I believe it is just as good in mithridate as in other medicines. If I wanted to make up an elixir or medicine from gems, I would first want to know two things: first, of what materials the gems are made, and second, if the stomach is able to digest them. But, since green stones are colored by copperas, they can only be enemies of nature.

Theory

Well, then, for the same reasons you give, many simples are put together because some of them are too rough, biting, corrosive, and laxative. And some of them are even harmful, taken singly: but to correct them, they are mixed with bland materials.

Practice

In this I find a very great difficulty, since I know that a mixture of three hundred simples cannot fail to contain some that are harder to digest than the others; which makes me think that when they are in the stomach, the ones that are soonest cooked are the first to be absorbed as food, according to the natural order; just as I have shown you, by means of certain marcasites, that substances that have some affinity are able to separate and join together in the womb of the earth; this, I think, can just as well be done in the stomach, (153) that is, the nourishing materials will be dispersed in the members and the harmful ones will be excreted, and if, among so many simples there is one that the stomach cannot digest, how can we hope that it will be useful? So I find the elixirs very strange, for they are medicines made from crushed stones, and I know that no other material is so fixed that the stomach cannot digest them. Now, an indigestible material cannot be useful to the stomach.

Theory

How dare you disapprove of mithridate? which has been approved so long, and many people, after eating some on an empty stomach, have been preserved from poison; and more, when King Mithridates had died, the recipe for it was found in his cabinet, among his most valued possessions, and because he took some every evening, he could never be poisoned.

Practice

That argument has no weight against me: because Mithridates' counterpoison was made up of only four simples, to wit, nuts, figs, rue, and salt; that is much less than three hundred. To know if a substance can be useful against poison, one must first know what poison is. Someone has written that there are three hundred kinds of it. If that is so, who will (154) say that a mithridate can serve against all kinds of poison? As for Mithridates' counterpoison, there is some broad reason by which its usefulness can be judged, and to pass on it, one must remember that sublimate, which is the commonest poison, is not of oily but of aqueous nature, and oily materials have no affinity for aqueous ones: It must be thought, then, that he who made up the counterpoison of mithridate from four simples had in mind that sublimate and other poisons, when they are in the stomach or bowels, attach themselves to the spot where they lie and cut into it, and in this way their action is pernicious and fatal: and to prevent this effect, it was necessary that the counterpoison should consist of oily and palatable materials so that the stomach would not refuse them. We cannot deny that nuts are oily and good to eat, figs therefore contain a salt which is so corrosive and dissolutive, that in the region of Agenés and thereabouts, where there are a great many fig trees, those who eat figs before they are ripe suffer from split lips, because of the mordant action of the juice of these figs. The juice of these figs has great power to dissolve viscous things: when painters use white of egg to thin their colors, they put into it little (155) figs chopped up, or else sprigs [86] of fig branches and as soon as these have been stirred into the white of egg, it begins to dissolve and becomes as clear as spring water, without any viscosity. I say this to explain that mithridate made up of these four things can grease the stomach and bowels, by the oily power of the nuts, and dissolve the poison by the power of the figs and rue: as for salt, it is certain that it is opposed to venom, as I shall tell you when I speak about salts. That is how mithridate cannot be harmful: not that it could be useful against all poisons or

[86] The word is *gittes* which Cotgrave translates as "a sprig; or putting out, in a branch."

venoms. If I knew the cause of it, I could talk about it. The venom of plague is invisible. It travels by day and by night as God has ordained. Some say that the causes of pox, plague, and leprosy are unknown. I know that all diseases are cured by their opposites: and if I do not know the disease, how can I know its opposite? It must not be doubted that many things are mortal through their frigidity, and others by their great heat and extreme mordication, and others which stifle the vital spirits, commonly affecting the brain, rising in airy vapor. In the Ocean Sea, around Easter time, a great number of fishes as large as a child are taken, which are called meagres, from which the fishermen make much money. I have (156) many times seen men and women whose body, hands, and face have been peeled because they ate the liver of these fishes, and they say that this happens if the fish is caught when in heat.[87] Now, since the nature of the various venoms is so hard to know, I have said under the form of a debate, that I cannot believe that a mixture of three hundred simples could be as good as that of Mithridates, which is made up of only four.

[87] There may be a grain of truth somewhere in this apparent old wives' tale, but it remains hard to believe that the fish is poisonous because it is caught when in heat.

ON ICE

Theory

Never did I see such a stubborn man as you are: because once you have an idea in your head, it is impossible to make you believe the opposite. That reminds me of one day when you were by the River Seine, opposite the Tuileries, where many people, even boatmen, said and argued that the ice that floats on the river, when it freezes hard, came from the bottom, but you maintained the contrary because of your stubbornness.

Practice

Do you call it stubbornness to maintain the truth? (157)

Theory

What! Do you still persist in your crazy opinion?

Practice

I do, and will do so as long as I live: for I know that what I say is true, that water cannot freeze on the bottom of the river, unless first the whole surface is frozen, and it has entirely stopped flowing: and I don't mind your blaming me for such an idea: for it will serve me as an argument to show that if for such a thing, so visible and easy to know, so many men uphold the opposite of the truth, saying that the ice carried by the river has formed at the bottom, how much more can they be mistaken about hidden things, as they have been with the golden tonic which has led me to argue about mithridate.

Theory

Don't you know that many have maintained to your face that in freezing weather they often see the ice in cakes coming up from the bottom? Don't you know also that many learned men have demonstrated to you by philosophical arguments (which you could not refute) that this was true?

Practice

The more you try to contradict me, the surer I am of my opinion, and no man in this world can make me blush for it, because I know that it is impossible for ice (158) to form at the bottom of the water.

Theory

But since your opponents give you natural reasons, you should also put yours forward: so that one may know if they are better than theirs.

Practice

If I should make an effort to find reasons, I should find a thousand more convincing than those of my opponents. First, it must be taken as certain that if rivers froze at the bottom, as they say, then all the fishes that are in the water would die, and that must not be doubted. Not a cake of ice coming up to the surface but would be filled full of fishes. I suspect you do not know the deadly effect of ice: its harmful effect is such that as the water freezes, it causes a great pressure that the things mixed in it cannot endure; likewise, living things must give up the ghost, however powerful it may be. Look at the wheat when it is frozen, you will not know that it is dead until it thaws. But when it has thawed, you will see that the pressure of the frost has killed the wheat stalk, and that it has died from no other cause. If you wished to make me believe that fishes are (159) harder than stones when frozen, you would be mistaken. I know that the stones of the Ardennes Mountains are harder than marble: and even so, the people of that country do not quarry stone in the winter, for they are very subject to frost: and many times, cliffs have been seen to fall before they were cut: by which many people have been killed, when these rocks were thawing. You know very well that the water of wells is warmer in winter than in summer: [88] for

---

[88] Palissy had no thermometer with which to verify his statement. It is very probable that the water in the wells remained at the same temperature summer and winter but seemed warmer in winter, just as some caves appear to be warm in winter and cold in summer although they remain at a constant temperature throughout the year.

the air, which is warmer in summer time, withdraws in cold
weather, to flee its opposite; and to prove it, don't you remember
when we went into the quarries of Saint Marceau, in which I was
all dripping with sweat, while outside the air was very cold; and
if the weather had been warm, we should have found the inside
of these quarries cold. Some say that for these reasons a man eats
better in winter than in summer: for natural heat stays well inside, helping the work of the stomach. Now here is another example which should be sufficient proof for you. When the rivers
freeze, they begin to freeze at the edges and on the surface, and
when they have frozen for a night, the main stream and the rest
of the water, which is not frozen, goes down and when it has
been lowered a little and has left its ice sticking to the (160) land
of the shore, it happens that the ice falls into the water, carrying
with it much earth and many stones, which cause the ice to sink,
and the ice being in the water and encountering the warmth at
the bottom, begins to melt and as it warms up, the earth and
stones which had forced it to go to the bottom fall off and let go
of the ice, and it being lightened, rises up to the surface: and when
there are many cakes of it, the water carries them along until they
find some bend or obstacle which stops them; and once stopped,
they stick to each other, and in this way rivers are completely
frozen across. This is why they are deceived and are led to maintain that the river freezes from the bottom. If that were so, where
would the fishes live when the rivers are frozen? It is quite certain
that many sea-fishes go to the bottom of the sea during very cold
weather: which can be confirmed by the fishermen of Xaintonge
who during the summer catch meagres and squid in such great
numbers that one man alone salts and dries more than five hundred pounds' worth every year: and none are caught in the winter.
And if that is true for the sea-fishes, how much more so for river
fishes? Even the frogs dive to the bottom, even into the muds,
(161) to stay alive during cold weather. For otherwise all the
fishes would die; some who have lived in Muscovy, Prussia and
Poland say that in winter, the fishermen of these countries go to
much trouble breaking through the ice of certain rivers and lakes:
and having made a hole on one side and one on the other, they
put their nets in one of the holes and through the other they
chase the fish, and thus take a large quantity of fish. Shuffle and
gather your opinions now; you can't make me believe that the
river is also frozen at the bottom, and that the fishes live between

two layers of ice. Another example: consider a little the form of
the ice cakes when the river begins to freeze, they have no other
shape but a flat one, like the glass that the glaziers work with, and
if they are not level, the knobby forms were caused by the second
freezing, because the first cakes impede the water that beats
against them, and afterwards comes a large number of cakes
which are forced by the current to pile up on top of each other.
But if these cakes were formed at the bottom of the river they
would necessarily have the shape of the hollows and concavities
of the river bottom: and besides it would be impossible for them
not to carry with them some of the soil or sand of the place where
they were formed: and if it were true that water froze at the
bottom, (162) the cold would have to come from underground:
which would be contrary to the truth. For if they came from below, then all the springs would have to freeze first, and therefore
wells and the wines in cellars: and if the cold comes from the air
(which is true) and it should cause waters to freeze at the bottom,
then the river would have to be more spongy than anything in
this world, and still it would freeze at the top first, since the cold
comes from the air. But far from being spongy, I can find nothing
more homogeneous: and to prove that, look at water when it is
frozen: for there is neither hole, nor vein, nor artery in it: you
can also prove this by diamonds, which are a congealed, pure
liquid: for if they were even a little porous, they could take no
polish. We must therefore conclude that the cold comes from the
air and that the river is homogeneous or condensed, like crystal,
and that the cold of the air acts on it and could not pass to the
bottom of the water, and that there is a natural heat at the bottom
of it, aided in part by many little springs that come from inside
the earth, which allow fishes to live in the deepest part of the
water.

Theory

Supposing that is so: still, it seems to me that there was no
need to make such a long (163) speech about it, and that the
time could better be used to talk about the other things that you
have promised me.

ON THE VARIOUS KINDS OF SALTS

Practice

I was sure that after drinkable gold and mithridate I would tell you about salts: but you yourself interrupted me, chiding me for the argument I had long ago about ice. Well then, let us return to our subject: For I want to show you that nothing exists without salt. If you are a man of wit (as I think) you will learn many secrets as I talk about these salts which will make you more certain of the impossibility of generating metals: and this all the more so since salts are much used by those who concern themselves with the adulteration, increase, and sophistication of metals.

Theory

How now? You say salts, as if there were many kinds of them.

Practice

I tell you that there are so many kinds that it is impossible for any man to name them all, (164) and I tell you, moreover, that there is nothing in this world that does not contain salt, either man, beast, trees, plants or other vegetative things: even metals: and I say further, that no vegetative thing could vegetate without the action of salt, which is in seeds; what is more, if the salt were removed from the body of man, he would fall into dust in less than a wink. If the salt were taken out of the stones in a building, they would suddenly fall into powder. If the salt were extracted from the beams, joists, and chevrons, all would fall into dust. I say the same for iron, steel, gold, silver, and all metals. If anyone asked me how many different kinds of salts there are, I would answer that there are as many as there are different kinds of tastes and odors.

Theory

If you want me to believe what you say, pray name a few.

Practice

Copperas is a salt,[89] niter is a salt, vitriol is a salt, borax is a salt, sugar is a salt, sublimate, saltpeter, rock salt, *salicor*,[90] tartar, sal ammoniac, all these are diverse salts. If I wished to name them all, I should never be done. The salt that the alchemists call salis alkali is extracted from an herb which grows in the (165) salt flats of the islands of Xaintonge. The salt of Tartary is nothing more than the salt of grapes, which gives taste and savor to wine and prevents it from spoiling; therefore I say again that the taste of all things comes from salt, which has itself caused the vegetation, perfection, maturity, and total goodness of foodstuffs. And although there are many trees and kinds of plants whose salt is more fixed and of harder solution than that of grapes or salicor: still there is some in all trees and plants, I say as much, or nearly so, as in the above. And otherwise, many kinds of ashes would be worthless for laundering clothes; by the effects of these ashes you can see that there is salt in all things. And you must not think that the ashes have power to launder otherwise than by the virtue of the salt, otherwise they would be used many times. But because the salt that is in these ashes dissolves in the water that is placed in the tub, it passes through the clothes, and by its power and sharpness, or mordancy, the dirt in the clothes is dissipated, softened, and drawn down with the water, which afterwards is called lye,[91] because the salt that was in the ashes remains in it, being dissolved by the water, and the ashes being thus desalted have no more virtue to launder clothes, and they are thrown away as useless. Another example: when (166) the saltpeter workers draw out the saltpeter that is in the earth, they do it in the same way as the lye, and when they have drawn out the saltpeter, the ashes

[89] The following passage is as clear and concise a definition of salt as one could wish for without using the language and concepts of present-day chemistry. It is far better, much less mystical a treatment than any of those published previously.

[90] *Salicor* is probably the same thing as modern French "salicorne," the salt-wort, *Salicornia herbacea*, or glasswort, a plant that produces much soda when burned, according to Bescherelle, and therefore the salt derived from it.

[91] It is not quite clear why the water is called lye only after it has been used. In modern French the word (*lessive*, which Palissy spells *lexive*) is an exact equivalent of the English "lye."

and the earth from which they have extracted the salt, are useless: because the salt, which caused the operation, is no longer in them. If you do not have enough examples to believe that there is salt in all woods and plants, consider the tanners: they take oak bark and having dried and pulverized it, they spread it between leathers which they tan in certain receptacles: and when the leather has remained a predetermined time in this bark, the tanner takes out his leather and throws away the bark, as a useless thing: it is true that where wood is expensive, chunks shaped like cheeses are made of this bark which are dried to be burned for lack of wood; but the ashes are worthless; because the salt is out of them. Can't you see by this that it is not the bark that has hardened and tanned the leather but the salt that was in it? For otherwise the bark could be used many times: but because the salt is dissolved and has gone into the leather, because of its moisture, and has attracted it to serve itself. You must note that in all kinds of wood the salt is almost always in the bark: and barkless wood never produces good ashes. Monsieur Sifly, physician to the Duke of Montpensier, some time showed me a stick of balsamum or cinnamon (167) which was about four feet long and about an inch thick: he made me taste the bark which had the natural taste of fine cinnamon: but the rest of the wood had no more taste than a stone. That is why tanners use only the bark: because the salt is in it, otherwise the rest of the wood, when pulverized, could serve as well as the bark. And continuing with my proofs, that there is salt in all things: The Egyptians used to salt down the bodies of their kings and princes, which we call embalming. The histories say that they embalmed them with niter and aromatic spices. You must note that niter is a preservative salt, which prevents putrefaction: nevertheless it could not have prevented putrefaction for so many thousands of years, except for the aromatic spices, whose salt has prevented the corruption of the bodies which were embalmed with them. And further, the flesh of these bodies is called mummy, because of these spices with which they are sprinkled. The Egyptian princes keep this mummy to serve them in their sicknesses. I would rather believe that such a food would be more useful than drinkable gold. Some moderns have wished to imitate the ancients, trying to make mummy with hanged or decapitated bodies. But whoever would try to soak it a little, it would turn into a stinking carrion: because it (168) has not steeped in spices having the same virtue as those of the ancient Egyptians. And so it is said that the odors and *ubarbes*,[92] gums and aromatic spices, are all adulterated before they reach us. And common salt has no power to preserve like the aromatics that come from Arabia Felix and other hot countries. And because our purpose is to prove that there is salt in all things, I shall advance this point, that glass can be made with all kinds of ashes: although some are harder to melt than others: and if there were no salt in wood and grasses, it would be impossible to make glass from them. That is enough proof that there is salt in all things: let us talk of their virtues, which are so great that no man has ever known them completely. Salt whitens all things: salt hardens all things: it preserves all things; it gives flavor to all things; it is a putty that binds and cements all things: it gathers and unites all mineral matters: and out of many thousands of pieces it makes one mass. Salt gives sound to all things: without salt, no metal would ring. Salt gladdens human beings: it whitens the flesh, giving beauty to reasoning animals: it keeps up affection between male and female, because of the vigor that it gives to the genital parts: it helps in generation: it gives voice to (169) created beings as well as to metals. Salt causes many finely pulverized pebbles to unite into one mass to form glass and all kinds of vessels: with salt, all things can be made into transparent bodies. Salt makes all seeds vegetate and grow: and although very few people know why manure is useful to crops, and use it only by custom and not through philosophy, still, the manure that is taken to the fields would be useless were it not for the salt which straw and hay have left in it as they rotted; therefore those who leave their manure at the mercy of rain are very poor husbandmen, and have little acquired or natural philosophy. For the rains that fall on manure, flowing into some valley, take with them the salt of the manure, which has dissolved in the moisture, and thus it will be useless when it is spread on fields: that is easy enough to believe: [93] and if you don't want to believe it, watch when the farmer has carried manure to his field, he will put it (as he unloads it) into little heaps, and a few days later, he will spread it over the field,

---

[92] No translation or explanation of this word has been found.

[93] These ideas are so close to a statement of the essential qualities of manure that they are worth noting as an example of Palissy's original thought. If we judge by comparison with a French treatise on agriculture published twenty years after the *Discours Admirables* (Olivier de Serres, *Théâtre d'agriculture*, 1600), Palissy was far ahead of the experts of his time and de Serres would have done well to study Palissy's book.

and will leave nothing where the piles were: and yet, after a field has been sown with wheat, you will see that the wheat is finer, greener, and thicker where the little heaps were than anywhere else, and that is because (170) the rains that fell on these heaps have taken up the salt as they passed through them into the earth. By this you can see that it is not the manure that is the cause of generation: but the salt which the seeds had taken in the ground. Even though I deduced this fact about manure long ago, in a little book [94] which I told you I had had printed as early as the first troubles, still it seems to me that it is not superfluous here: for thus you will understand why all excrements can help the generation of seeds. I say all excrements, either of man or beast. It is further confirmation of a fact that I have repeated many times in speaking about alchemy, which is that when God made the earth, he filled it with all kinds of seeds: But if someone sows a field for many years without manuring it, the seeds will draw the salts from the earth for their growth, and thus the earth will be deprived of salt and will no longer be able to produce: therefore it will have to be manured, or allowed to rest for a few years so that it can regain some saltiness, coming from the rains or clouds. For all earth is earth: but some are much saltier than others. I am not talking merely about common salt, but of vegetative salts. Some say that nothing is more harmful to seeds than salt, and therefore, when a man has committed a grievous crime, he is condemned (171) to having his house razed and his land ploughed and sown with salt so that it may never produce a crop: I do not know if there is a country where salt is harmful to crops: but I know well that on the mounds of the salt pans of Xaintonge, wheat is harvested that is as fine as any where I have been: and yet these mounds are made of the scrapings from the salt pans: I say the scrapings from the bottom of the tidal flats, which scrapings and muds are as salt as sea water: yet the crops are as good there as in any land I have ever seen: I do not know where our judges got the idea of having salt sown over a land as a sign of malediction unless there is some country where salt is harmful to crops.[95]

Theory

Perhaps the judges do it not because salt is harmful to crops but rather because salt is a seed that does not germinate.

[94] Again, the *Recepte véritable* of 1563. See note 84.

[95] This fine passage on salts and others on chemical subjects brought Palissy recognition as a chemist a century and a half after his death. His chemical

Practice

Say what you will, but I know well that many physicians and others have tried to persuade me that salt is harmful to crops: And that is why I have brought out this point, in order to speak at length about salts: And to continue with my argument, to show you that salt is not harmful to vegetable or sensitive natures, the grapevines of the Xaintonge country, planted among the (172) salt pans, bear a kind of black grape, which is called *chauchetz*,[96] from which is made wine not to be prized less than hippocras, and it is used in cooking, just like hippocras. And these vines are so fertile that one plant bears more fruit than six Parisian ones. That is why I say that salt, far from being harmful to natures, on the contrary favors the goodness, sweetness, maturity, generation, and conservation of these wines. And not only does salt favor these things, but so does the air whose exhalations are salty. In these islands and among the salt pans, is gathered a salt grass from which the finest glass is made, and which is called salicor. Absinthe is also gathered there, called Xaintonnic from the country of Xaintonge. This herb has such power that when it is boiled and its decoction is mixed with flour to make doughnuts fried in pork fat or butter, and these doughnuts are eaten, they chase out the worms from the bodies both of men and children. Before I knew about this herb, worms caused the death of six of my children, as we found out by autopsy as well as by the fact that they often voided them by mouth; and when they were near death, the worms came out of their nostrils. The regions of Xaintonge, Gasgony, Agenès, (173) Quercy, and the country beyond Toulouse are very subject to worms, and few children are free from them: because the fruits of these countries are very sweet. I say that because the physicians of Paris have assured me that it was a rare thing to find worms in children of this place: yet in the region of the Ardennes they are very subject to them. I don't know if it is caused by beer or dairy products. I can give witness only for the countries I have lived in. In the rocks of the islands of Xaintonge is also gathered the *criste-marine* [97] otherwise

---

work is praised by Venel in the *Encyclopédie*. See the article "Chymie," vol. 3, p. 432.

[96] Cotgrave and Bescherelle give the verb *chaucher* to press or tread. In this context, perhaps "pressing grapes" is meant.

[97] According to Bescherelle, the common name for several plants eaten after steeping in vinegar, i.e., as salads.

called saxifrage, which has a marvelous goodness and odor, because of the vapors of the sea; when it is fresh, it makes very
good salads, and many people preserve it for the entire year. In
Paris some have planted this *criste-marine:* but it is far from
being as tasty as the one which grows naturally on the rocks near
the sea. I do not wish to prove by that that common salt is
pleasing to all kinds of plants: But I am sure that the salty soil
of Xaintonge bears all kinds of fruits that are planted in it,
which are as sweet and pleasant as anywhere I have been. The
wild plants, thorns and thistles, grow there as stout as in any
country. It is still confirmation of my argument, against those
who say that salt is harmful to plants. If that were so, it would be
harmful to (174) human natures. The Burgundians will not say
that: for had they known that salt is harmful to human nature,
they would not have ordained that salt be put in the mouth of
little children when they are christened, and they would not be
called "salty Burgundians," as they are. Brute natures will not
say that salt is harmful to them: for goats will eat as much of it
as they are given, and even seek out pissing walls, to lick them,
because of the salt in urine: pigeons, when they cannot find salt
easily, find some old wall, whose mortar is made of lime and
sand, and if it has started to fall apart, the pigeons will be seen at
it every day; and men who live without philosophy say that the
pigeons eat the sand. But that is ridiculous: it would be the
drinkable gold of pigeons: for it is indigestible, and one must
not think that they seek anything else but the lime that is in the
mortar,[98] because of its saltiness, and if they swallow some grain
of sand, it is against their will and intention. Oysters for the most
part feed on salt, and their shells are made of it, which they have
themselves built up; and that this is true is obvious: for when
these shells are thrown in the fire, they burst apart like common
salt. And if salt has power to affect the genital parts (175) (as I
have said) it is certain and generally proved that oysters do the
same thing; which is evidence of what I have said, that oysters
feed for the most part on salt. And the better to show that salt is
not harmful to vegetative natures, let us look at what the Ardennes farmers do; in some parts of the Ardennes, they cut wood
in great quantities, lay it and arrange it on the ground, so that
there is air below it: then they put many clods of earth on the
wood, that is, grassy earth in the form of turfs, then they burn the

[98] It seems that Palissy was wrong here and that the pigeons did eat the
sand, to serve as grit in their crop.

wood under these clods, so that the roots of the grasses in this earth are burned, and when the earth and roots have been exposed to much fire, they spread it on the field as manure, then they plough the ground and sow it to rye: in the place where there were only woods, the rye is very fine: and they do that every sixteen years: for they leave it fallow sixteen years, and in some places six years, and elsewhere only four: during which time the earth being unploughed, produces wood as tall and thick as it was formerly; and as much land as they need they sow each year, so much wood do they cut and burn (176) the clods, as I have already said, and consequently every year, to the number of sixteen: and then they start over at the first piece of land which they had ploughed sixteen years before, on which they find the wood as tall as the first time. I have said this for two reasons, one because my statement on salt is not finished, and because the farmers of this region say that the earth is warmed up in this way, and that otherwise it would produce nothing, because the region is cold; to which I say that, just as water that has been boiled is more subject to freezing than the other,[99] so the fire that they make does not cause the growth of fruits, but we must believe that it is the salt which the burnt trees, grasses and roots leave behind. The other reason is to show how fortunate are those who live in temperate and fertile regions, that produce every year. These poor people are very badly off, when the year is rainy, because they cannot burn their wood at the proper time; in their best years they harvest neither wine nor fruit, nor anything except rye: and in every village the poor man has as much land to till as the rich man. If salt were harmful to crops, it is certain that the wood and grasses that they burn would not better the land but would make it useless: for in burning the wood, the salt in it stays in the ground. If I (177) knew all the virtues of salts, I think I would do marvelous things. Certain alchemists whiten copper with Tartary salt or other kinds of salt, and salt is very useful in dyeing. Alum, which is a salt, attracts the colors of brazil wood,[100] of gall and other substances, to give them to

[99] The observation is quite correct. Boiling drives out the gases dissolved in tap water and permits it to freeze more quickly. Any dissolved gas or solid in water lowers its freezing point. Palissy may have been the first to make the observation in print.

[100] The *Shorter Oxford Dictionary* has an interesting note on the word. The wood was originally that of an East Indian tree from which dyers obtained a red color. Later the term was also applied to a South American

cloth, to leather or silk, so much so that when dyers wish to dye a white cloth red, they soak it in alum water: the alum salt, dissolved in water, will cause the cloth to receive the dye prepared for it, and another cloth which has not been soaked in alum water will be unable to do so. Salt is therefore a handmaiden who takes color away from one and gives it to another. Some salts harden iron and the cutting edge of weapons, so that iron is cut with them as if it were wood. I am unable to describe the excellence of salts nor their marvelous virtues: nevertheless, when I talk about rocks, I shall say some things about them that will have been forgotten here, especially since one cannot speak of rocks without talking about salts.

Theory

You have been talking about salts for a long time, but up until now you have not said a word about the definition of a salt, and yet, the main thing is to know what a salt is.

Practice

I could say nothing else about it except that salt (178) is a fixed substance, palpable, and known by itself, preserver and generator of all things, and in other things, as in wood and in all kinds of plants and minerals. It is an unknown and invisible body, like a spirit, and yet, it occupies space and sustains the thing in which it is enclosed, and if it never felt humidity, many things in which it exists would last forever: as the salt in wood which would prevent it from ever rotting: and if it received no humidity, worms would never form within the wood: for generation can never take place without a humor warmed by putrefaction. If hay, straw and similar things, well dried, without receiving any humidity, were kept in a dry place, they would last forever by the virtue of the salt that is in them. Some salts that hold their form in dry places, turn to oil in humid ones, of which Tartar is one and the salt of salicor is another. This point well understood can help a great deal in understanding what I have said on the generation of metals: therefore it is necessary that you understand all of it: because all things are intimately related together, so that the one makes you understand the other. (179)

---

species. The name of the wood gave its name to the country, Brazil, the *terra de brasil.*

ON COMMON SALT [101]

Theory

I would not have thought that there were so many kinds of salts nor that they had so many virtues, had you not told me: But since we are talking about salts, before we go on, I pray you tell me about the way common salt is made, as it is done in the islands of Xaintonge, and give me a picture of the way salt pans are made: because you know it well, for I have heard you say some time ago that you were there with orders to make plans of these salt pans.

Practice

That is true; it was at the time when the salt tax was to be established in that country. So, since you want to hear about it, listen to me and I shall be glad to tell you about it, then I will show you a drawing of it.

In the first place, you must understand that the sea is almost entirely hemmed in by great cliffs or lands that are higher than the sea. To make salt pans, it was necessary to find some meadow that was lower than the sea: (180) for otherwise it would have been impossible to find a way to make salt by the heat of the sun: And we must believe that if some suitable place for making salt pans had been found in some other part of France that was near the sea, there should be others in many places. Now it is not sufficient to find a tide-flat or meadow that is lower than the sea: but it is also required that the earth, where we wish to make salt pans, shall be firm, sticky or viscous, like that used for making pots, bricks and tiles. A nobleman of Antwerp has spent a great deal of money

[101] Palissy's account of salt manufacture was probably the first to be printed in French. There is indirect evidence of this in the way Cotgrave (1611) lists the technical terms (e.g., *jard, conches, viresons*) used by Palissy and the handling of these terms in French dictionaries (e.g., Bescherelle, ca. 1906) which constantly refer back to Palissy to explain their meaning by appropriate quotations from Palissy.

trying to make salt pans in low lands, on the model and form of those of the islands of Xaintonge. But although he found enough low places to let in the sea water, because the earth was neither sticky nor firm like that of Xaintonge, he was unable to achieve his purpose, and his outlay was lost: for the lands that he had caused to be dug out were arid and sandy, and could not hold the water.

Although our predecessors of the Xaintonge islands had found certain tide-flats or low places, near the sea, and although the earth of the bottom was found to be naturally sticky and clayey, that was not sufficient to attain their ends: for some way of tamping this earth had to be invented, of the kind and in the manner that I will (118, err. pro 181) tell you about later.

If our predecessors had not used great judgment and thought in making the salt pans, they would have done nothing that was worthwhile; having, then, thought about the tide-flats lower than the sea, they found they would have to dig a canal which could easily bring the sea water to the places where they intended to make salt. Having thus dug certain canals, they brought the sea water to a great receptacle that they called the *jard,* [102] and having built a lock on this jard, they made at the end of the latter other great receptacles which they called *conches,*[103] into which they allow the water of the jard to flow in smaller quantities than in the jard, and from these conches, they bring the water into *forans* [104] by means of a pierced log, which they call the *amezeau* [105] which is under the causeways and from the *forans* the water passes, by means of two pierced logs which they call the *pertuis de poelles,*[106] to come into places which they call *entablements, viresons et moyens,*[107] which are made in such a way that the water, from which salt is to be made, must twist and turn a

[102] Cotgrave lists this word but gives only "the first great receptacle, or pond of salt water whereof Salt is made." The word seems to have no English equivalent.

[103] The second reservoir of a salt-pan (Bescherelle).

[104] Cotgrave lists the word but has no English equivalent for it. He says: "A certaine receptacle for Sea-water (whereof Salt is made) conueyed into it out of others by a trunk, or pipe of wood."

[105] "Pipe or trunk of wood" (Cotgrave). See also note 104, above.

[106] "Two trunkes, or gutters of wood, whereby sea-water (for Salt-making) is conueyed from the receptacle called Forans into those which are called Viresons" (Cotgrave).

[107] These terms are more or less synonymous, according to Cotgrave, but they were undoubtedly distinct for Palissy and the salt makers.

very long way and on various levels, before it is allowed to enter into the floors of the square intended for making salt. It must be noted that although the water is made to pass through many enclosed levels to the receptacles, nevertheless, from one receptacle to the other, (182) the water is diminished, flowing from one to the other as it diminishes, in order to be well prepared and warmed before it is placed in the salting areas, where it is made to congeal into salt, that is, before it is allowed to enter these areas. For there are certain little tablets that are raised to let the water flow into the areas, which comes from the *vitesons*,[108] *entablements* and other levels.

But to show that they have not been built without much labor and during a very long time, it was necessary to dig the square of the tide-flat lower than the canal coming from the sea and the jards and conches, to give slope and inclination to the levels and members mentioned above: so as to bring the water to the great square of the tide-flat. And it must be noted that in digging out this great square it was necessary to carry the earth and rubble all around it, which being placed all round, made a great platform which is called a *bossis,* which is used to hold great piles of salt which are called salt cows, and when winter comes, and the time of salt-making is over, they cover these heaps of salt with reeds, which sell well, because of their usefulness. These bossis also serve to go from pan to pan, for men and horses to travel over at all times: they must be very wide, for when someone (183) has sold a salt cow or two, according to the distance, to bring the salt to the ship for great distances, a great many animals are needed to carry the salt aboard, and this is done with marvelous dispatch, so much so that anyone who has not seen this would think these were squadrons about to fight a battle. There are men aboard the ship who do nothing but empty the sacks, and another who tallies, and each animal bears only one sack at a time, and those who tend the horses are usually little boys who, as soon as the horse is unloaded and the salt emptied, scramble quickly up on the horse and gallop as fast as they can to the salt cow, where other men fill up the sacks and load them on the horses, and when they are loaded, these boys hustle them quickly back to the ship. And because all of them come and go in a hurry, it is necessary that the bossis or platforms should be very wide: for the horses would meet each other. See now what industry had to be used

[108] Probably a misprint for *viresons.*

to render the pans such that the earth should not soak up the water that is placed in them to make salt. When the great square had been dug out and the rubble taken away from it, before making the channels and parks, they bring in a number of horses and mares, which they tie to each other, as if to walk them around, then they put them into this great square, (184) where they wish to make salt pans; there is a person who leads the first horse with one hand and has a whip in the other, who walks the horses and mares about quickly, until the earth of the bottom is well tamped and can hold water, like a bronze vessel. And when the earth is thus well tamped, they lay out their channels and parks in straight lines, giving the required slope from level to level, so that no mason or surveyor could level it better, with all the tools of surveying, than they do with water: for water shows them clearly where the high and low places are.

After the earth has thus been tamped, they lay out their channels and parks as if it were potter's earth; that is why I have told you that besides finding places lower than the sea, it would be impossible to make salt pans if the earth is not naturally viscous or clayey, like that of the potters.

There is still another great work that our predecessors had to undertake to set up the salt pans; it must not be doubted that the first men who built some had chosen a place near some natural canal: for if there were no canal, it would be hard to bring the salt made in the pans to the ship on the open sea, for large ships cannot come near the shore, because of their size: hence (185) those who sell salt bring in small boats that come into the tide-flat as close as they can to the salt they have sold; they drop anchor, and thus the salt is brought first into the boat, then the the boat goes and unloads into the ship: and it must be noted that in certain canals boats can come in only at high tide: and to get out at low tide, they must wait until the next high tide: And even though some natural canals were found, still it was necessary to aid nature, so that the boats and little ships could come near the places where salt is made: and we must not doubt that our predecessors were also forced to make canals in places where no natural ones were found: for otherwise they could not gather the salt from the pans: the more so as the platforms are made so oblique that they are like a labyrinth, and that one could not travel one league across them without going up to six, because of the windings that must be made to get out of them:

and if some stranger were trapped in them, he would scarcely be able to get out without a guide, for one must find many bridges, which must be searched for to right and left, sometimes in quite the opposite direction from the one he wishes to follow: for it must be understood that the whole tide-flat of the pans is full of canals, jards, and conches or tide-pools; some of (186) these flats are square and others are long and narrow, others in the shape of a set-square; finally, that the whole region is used as a pan: just as in a city the first builders have usually taken up a square area at their convenience, and the last have taken the spaces and left-overs of the others, as they stood: the same has been done in the pans, for the first ones were placed conveniently as close as possible to the canals and to the sea, and the last have taken the places left, not as they wished, but have sometimes built them very far from the canals and the shores of the sea which causes them to be sold less often: the more so as the cost of carrying the salt is too great.

Others have built pans of little value, because very often they lack water when they need it most, the more so as the canals, jards, and conches are not low enough in the ground to gather enough sea water, and we must note here a peculiar fact which is that in each pan there is a canal built by hand to bring sea water into the jard and other canals like little rivers that are used to bring the boats between many pans, in which the salt is carried to the great ship, as I have said another time: in this way the earth of the pan-meadow is ploughed, trenched and re-trenched for the purpose of the salt, and (187) for these reasons I have said above that if a stranger were in the middle of the pans, even if he saw the place where he would like to go, he could hardly get out of them: because he would often have to turn his back on it to find the bridges. Also because there are no roads or paths except only the causeways which run in oblique lines, and it is not possible to find a road or one's way in these pans, other than the causeways, which are raised high, because all the rubble from the tide fields has been put there, and if it were winter, one would see all these fields covered with water, like great ponds, without seeing the shape of them. Which is why certain painters having been sent to these islands to find out why it was impossible for an army to cross these pans, have been deceived: because they went there in seasons when the water was in the pans, and have brought back inexact plans of them. At the time when it was desired to impose the salt tax in Guyenne, my lord de la Trimouille and general Boyer sent one master Charles (a very good painter) to the islands, to note the passages; this painter brought back exact and accurate plans of the towns and villages: but as for the shape of the pans, his plan was nothing but confusion: because at the time the pans were covered with water; and to make you understand this better, (188) it is necessary that after the hot weather is over and there is no more chance of making salt, the salt-makers, to preserve the pans, open certain bungs of the canals that pass through the jard and conches and allow the water to enter the pans until all the forms are covered. For if they left the pans uncovered, the frost would break them up so badly that they would have to be made over each year: but by means of the water, they are preserved from one year to another.

And so that you may understand that salt is not something that can be made easily and at little expense, it must be noted that it can be made only during three or four months in the year, during very hot weather. And for the first preparation of the salt, the sea water must be taken in the full of the moon of March. For at that time, the sea is higher and more swollen than in any other season, and when it is at its full, the salt-makers open the conduits of the canals and great trenches, to fill this great container that they call the jard, which must contain as much water as will be needed to make salt until the full moon of July, at which time the sea is high again, as in March, and then every salt-maker busies himself with filling the jard: however, whatever labor and hurry the old salt-makers were (189) able to expend, if the summer is very dry, many a pan is idle part of the summer: for when the water of the jard is exhausted before the time, they have no means of replenishing it, except at the time of the great *malignes* [109] (as they call them) which is when the sea is at its superb height. That is why the pans that are near the port, and which can have water at the full of every moon, are much more prized than the others.

Another point must also be noted, which is that if it should rain for a night or a day, even only two hours, while salt is being made, it could not be made for fifteen days after: because it would be necessary to clean out all the pans and remove the water from them, the salt as well as the fresh, so much so that if it should rain every fifteen days in a particular year, no salt would

[109] Equinoctial tides according to Bescherelle; Cotgrave gives "A Spring-tyde; called so by the Salters of Xaintonge."

be made by the heat of the Sun: by which it must be believed that in rainy and cold regions and countries, salt could not be made the way it is in the islands of Xaintonge, even if they had all the other requirements named above.

We must also understand that before making salt, all the water that is in the pans, which was put in them to preserve them in winter, must be taken out: which is no small task; and when they have cleaned out the pans, usually in the month of May, when the weather (190) warms up, they pull out the bungs, to allow as much water to enter as they wish, which they cause to flow through the *conches, entablements, moyens* and *viresons,* so that it may start to warm up, and when it is warm, they put it in by degrees into the areas where the salt is made to cream. And to show you again the expense of these pans, it must be understood that in each pan-field there are two locks made like a bridge, which cannot be built without great expense, because of the size of the lumber: for the uprights must come up from the bottom and concavity of the rather deep canal, and the cross-pieces must be used for men and horses to cross over: they call these bridges, one the *varengne* and the other the *gros mas:* [110] because it also serves to hold back the waters of the jard. Besides these bridges, there are in each pan many pieces of wood that are pierced all along their length, to lead the water from level to level. In each pan-field there must be a log as long as the trunk of a large tree, that is pierced lengthwise, which they call the *amezeau,* and this tree trunk must be very large; and the other logs, which are smaller, are pierced according to their size. I tell you this so that you will understand that when the lumber of the pans has rotted away or has burned, the forests of Guyenne would be insufficient to replace them. And no man who has seen the works of all the pans in (191) Xaintonge but would agree that it has taken more money to build them than would be needed to build a second city of Paris.

Theory

Very well, but those who have written before say that the salt comes from sea foam, and one author (who has written, since

---

[110] Literally, big post or mast. I have found no English equivalent for "varengne" which appears to be something quite like the "gros mas" but distinct from it.

salt is so expensive, a little book on the excellence, dignity and usefulness of salt) has said so, and likewise has said that we would be very fortunate if we had a salt-water spring in France, as they have in Lorraine and other countries.

Practice

You must have understood by my talk the opposite of what they say, there is no need for me to repeat any of it. And as for the author you mention, he does not understand what he has put in his book, and many, believing him, can fool themselves: For even if there were a hundred salt-water springs in France, they would not be enough for half the kingdom. And what is more, even if there were a thousand, they would be useless. For where is the wood to make this salt? I dare say that all the forests of France could not in a hundred years make as much salt from springs and salt wells as is made in a single year in Xaintonge, by the heat of the Sun; not even in one year, but from mid-May to mid-September. For they could not make any at other times. (192) There are wells and springs in Lorraine, from which great quantities of salt are made: but I pray you, think a little about the great expense of it. The cauldron, in which the water is boiled, is thirty feet long and as wide, it is built over a furnace with two openings and at each opening there are two men who never stop throwing wood into them. There are many carts to carry the wood, and men to put it near the furnace, others are in the woods to cut it down. It is certain that every year a thousand arpents [111] or quarters of woods must be cut to supply these furnaces, and the order is that there are four thousand quarters of woods set aside for the feeding of the furnaces: and every year, a thousand quarters are cut, and at the end of four years, when the four thousand quarters have been cut, they start over at the first thousand that had been cut. Now think, if someone in France had a thousand quarters of woods, would he permit the cutting of these woods for the price of the salt that could be made from ten thousand quarters? It is certain that the wood would be worth more, and would bring more money than the salt. And although the wood costs the Duke of Lorraine nothing, still the cost of making the salt with fire is so great that salt is three times more expensive

[111] See previous note (50) on the meaning of this term. The context seems to indicate that an arpent and a quarter are the same thing.

in Lorraine than in France. O how much greater is the well-being of France in this respect than that of the other (193) nations! And although some is made in Portugal by the heat of the Sun, still it is less natural than that of Xaintonge: for it has so great and corrosive a sharpness that many who have salted pork with it have found holes and incisions that the large grains of salt had made in the pork. As for that of Lorraine, it is so far from being as good a preservative as that of Xaintonge, that very often the salt pork of that region is all filled with worms after having been salted. Many foreign kingdoms, who have some quantity of salt in their country, still come to France to get some, and when they have it, they increase and multiply it with their own: the people of the Ardennes know very well that the salt of Xaintonge is better than that of Lorraine, and for these reasons they make sure of having some: they know it by its color and size: for the grains of the salt that is congealed by the Sun are larger than those of the salt made by fire, and we must believe that the salt of Xaintonge is as white as any other could be. But because the earth of the pan is black, those who make the salt cannot get it out of the pans without raking and mixing in a little earth: which robs it of part of its whiteness: however, when the salt-makers begin to make salt, they make it as white as snow, for table use, and make presents of it to their relatives and friends, who live here and there on land where there is no salt.[112] They take this white salt (194) from the very top, before they rake down to the bottom, and without touching the earth below. It is therefore not the fault of the water, if the salt of Xaintonge is not as white as that of other countries. And we must now discard the opinion that it is made from sea foam, as has been believed until now.

Salt whitens all things.

And gives tone to all things.

And thus fortifies all things.

And thus is the companion of all natures.

And thus strengthens the friendship between male and female.

And thus helps in the generation of all animate and vegetative things.

It prevents putrefaction and hardens all things.

It helps sight and eyeglasses.

[112] Palissy says *terres douces*, meaning literally "sweet lands." The context shows that he means lands that contain no common salt, as contrasted with the earth in the vicinity of the salt pans.

Without salt it would be impossible to make any kind of glass.
All things may be vitrified by its virtue.

It gives taste to all things.

It helps the voice of all living things, even that of all kinds of
metals and musical instruments. (195)

ON ROCKS

Theory

I am very glad to have heard this talk on common salt: for I did not think it was made with such trouble, and that would be well worth bringing out. For I firmly believe that none of the cosmographers has ever mentioned it. Now I pray you tell me about rocks: all the more so since you have told me that in talking about them I would learn some fine secrets. I would really like to know what you have to say about them: for some say that they were formed at the time of Creation, and others say that they grow every day.

Practice

Because I have seen you so strongly attached to alchemy, I am glad to talk to you about rocks: perhaps while I talk about their formation and essence, you may be brought around to my opinion. Those who say that rocks were formed when the world was created are in error, and those who say that they grow likewise err. But you must remember what I have said many times while I spoke about fountains and alchemy, that nothing under the sun is at rest, and that all things are worked as they form, and in transforming themselves often change (196) from one nature to another, and from one color to another. If it were true that rocks were formed as early as the beginning of the world, and that they were no longer being made, no more could be found at present. Consider the great quantity of rocks that is destroyed every day: some by frost, which breaks them up as fine as ashes: some by lime-kilns: others by masons and stone-cutters. It is certain that in building a house with stone, half of it will be lost in dust by hammering; also you know that horses, carts and wagons, as they come and go, destroy a great quantity of them. If you have looked carefully at the rocks along the seashore, you have seen how its wild waves have undermined a good part of these rocks. On the other hand the East and South winds cause the dissolution of the salt that keeps the rock together, so much so that it crumbles to dust: and that is why some say that certain rocks are frosty or windy.[113] In truth, rocks from which water has gone out before their decoction was finished, if they are soaked with water when the frost hits them, will not fail to crumble to dust: and that is how rocks are subject to destruction by winds and frost. If you think of all this, you will understand that if rocks had been made at the beginning of the world, and that none had been made since, (197) no more could have been found long since. I am not telling you that God has not created both mountains and valleys right at the beginning, which mountains are caused simply by rock cliffs, as I have told you in talking about fountains.

Theory

And why then have you denied that rocks grow?

Practice

I still deny it emphatically: for rocks have no vegetative soul, but an unfeeling one; hence they cannot grow by vegetative action: but by a congelative increase.

Theory

And what do you call congelative increase?

Practice

It is a fact that will be very useful to you in learning about the generation of metals. I call it congelative increase if one were to throw molten wax on a mass of wax already congealed, and that it should congeal with this mass, which would be increased by as much as had been added. In the same way, the rocks of the mountains are increased by any fall of rain which brings with it a stony material. But the true addition of rocks and the most certain, is that which happens to rocks that are still in the womb of the earth. For just as I have said for metals, that they cannot be generated outside the matrix of the earth (198) and that they must be enclosed in humid and aqueous places, as for the formation of human nature: so likewise the rocks of quarries cannot

[113] That is, subject to destruction by frost and wind.

be generated except in deep and hidden places in the interior of the earth, and there they receive every day a congelative increase, and that is done in the way I have often described, and which is the main basis of my arguments: namely that as soon as God had created the earth, he filled it with all substances. Now, because all stony and metallic substances are unseen in the earth, and therefore in waters, the rains that pass through the earth take up the salts that are also invisible, which salts or metallic matters are fluid and flow with the waters that enter the earth until they have found a bottom that stops them: and if they are stopped by a quarry or rock mine, these matters, being liquid, begin to congeal and harden and make one body and mass with the other rock. That is why I have told you that rocks do not grow, but that they can increase by congelative addition: and that is why all hard-rock [114] quarries have horizontal partings,[115] veins and assemblages, and not vertical ones, which is real evidence that the congelation of these (199) rocks did not happen all at one time: otherwise they could never be split, because they would be as hard in one place as in another. And when one wants to split them, one usually finds certain joints which are called *sins* and which are well named: for it is the end of a congelation made at one time, just as I have said that the congelation of adjoining rocks or quarries, did not happen all at once.

Theory

And where have you found this written down? Or tell me, what school have you been to, where you could have heard what you say?

Practice

I have had no other book than the sky and the earth, which is known to all, and it is given to all to know and to read in this beautiful book. Now, having read in it, I have studied earthly things, because I had not studied astrology in order to contemplate the stars. And having looked very closely at natures, I have learned from the form of many rocks, which were made like the

[114] Palissy uses the word *contigües* which means dense or closely packed, hence hard-rock in this context.
[115] I have translated as "partings" the word *sins* of the original. I have been unable to find the word *sins* with this meaning in any dictionary.

icicles that hang from the eaves of houses in freezing weather, that the rocks were made and engendered by some liquid and distilling matters like water; I have held the opinion for ten years that ordinary water was reduced to rock by some congelative power, and particularly crystal, which I found in no way different from ordinary water. However, as the (200) sciences reveal themselves to those who seek them, I have known for some time that crystal formed in water; and having found many pieces of crystal formed into diamond points, I have begun to ponder over the cause of this: and while daydreaming about it, I have thought about saltpeter, which, when dissolved in hot water, congeals in the middle or on the sides of the vessel in which it has boiled: and even while it is covered with water, it does not congeal. By this means I learned that the water that congeals into stones and metals is not ordinary water. For if it were ordinary water, it would congeal equally all over, as it does by freezing. Thus I have learned by the congelation of saltpeter that crystal does not form at the surface, but instead forms in the middle of ordinary water, so much so that all stones with a square, triangular or pentagonal form are congealed in water. Since learning this, I have found many pieces of iron, tin and silver ore which had crystal forms, which has led me to believe that all these things were congealed in water, as I have said in speaking on alchemy. And in confirmation of what I say, I have known a lapidary (named Pierre Seguin) who had found a piece of crystal inside which was some water that had not congealed, and inside this water was a little black speck that was lighter (201) than the water: for when he turned the stone from side to side, this speck always stayed up. And as this lapidary had had it cut and mounted in a ring, some people firmly believed that a spirit was enclosed in it, not suspecting the secret of this philosophy. There was a man named de Troisrieux, a curious man and with good judgment, who had another piece of crystal in which some water was enclosed, like the one above: but he was badly deceived: for having given it to a lapidary to cut into a teardrop, while cutting it he found a little flaw through which the water (which was not congealed) escaped. I have also found many twisted pebbles that were hollow inside and had many points like diamond points: [116] this has taught me that while these pebbles were forming, they were full of water, and that

[116] Such "pebbles" filled with crystals are now called geodes.

later the ordinary water had evaporated and had left the congelative matter in the form of a hollow pebble. These are the books in which I study.

Theory

And do you think I'm going to believe that water can be reduced to stone?

Practice

I have told you that I have long held that opinion. But now I tell you that it is not ordinary water, but a salty water, which you could not distinguish from the ordinary one. Still, it is fluid and just as clear as ordinary water. And (202) of that I have good evidence: for when I was in Paris last year, 1575, there was a physician, Monsieur Choysnin, whose company and conversation were a great consolation for me, who after he had heard me speak thus of natures, and knowing that he was a lover of philosophy, I asked him to come with me into the quarries near Saint-Marceau, in order to remove all doubt on what I had told him concerning the origin of stones. And he, moved by kindly zeal and without sparing trouble, had wax torches brought immediately, and taking with him a medical student named Milon, we went into these quarries for nearly one league, guided by two quarrymen: And there we saw what I had long since learned by the form of stones that had been brought from Marseilles by order of the Queen, the King's mother, from a cavern called *la Mauve louvière,* which is so named because wolves often go there to eat the goats and sheep that they have stolen. I had also seen a great many such stones at the grotto of Meudon, which have been brought from near the sea. I have also seen them in the cliffs along the River Loire: but when we were in the quarries of Paris we saw being distilled the water that was congealing in our presence. Hence you cannot deny me this point: for I have good evidence. (203)

Theory

Here is a very strange thing to say that rocks are being formed every day.

Practice

I say not only just rocks alone, but also metals, and I tell you that wood and grasses can be changed to stone.

Theory

If you say that, few people will be willing to believe it, and I advise you never to utter an opinion so far from the truth.

Practice

Long ago, I found asses like you who found my statements very strange, and who shouted at me, as at a fox, so that often I was ashamed of it: nevertheless, I always comforted myself with the idea that science has no greater enemy than ignorance. Now no one can make me blush for them: I am too certain of my facts. And I say that not only wood may be turned to stone, but also the body of man and beast.

Theory

That is something more than strange, that man, beast and wood can be turned to stone.

Practice

As to wood, I shall show you more than a hundred pieces turned into stone or pebbles: as for man I have not seen any: but I have good witness from a good man, a physician, who says he has seen in the cabinet of a nobleman, the petrified foot of a man. (204) And another physician has assured me that he has seen the head of a man, also petrified. A certain Monsieur Julles, living in Paris, has assured me that there is a prince of Germany who has in his cabinet the body of a man, most of which is petrified. I am quite sure that if a body were buried in a place where there was some stagnant water, in which there was some congelative water, from which crystal and other metallic and stony matters are formed, that this body would petrify: because the congelative seed is of a salty nature, and the salt of the man's body would attract the congelative matter, which is also of a salty nature, because of the affinity that species have; they would begin to congeal, harden and petrify the dead body, and this I prove by beech wood, which is the saltiest of woods, and from which glass is most easily made.

Theory

That is a statement farther from the truth than the others, in my opinion, and I do not believe that the human body can be turned to stone.

Practice

I say not only into stone, but I say that it can be changed into metal, both man, wood and grasses. And that can be done if a man should be buried in some watery place, where the earth is full of seed of vitriol or copperas. For this seed is nothing else but a salt (205) which is never idle. And, as I have already said, salts have some affinity for each other. The salt of the dead body in the ground attracts the other salt, which will be of another kind, and the two salts together will be able to harden the body of the man and reduce it to metallic matters: because the nature of the salt called copperas or vitriol can do nothing else but convert to bronze the things it finds where it exists. I give you this example as an invincible and very certain point.

Theory

You say it, that it is a very certain point. Yes, if I wish to believe you. That is all the certainty I can get from you.

Practice

I have not advanced these points without being very certain of them. A long time ago I was assured that there is a nobleman, in Auvergne, who has a stake, which has been pulled out of a pond, and was found to be partly wood, partly stone, and the rest iron. Namely, the part that was in the ground was covered with iron, and the part that was above water was still wood. When I heard of such a thing, I made a point of knowing the cause of it: And one day, while looking for clayey earth, I found many pieces of wood changed (206) into metal: And I saw that in this earth there was a great quantity of vitriol: then I knew that, as the wood rotted in the ground it was soaked with this salsitive or vitriolic matter, which caused the congelation and transmutation of the nature of the wood into metallic matter: and because I knew very well that the saltiest wood was changed soonest into stone, I took pains to find out what kind of wood these metallic pieces were made of, and I found out by their shape: for remembering that the place where I had found them had formerly been planted with grapevines, which had been pulled up, to take out clayey earth and make tiles, I saw that these metallic pieces of wood were like branches and trunks of the vines that had been pulled up at this place; then I doubted no longer that these were the trunks of grapevines which had been transmuted from wood into metal: not by means of fire, as alchemists attempt to do it, outside the womb of the earth. For I found and examined very closely that these things had been transmuted within this clayey earth, which is of a cold nature: and for this reason some say that it stops the flow of blood when it is placed on the temples with vinegar. After I was very sure that the grapevine was congealed and transmuted into metallic matter by the power of copperas, I knew that there was still another cause operating (207) and aiding this copperas: And just as the salt of a dead body in the ground in a wet place can attract other salts because of their affinity for each other: so the salts of the grapevine can have aided the congelation and transmutation of the wood; and of this I am quite certain, knowing well that the salt of the vine that is called tartar has great power over the metals. I know that many alchemists use it to whiten copper, which has caused many of them to abuse of it. Some make a brightener [117] from this tartar, which I dare not tell about, fearing that you will think I am a liar: because the thing seems impossible. Hence, having truly learned these things, and being very certain of them, I have considered that I had spent much time learning about rocks, stones, waters and metals, and that old age presses me to multiply the talents that God has given me, and that therefore it would be well to reveal all these beautiful secrets, to leave them to posterity. But because these are lofty matters and known to few men, I have not dared risk myself, until first I had found out if the Latins had more knowledge of it than I: And I was sorely troubled, for I had never seen the opinion of the philosophers, to know if they had written about the above things. I should have been very pleased to understand (208) Latin and to read the books of these philosophers, to learn from the ones and to contradict the others: And being of this uncertain mind, I thought of having signs put up on the street corners of Paris, in order to assemble the wisest physicians and others, to whom I promised to reveal in three lessons all that I had learned about fountains, rocks,

[117] The original has *tire-poil*, literally hair-puller, which Bescherelle explains as follows: "Process formerly used in minting, to give color to pieces of gold and to whiten silver pieces." He does not say anything concerning the materials used. Vannoccio Biringuccio (1540) is not so reticent concerning the process which he describes in his *Pirotechnia* and calls a blanching liquor. Lazarus Ercker (1580) mentions that the blanching of small coins affects the uniformity of their composition.

metals and other things. And in order to have there only some of the wisest and most curious, I put on my signs that no one would enter unless he gave an *écu* [118] at the entrance of these lessons, and this I did partly to see if I could draw some contradiction from my hearers, which would seem truer than the proofs which I advanced; knowing well that if I lied, some of the Greeks and Latins would oppose me to my face, and would not spare me, as much because of the *écu* which I had taken from each one, as for the time during which I had entertained them: for there were few of my hearers who would not have drawn profit from something while they were at my lessons. That is why I say that if they had found me to be a liar, they would have contradicted me thoroughly: for I had put on my signs that unless the things promised on them were true, I would give them back fourfold. But thanks to my God, never did anyone contradict a single word of mine. Which considered, and seeing that I could not have more faithful witnesses, nor of (209) more certain knowledge, I have made bold to tell you about all these well attested things, so that you should not doubt that they are true. And to make you still more certain of them, I shall give you here a catalogue of the good, honorable and very learned men who have been present at my lessons (which I gave during Lent of the year 1575) at least of those whose name and position I know: who have assured me that they will always be ready to give witness of the truth of all these things, and that they have seen all the mineral rocks and monstrous formations that you have seen during my last lessons of the year 1576,[119] which I have continued, in order to have a greater number of witnesses.

Follows the catalogue of these witnesses who have seen the above things before the printing of the book.[120]

And first, Master François Choisnyn, and M. de la Magdalène, both physicians to the Queen of Navarre.

Alexandre de Campège, physician to Monsieur, the King's Brother.

Monsieur Milon, physician.

[118] *Ecu:* "A crown in money," according to Cotgrave, who lists several varieties.

[119] If the dates are correct, there is evidence here to show that Palissy gave his course of lectures at least twice, once in 1575 and again in 1576. Leroux (1927, p. 91) states that they continued for at least ten years.

[120] See Leroux (1927, pp. 66 ff.) for biographic notes on some of these friends of Palissy.

Guillaume Picard, physician, of Saint-Amour, in the County of Burgundy, diocese of Lyon.

Philibert Gilles, physician, native of Muy, in the Duchy of Burgundy.

Monsieur Drouyn, physician, native of Brittany. (210)

Monsieur Clément, physician, of Dieppe.

Jean du Pont, in the diocese of Aire, physician.

Monsieur Misère, physician of Poitou.

Jean de la Salle, physician of Mont de Marsan.

Monsieur de Péna, physician.

Monsieur Courtin, physician.

All these named above, are learned physicians.

Monsieur Paré, first surgeon to the King.

Monsieur Richard, also surgeon to the King.

Messrs. Pajot and Guérin, apothecaries of Paris.

Messire Lordin, Marc de Saligny in Bourbonnais, Knight of the Order of the King.

Monsieur d'Albène, and the abbé d'Albène, his brother.

Jacques de Narbonne, precentor of the Cathedral Church of Narbonne.

Monsieur de Camas, gentleman of Provence.

Nobleman Jacques de la Primaudaye, of Vendomois.

La Roche Larier, gentleman of Touraine.

Monsieur Bergeron, attorney in the Parliament of Paris, a learned man, expert in mathematics.

Master Jean du Clony, diocese of Rennes in Brittany, also an attorney in the Parliament of Paris.

Brunel de Saint-Jacques, Béarnois, of Salies, diocese of Dax, licentiate in laws.

Jean Poirier, law scholar, Norman.

Monsieur Brachet of Orléans, and Monsieur du Mont.

Master Philippe Olivin, governor of the Seignior of Chasteaubrési, a man learned in Letters. (211)

Master Bertolome, prior, a man of experience in the arts.

Master Michel Saget, a man of judgment and good ingenuity.

Master Jean Viret, an expert in arts and mathematics.

Now, long ago I saw in a book that Cardan [121] had had printed, subtleties in which he treats of the reason why there are a great

[121] Jérome Cardan was born in Paris in 1501 and died in Pavia in 1576. He was a professor of mathematics and later of medicine at Milan. He wrote numerous books, among them *De Subtilitate* referred to here; it was pub-

many petrified shells even at the top of mountains and in the rocks: I was quite pleased to see such a clumsy error to have the opportunity of contradicting one so esteemed: on the other hand I was sorry that the books of the other philosophers had not been translated into French, as this one was, to see if perchance I could have contradicted them, as I contradict Cardan in this matter of lapified shells.

Theory

How's that? Do you dare contradict such a learned man, you who are nothing? We know that Cardan is a famous physician, who has been a regent at Toledo, and has written many books in Latin: and you, who know only your mother tongue, what do you dare contradict him about?

Practice

About what he has said, that the petrified shells scattered about the world came from the sea at the time of the Flood, when the waters rose above the highest mountains, and as (212) the waters covered all the earth, fishes roamed over the world, and that once the sea returned to its bed, it left the fishes behind: and shell-bearing fishes have turned to stone without changing shape. Here is the judgment and opinion of Monsieur Cardan.

Theory

Certainly it is very good reasoning, and I could not believe that the truth were otherwise.

Practice

Nevertheless you cannot make me believe such gossip. For it is certain that all kinds of souls know something of the anger of God and the movements of the stars, lightning and tempests: and that is to be seen every day on the sea coast. There are many kinds of birds who, before storms at sea, take shelter in rivers until the storms have passed, and afterwards return to the sea as before. Amongst which birds, there is one kind that is white and

---

lished in Latin in 1556, according to Leroux (1927, p. 123). The same Henry Morley who wrote a biography of Palissy has also published *The Life of Jérome Cardan, of Milan, Physician* which I have not seen but which certainly appeared before 1855.

as large as a pigeon, called gulls, which at times of storms know
how to take refuge in fresh water. One commonly sees the
porcilles [122] which are large fish, come to the sea coast before a
storm, which is a sign that lets the people of the country know
that a storm is near. And as for the shellfish, at the time of the
storm they (213) cling to the rocks in such a way that the waves
could not tear them away, and many other fishes hide at the
bottom of the sea, where the winds have no power to stir either
the water or the fish. Here is proof enough to deny that the fishes
of the sea spread over the land at the time of the Flood.[123] If
Cardanus had read Genesis he would have spoken otherwise: for
in it, Moses gives witness that in the days of the Flood, the
abysses and floodgates of Heaven were opened, and it rained
for forty days, which rains and abysses brought the water on the
land, and not the overflowing of the sea.

Theory

But where would you wish to find the cause of these shells in
the rock, if not by the means that Cardanus has set down?

Practice

If you had thought about the great number of petrified shells
that are found in the earth, you would know that the earth produces hardly fewer fish bearing a shell than the sea: including in
it rivers, fountains, and brooks. In the ponds and brooks, one can
see many kinds of mussels and other shellfish, so that when these
shells are buried, if there is in them some salsitive seed, they will
eventually petrify. (214)

Theory

I shall never believe that there are on land nearly as many
shell-bearing fishes as in the sea, and it is well known that there
is no place in the sea that is not all covered with them, and that
on land and in rivers they can be found only in certain places
and very seldom.

---

[122] "A Sea-Hog" (Cotgrave). Possibly porpoises, although there was another
word for these in French in Palissy's day.

[123] An original, and very telling, argument against accounting for fossil
animals by assuming that the sea spread over the land. Burnet, Whiston,
and Woodward probably did not know about this argument; if they did
they would have had trouble explaining it away.

Practice

You are mistaken in thinking that there are shell-bearing fishes in all parts of the sea: for just as the land produces plants that cannot grow in one country as well as in another, just as the orange, fig, palm, almond and pomegranate cannot grow in all countries: so in the sea there are certain places where mackerel are caught, others where herring is caught, in other places cuttlefish, in others bars, and we must even fetch cod from Newfoundland. All shell-bearing fishes stay close to shore, and grow in part from the salsitive materials, which are brought in from the coast of the land near the sea. And still, one must not hope to find these fishes in all parts of the sea coast. It must therefore be concluded that there are some places where the seeds of the fishes can obtain food, and others not. Just like the plants. I do (215) not mean to say that there are now as many shellfish on land as there were formerly. For it is certain that animals and fishes that are good to eat are so closely pursued by man that in the end he causes them to lose their seed.[124] I have seen many brooks where great numbers of lampreys were caught, where now no more are found. I have also seen other brooks in which crayfish were caught by the thousand, where now no more are found. I have seen rivers where salmon used to be caught, and now there are no more to be found. And that the land and its rivers produce shellfish as well as the sea, I prove by petrified shells, which are found in many places by thousands and millions, of which I have a great many petrified ones, whose seed has been lost, because they have been hunted too much. And this is something that we see every day, that people eat meats that formerly no one would have eaten for the world. And in my time I have seen that there were few people who would eat turtles and frogs, and now they eat all things that they formerly did not eat. I have also seen in my time that they would never have eaten the feet, the head, or the stomach of a sheep, and now that is what they prize most. Therefore I maintain that shellfish, which (216) are petrified in many quarries, have been born on the very spot, while the rocks were but water and mud, which since have been petrified together with these fishes, as you will understand more clearly later, in talking about the rocks of the Ardennes.

[124] That is, causes them to become extinct.

Theory

By this argument, you have done nothing against the opinion of Cardan: for you have not named the cause of the petrifaction of the shells.

Practice

Some are thrown to the ground, after the fish has been eaten, and when they are in the ground, their salsitive virtue has attracted a generative salt, which when combined with that of the shell in some watery or moist place, the affinity of these matters being joined with this mixed body have hardened and petrified the main mass. That is the reason, and you need seek no other. And as for the rocks in which there are several kinds of shells, or in one rock there is a large quantity, of the same kind, like those of the suburb of Saint-Marceau near Paris, those are formed in the following manner, to wit, there was some great body of water, in which there was an infinite number of fishes with shells in the form of a pyramidal snail. And these fishes were formed in the waters of this body of water, by a slow heat, either (217) coming from the sun in the open, or by a slow heat that exists below ground, as I have noticed in the said quarries. I put forth this difficulty, because there is in these quarries a vein of rock, only five or six feet underground, that contains as many shells as all the lands around, and it is scarcely a foot and a half thick, but it is very extensive. The cause which I think most certain is that there was formerly some large lake, in which these fishes existed in as great numbers as their shells are found there: And because the lake was filled with some salsitive and generative seed, it has since congealed, that is, the water, the earth and the fishes. You will understand this better later when I talk about the rocks of the deserts of the Ardennes. And that is why we commonly find, in the rocks of the sea, all sorts of fishes bearing shells. It follows, therefore, that when the water has failed the fishes, and that the earth and mud where they lived have been petrified by the same generative power as for the fishes, we find as many shells petrified in the rock that has been congealed from these muds, as there were fishes in it, and the mud and the shells have changed their nature, by the same power and the same efficient cause. I have proved this point before (218) my hearers, by showing them a large rock that I had cut away from a cliff near Soubize, a city near the sea: which rock was formerly covered by sea water, and before it was changed to stone, there were a great many shellfish of many kinds, which had died in the mud, and after the sea had retreated from the spot, the mud and the fishes were petrified. It is certain that the sea has retreated from there, as I have verified, at the time when sedition raged in Xaintonge, when it was desired to establish the salt-tax there. For in those days I was commissioned to make plans of the salt-pan country: and being in the island of Brouë, which juts out into the sea, where there is still a ruined tower, the people of the country have assured me that formerly they had seen the channel of the port of Brouage next to this tower, and that this tower had been built to prevent the pirates and sea robbers from entering, who in time of war often came for water to a fountain which was near the tower, and this tower is called the tower of Brouë from the island on which it stands, which is called Brouë, from which the port of Brouage takes its name. And because today it is impossible to reach the tower by the channel, we know from this that the sea has retreated (219) from this region, and that it may have advanced as much elsewhere: for example, near the coast of Alvert, not far from the Maumusson channel, which is so dangerous, the people of the country say that formerly they crossed easily from Alvert to the island of Oléron, simply placing a horse or ox skull into a little ditch, or little arm of the sea which connected at both ends with the open sea. And nowadays, ships of all sizes go through there as the shortest way from Bordeaux to La Rochelle or to Brittany, Flanders and England: and before that it was necessary to go around the isle of Oléron. Here is evidence of how the sea, diminishing in one place, grows in another. From which I have drawn evidence that the rock that is all full of various kinds of shells was formerly marine muds, producing fishes. If anybody will not believe it, I shall show them this rock, to put an end to all arguments. And because there are also rocks filled with shells, even on top of high mountains, you must not think that these shells were formed, as some say, because Nature amuses itself with making something new. When I had examined the forms of rocks very closely, I found that none of them can take the shape of a shell or other animal, if the animal (220) itself has not built its shape: from which you must believe that there have existed, even on top of mountains, shellfish and other fish that were generated in certain receptacles [125] or bodies of water, which water mixed with earth and congelative and generative salt, the whole has been changed to stone, with the shell of the fish, which has kept its form. And you must not object that therefore rain water carries some salsitive and generative substance, and you must not doubt this: for if it were otherwise, the toads and frogs that often fall with the rain could not be generated in the air; on the other hand you often see very high walls where there are bushes and grasses, which have been produced and generated by nothing else than the seeds and humors brought by the rains, and unless the rains bring with them some generative substances, they could not aid the growth of the seeds; and even the fruits, watered with saltless water, would soon rot away. This is the reason why I have told you that salt is the generative and preservative glue and putty of all things: nevertheless, I have not said that all salts were combining and mordant: you will find that all petrified shells are harder than the mass of the rock that surrounds them, and this is because they contain more salsitive matter. Now, (221) although I have, by the above, sufficiently disproved the opinion of Cardan on monstrous stones, still I am inclined to give further proofs of my opinion, which is opposed to his, especially since very few people do not agree with him that the shells of petrified fish, in mountains as in valleys, are of the time of the Flood, to oppose which and prove the contrary, I have drawn many pictures of petrified shells that are found in thousands in the Ardennes Mountains, and not only shells, but even fishes that have been petrified with their shells. And to show more clearly that the sea did not bring in these shells at the time of the Flood, I shall show you presently the picture of a rock of these Ardennes, near the city of Sedan, in which rock and in many others, are found shells of all the kinds shown in this paper: from top to bottom of the mountain, although the mountain is higher than any of the houses or even the steeples of Sedan, and the people of this city daily quarry rock from this mountain, for building, and in doing so, find shells at the bottom as well as at the top, even inside the hardest rocks; I can affirm that I have seen some of a kind sixteen inches in diameter. Now I ask (222) anyone who follows Cardanus' opinion, by what door did the sea enter to bring these shells into the hardest rocks?

[125] *Cassars* in the original. Cotgrave, under *cassard*, gives "a chest-like cover, a case-like receptacle; also a Buzzard."

I have explained to you above that these fishes were generated in the very place where they have changed their nature, keeping the form that they had when they were alive. Therefore I will repeat the same statement, saying that inside the above rocks are found many concave trenches, and bodies of water, which enters by the cracks in these rocks, descending from top to bottom, and in descending it is obvious that they petrify in the shape of icy waters that flow from the top to the bottom of mountains. It must therefore be concluded that before these shells were petrified, the fishes that made them lived in the water of the receptacles in these mountains and that since then the water and the fishes have been petrified at the same time, and that must not be doubted. In the Ardennes Mountains petrified mussels are found by the thousand, quite similar to those in the Meus River which is near these mountains. Long ago I examined the shell of the oysters of the Ocean sea: but I never saw natural oysters nor their shells in greater quantity than in many rocks of the Ardennes: the latter, though petrified, (223) still were once alive, and this must convince us that in many places of the earth the waters are salty, not as much so as those of the sea: but they are salty enough to produce all kinds of shellfish. And we must believe what I have said above that just as the earth produces trees and plants, of one kind in one region, and in another region it produces some of another kind: and just as some fields produce ferns and others bloodwort, and others thistles and thorns: so the sea produces some kinds of fish in one place, which could not live in the other. It is certain that oysters, mussels, hard-shell clams, scallops, cockles and all kinds of snails [126] that have a shell like a snail's, all these kinds, I say, live around rocks near the sea, which the other kinds of fishes do not do. Those who go fishing for mussels three or four hundred leagues away, are witnesses of what I have said. And just as oranges, figs, olives and spices could not live in cold countries, so likewise fishes live only where God has pleased to sow the seed of their generation and nourishment, just as I have said above that He has done with the seeds of metals and of all minerals, and of plants. Until now, I have spoken only about petrified shells, and as I was searching and inquiring everywhere about places where I could collect some as evidence (224) of my conclusions, I was told that in the Valois region, near a place called Venteul, there were large quantities of petrified

[126] See previous notes (42–44) on the same words.

shells, which caused me to go to this place, near a hermitage, at the foot of the mountain of this place where I found large numbers of various kinds of shellfish similar to those of the Ocean sea and others. For among these shells are found purple shells and whelks of various sizes, quite often as long as a man's leg, which shells have not been petrified, but are still as they were when the fish was in them; which must make you believe that there were formerly waters in that place, which produced the fishes that have built these shells: but since there was a lack of ordinary and generative water, the mountain could not be lapified, but has remained sand, and if this mountain had been petrified like that of the Ardennes and many others, these shells would also have been petrified, and in whatever place the rock would have been cut, they would have been found encased in this rock, in the same way as those you see in the quarries of Saint-Marceau near Paris. After having seen this mountain, I have found another mountain, near the city of Soissons, where there are thousands of various kinds of petrified shells, so closely packed that one could not (225) break the rock of this mountain anywhere, without finding great quantities of these shells, which give witness that they have not come from the sea, but rather have been generated on the spot, and have been petrified at the same time as the earth and the water in which they lived were petrified. Some time after I had collected many petrified shells and fishes, I thought I would draw those that I had found lapified to distinguish them from the common ones, which are commonly in use at present: but because time has not permitted me to carry out my intention when I was disposed to, having postponed for some years my intention stated above, and having always searched all I could for more and more petrified things, finally I have found more kinds of fishes or their shells, petrified in the earth, than of modern kinds that live in the Ocean sea. And although I have found petrified shells of oysters, cockles, hard-shell clams,[127] *jables*,[128] mussels, angel-wings,[129] razor-

---

[127] See previous notes (42–44) on the same words.

[128] This is some kind of marine animal, judging by the context. Cotgrave lists the word but he is of no help here; he says: "The Croes of a piece of caske; the furrow, or hollow (at either end of the pipe-staves) whereinto the head-pieces be enchased."

[129] *D'alles* in the original; a variant of *dailles* which is explained by Bescherelle as the common name of the Pholad on the coasts of France. I have used "angel-wings," the common name for the same genus in North America.

clams,[130] scallops, sea-chestnuts, crayfish, snails and all kinds of other snails that live in the Ocean sea, still I have found some in many places, as much in unsalted lands,[131] of Xaintonge as in the Ardennes, and in the Champagne region some kinds whose like is unknown to us, and none are found (226) except they are lapified: therefore I have dared say to my disciples that Monsieur Belon [132] and Rondelet [133] had taken pains to describe and figure the fishes that they had found in their voyage to Venice, and I thought it strange that they had not tried to become acquainted with the fishes that long ago lived and generated abundantly in regions whose rocks, in which they have been petrified at the same time as the rocks congealed, now serve as a register or original of the forms of these fishes. Some are found in Champagne and in the Ardennes that are similar to certain purple shells, whelks and other large snails, which kinds are not found in the Ocean sea, and are not seen, except through sailors who often bring some from the Indies and Guinea. That is why I have understood that in many and various places in unsalted lands [134] there was long ago presence and generation of these fishes, and this because, as I have said, some are found that have not yet been petrified, because they could not be, for the earth in which they lived is still earth, or rather sand. But the others, that are in the rocks of mountains, have been petrified when the place where they were has congealed, that is, the water and mud, and everything that was in them, as I have told you so many times to (227) make you understand it. You will see in my cabinet, that I have arranged for this purpose many forms of these fishes, of those that are armored: for few others are found petrified: because the softer parts rot away before being petrified: and to prove this, I have found many shells or armor of petrified shrimps and crayfish which were separated one from the other [135] be-

[130] *Couteleux* in the original. Cotgrave translates "a long and round shell-fish" but it has other meanings also. In this context, "razor-clam" is almost certainly what Palissy had in mind.

[131] See previous note (112) on the same words.

[132] Pierre Belon (1517–64), author of two books on "fishes," a term under which he included all marine animals.

[133] Guillaume Rondelet (1507–56) of Montpelier, in southern France. His book *De piscibus marinis* also gives a very comprehensive meaning to the term "fish." Palissy uses it in much the same way, e.g., *poissons armés*, shellfish or Mollusca and Arthropoda.

[134] See previous note (112) on the same words.

[135] That is, had fallen apart.

cause putrefaction had attacked the meat, before petrifaction: however I have found in the Ardennes Mountains some of those large mussels that commonly live in ponds, in which the fish was as well petrified as the shell. And since we are talking about rocks, we must first study their forms, and in searching for their cause, I have found that crystal takes form in water, and that otherwise there would be no points or faces such as one sees in crystal. I find also that all marcasites and minerals having some pentagonal, triangular, quadrangular or hexagonal form are all formed in water, as I have said above, that some iron ore rocks are found with pointed shapes. In the quarries where slate is produced in the Ardennes country, there is in the water, among the slates, a great quantity of naturally square marcasites, (228) formed with four squares, or polished faces equal in size, and these marcasites are the color of iron or lead, and rather smooth.[136] I have seen others that have seven or eight faces naturally formed like the above. A certain gentleman has assured me that some are found in Languedoc and Provence, of which marcasites each has thirty-six faces divided into equal parts. Now all these forms are not made and cannot be made save in water. We see also that the salt that is congealed in water, if it is allowed to congeal without moving it, it will take some pentagonal or quadrangular form; as I have said for saltpeter. But as for the pebbles and other peculiar rocks that have no divided shape, they take their form according to that of the hole or container where the material will stop and where they congeal: and that kind of rocks or pebbles is being formed every day: for toward the end of summer, when grasses, straw, hay and other herbage begin to rot in the fields, rain water picks up and carries away the vegetative salt that is in these straws and grasses, and in all plants that are burned by heat, and when it is thus dissolved and liquid in the earth, the salt itself causes the generation of new plants and rocks. And this kind of stones is commonly made according to the size of the material, (229) sometimes large and sometimes small, and sometimes as fine as sand, according to the small amount of material available. As for the great dense [137] rocks I have talked enough about them

[136] Palissy says *assez visantes*, which is not quite clear. Cotgrave gives "Ayming, levelling at" for *visant*. Palissy has already said that the marcasites are polished; perhaps by *visantes* he meant that they were "level" or smooth, or perhaps he meant that they were regularly shaped.

[137] Palissy's word is *contigües* but the context indicates that he means

at the very beginning. There is another kind of rocks from which whetstones are made to sharpen all kinds of cutting blades. If you look at them very closely and consider the roughness of these stones, you will find that they were originally made of sand, and after the sand has been in the ground a while, it happened that by the action of rain, this sand has soaked up waters and congelative salts that have gathered and joined together all these grains of sand into a large rock, and because the sand is of purer water than the second generation of the rock, that is why it is harder than the second mass, and hence this mass, being softer, is broken up and spoiled in sharpening irons: therefore the grains of sand always remain higher, and the depressions between the grains cause a sharpness and roughness in the whetstone, from which is derived its power and action in sharpening tools. And this is what has given me knowledge of these things: one day I bought a full *muy* [138] of Etampes sand, and in sieving or shaking it, I found many stones made of this sand, so stuck together by the secondary liquor which had agglutinated this sand (230) that one could see clearly that these rocks were made of this sand. Here is how little by little I have come to know about these things. There is another kind of rocks which have no shape, yet are dense [139] like the rocks of quarries, and that kind cannot be produced unless it is at least as hard as marble. These are the rocks produced by clayey soils which are very often changed to marble, jasper, chalcedony and other such hard stones. But because I wish to treat separately of hardness, weight and color, I shall keep this item to treat of it when the time comes, and shall continue to speak of shapes, of which I have good knowledge. As for petrified wood, it keeps its shape as before: there are many kinds of fruits which, once lapified, keep the same shape as before: I have lost a petrified pear as well formed as it was before it changed its substance. I still have in my cabinet a petrified quince, a fig and a turnip, having the same form as they had before they were petrified. Monsieur Race,

---

dense. Cotgrave gives "Neere adioyning, fast by, close together, touching one another."

[138] The *muy* or *muid* is a measure of volume which Cotgrave does not translate but he does give us its equivalent in English measure of his time; it is "about five Quarters, a Combe, and a Bushell of London measure." The value varied somewhat, for Cotgrave says that a muid or coal was ". . . about 30 of our Bushels."

[139] See note 137 on the same word,

a famous and excellent surgeon, has shown me an entire petrified crab; he has also shown me a petrified fish and many stems
of a certain herb, also petrified. I have also seen many sea-
chestnuts (231) petrified without having lost anything of their
form. There is in the city of Angers a master goldsmith, named
Marc Thomaseau, who has shown me a flower turned to stone,
a most admirable thing, since in it are seen the top and bottom
of the finest and most delicate parts of the flower. I have found
a deposit of clay earth in which there is an infinite number of
metallic marcasite stones of many sizes, the ones as large as the palm
of the hand, the others like *jocondales* [140] and *testons,*[141] which
have taught me more philosophy than Aristotle: And it is because I
cannot read Aristotle and have read much in these marcasites,
and have understood through them that the generative materials
of metals are fluid, liquid and aqueous, and this I have learned
by examining their shape: for they are formed in such a way
that, if one had thrown down melted wax in fair quantity, and
as the first was thrown down in greater quantity than the second, and being thrown down in ever smaller quantities, in hard-
ening it would take a more flattened form than the second, and
the second more flattened than the third, and this would happen
because of the lessening of the material. For I saw clearly in
these marcasites that the drops that fell last, showed signs of
lessened material. This (232) cannot be understood easily without
seeing the thing itself: therefore you can come and see it in my
cabinet. There are many other stones that are formed after the
subject they have taken, such as some other stones which I have
seen, which are called eagle stones. Whatever is said about them,
I think they are nothing more than lapified fruits, and that
which rattles inside them is the pit which, being worn down
when the stone is shaken, strikes both sides of it.[142] That is how
stones can have various shapes through various subjects: which
things are unknown to us for lack of looking into it. Many have
assured me that there is a lake at Rome, named Thioli [143]

[140] Cotgrave gives "A Daller; a piece of money worth about 3 s. sterl." Could
jocondale be a French adaptation of Joachimsthaler?

[141] See note 65 on this word.

[142] Palissy was quite wrong in this opinion. See Adams (1938, p. 98) for
a summary of ancient ideas on eagle stones. At least, Palissy's opinion is less
fanciful than that of his predecessors who thought that eagles needed one
in their nest before they could lay their eggs.

[143] Lake Tivoli.

whose waters flowing along its banks, stick to and congeal on the grasses, and other things that hang from the banks; I have seen many of these stones, which have been brought from this lake, which are very white and beautiful, because of the pores and open, spongy cavities masked by the various forms which the grasses have given them. I shall end the subject of shapes, and speak of the cause of colors.

There are a great many materials that cause the colors of stones, and many of them are unknown to man; still, experience, which at all times is mistress of the arts, has shown me that iron, lead, silver and antimony can yield no color except yellow. (233) Having therefore such a certainty, I can safely say that many yellow stones have taken their color from one of these minerals: I mean when waters pass through earth in which there is seed of these minerals, having brought with them some of the said substance, which will have acted in the coloring and congelation; for all these metallic materials are salsitive, and, as I have said so many times, no congelation takes place without salt; also this coloring came about at the same time as the essence of the rock, before the materials were hardened. I include in the yellow stones, rare stones as well as common ones, such as topaz. I also include in them sand, of which there is much of a yellow color. Here is one cause of yellow stones. There is another very certain and true cause, that wood, rotting in the ground, having given off by dissolution and putrefaction the salt it contained, and that the waters and congelative materials (by a *defluxion* [144] which occurs in rainy weather, the salt of the wood carrying its dye with it) cause the congelation and the color of some rock which will be formed in the nearest container where such fluid material comes to rest: and this must not be doubted, for I know that the yellow glass made in Lorraine for the glaziers is made from nothing else than rotten wood which is evidence (234) for what I say, that wood can stain wood yellow: if you have looked some time ago at planks or floors and other lumber when the wood was green and freshly sawed, if it rains on it, you will see that the water that drips from it will be yellow. There are also many kinds of grasses and plants that can stain the materials from which rocks are made: among others, oat straw carries a strong yellow dye. Xaintonnic absinthe has a strong yellow dye: it is also known

[144] Bescherelle gives this as an older synonym of fluxion. The context indicates that here it means approximately the same thing as leaching.

that dyers use a grass which they call weld, from which they make their yellows.

I know no plant or mineral, nor any matter that can dye rocks blue or azure, except *saphre* [145] which is a mineral earth, extracted from gold, silver and lead, which has little color except gray, with a little violet: yet when this *saphre* combines with glassy materials, it makes a marvelously beautiful azure: can we know by this that all azure colored stones have taken their dye from *saphre*? And so that you may have sure confirmation of what I say, consider a little the stones that are called lapis lazuli, which are of azure color, as bright as any in the world, and in these stones are found many little veins and flakes of gold; also in them are found (235) green areas resembling the chrysocolla of the ancients which we now call borax. Those who now make borax make it white by some process that they keep very secret. The borax of the ancients which they call chrysocolla, was gathered in streams that flowed from copper and *saphre* mines. And since I have told you so often that there was salt in metals and that their congelation was accomplished through this salt, you must now note this point above all others, which is that chrysocolla or borax is nothing but a salt that water has picked up in passing through copper mines: and the fresh rain water in coming out and flowing from the mines, having drawn out this salt, evaporates, and having evaporated the solid remains, which is the salt that congeals alongside the outer streams, where the water has brought it: thus congealed, it was used to solder gold, silver and copper. Now, do note that this chrysocolla was green only because of the copperas salt, which had generated the copper mine. It was not my intention to speak here of green colors, but of azure: but since there is green in lapis lazuli, I could not avoid speaking of both together. By that you can understand that *saphre* is gathered in gold and copper mines: for if there were no gold in the mine of this *saphre*, it would not be found in lapis, and if there were no (236) copper, it would not be green. That is how matters are collected together and how little by little, the occasion is presented of always producing the virtue of salts.

[145] Bescherelle gives this word but spells it *safre*. He notes that it is an old-fashioned word for cobalt oxide after it has been roasted to rid it of arsenic. Cotgrave also spells the word *safre* and gives: "A heauie minerall, which melted with glasse, or some other the like substance (for alone it will not melt) resolves into a blewish water, wherewith glasses, and earthen vessels be painted."

Theory

It seems to me that your argument is very far from the truth, and this inasmuch as you say that *saphre* causes such a fine color in lapis, and yet you say that this *saphre* has neither a vivid nor beautiful color; how then could this be? Could *saphre* yield something it does not have?

Practice

Certainly your argument is well founded: still I am very sure that azure glass is made with *saphre,* and I also know well that before it is melted with glassy materials it has no color: Also I know well that saltwort gives it its bright color: though it has no color, no more than common salt, that is to say it causes it to melt or liquefy with pebbles or sand: and I also know well that the three materials together produce a very fine azure, I say after the materials are liquefied and then hardened, and made into whatever kind of glass vessels one wishes to use them for.

Theory

I have now two arguments to put before you against what you say; in the first place you say that the salt of saltwort causes *saphre* to turn azure color, (237) and then you say that this is done by means of fire. Therefore lapis lazuli cannot acquire its color by these two means, since there is neither fire nor saltwort where it is found.

Practice

To this I reply that salt of vitriol does in the earth what saltwort does in the glaziers' fire. As for the decoction, it is not unusual for many decoctions to take place in the womb of the earth. For it happens in all kinds of stones and metals, and even in clayey earth, the ones that are black at first become white later.

Theory

And do you wish to conclude from this that no other material but *saphre* can produce azure color?

Practice

I know of no other.

Theory

Therefore you know nothing about it: for it is obvious that lapis and sapphire are of a bright azure color, and yet turquoise is more bluish than any other color: nevertheless there is a great difference between them: for it is a little greenish: on the other hand sapphire is transparent and turquoise and lapis are opaque. I prove by this that these different colors cannot be found in the same subject. (238)

Practice

You delude yourself: for the reason why sapphire is transparent and diaphanous is that it is formed of aqueous, pure and clean materials, but that is not true of lapis: for with the materials of the latter, earth is mixed which gives it its opaque color. Hence lapis is much weaker, as one can see that it has many veins where it cannot take as fine a polish, in one place as in another: the little veins of gold and the green parts of it give witness that the materials of its essence are poorly mixed. As for turquoise, the same argument must be used, that is, that it contains earth which makes it dark, and its greenness is caused by nothing else but some copper substance mixed in with the other materials. That is why one must always give the honor of all azure colors to *saphre,* as its main foundation; the stones that have a purple color are made of similar materials, save that there is some kind of red material that turns the azure to a purple color.

Theory

You say you know of no material except *saphre* that produces azure, yet some people make it out of copper.

Practice

It is not according to nature if they do so, it is by accident. (239)

Theory

And how could you maintain that only *saphre* produces azure, when we see so many thousands of blue flowers, and among others, the blue flag [146] from which blue color is made?

[146] Palissy uses the word *flambe* for which Bescherelle gives *iris des marais.* Cotgrave says: ". . . also the blew Flowerdeluce (called otherwise) Garden flags. . . ."

Practice

Your answer is not to the point: for I speak to you about the colors of stones, and you answer me about painters' colors. It is a long way from mineral colors to the colors made from plants: for all those made from plants do not last long, as saffron, bladder green,[147] sunflower and other similar colors. But those of the rocks that come from mines or are made from calcined metals cannot lose their color.

Theory

Even though you are a good arguer, still you have caught yourself this time, so that you cannot justify yourself: since you told me before that yellow stones could take their color from rotten wood and various kinds of plants, and now you say quite the opposite.

Practice

What I have said is well said and I am not ready to unsay it. When I told you that rocks sometimes could be dyed by rotten wood and plants, I did not tell you that the rock could be dyed after its materials were hardened: but I did tell you that when (240) materials are liquid and flowing, they can be dyed by some woods and some kinds of plants and the materials once they are hardened can retain these colors: and the reason why they can obtain their color, like those of painters, is that they are enclosed in the mass, and since neither air nor wind can penetrate into this mass, their colors are preserved in it. If you ask painters about colors made with plants, they will tell you that they are subject to fading; and to understand this fact better, consider a doublet, you will find some lapidaries who will make very fine ruby and garnet color, from dragon's blood or other material, and having cut two pieces of crystal they will stain one with this red color, and then will cement the other on top of it, and thus the red will preserve its beauty between the two stones: otherwise it could not keep its color. In the same way, natural colors keep their colors enclosed within themselves. I have two more arguments to give you about this, one is that when I told you that the colors of stones can sometimes come from wood and

[147] In the original, *verd de vessie;* here translated literally. I have found no clue to its meaning.

plants, I did not talk about flowers, for the colors of flowers are of little duration, as one sees that roses, carnations and other flowers lose their colors in a moment; but that is not so for colors that come from (241) rotten woods: for I have told you above that rotten wood is used to make yellow glass. It is just as if I told you that the dye of the wood has been fixed in its putrefaction and cannot be lost for this reason, in the extreme heat of the oven, an admirable thing. Similarly there may be many simples whose dye can be fixed. Now, here is the second argument, which is very noteworthy. If you point out that the colors of plants cannot be stable, I will answer you the above, that rotten wood produces yellow glass. And assuming that you should not be satisfied with such a proof, I shall tell you that among all colored stones, few will be found whose dye is stable. I have many times calcined black marble, black pebbles and rocks, and others of various colors, such as jasper, chalcedony, and figured marble: but I have never found any whose colors were not lost in fire: and although agate and chalcedony cannot be calcined, but rather are vitrified, still when they are searched with fire, they lose all their colors: from which one must no longer doubt that plants cannot give any color to the material of stones, before they are hardened, as I have said before. As for emeralds, it must not be doubted that their colors are caused by copperas, that is to say of some pure water that has passed through (242) copper or copperas mines. As for black stones, their dye can be caused by several means and many kinds. We have many trees whose dye is black, as well as gall nuts,[148] among others the black ones, alders or *vergnes* [149] yield black dye; when they are rotten in the ground their dye can be retained to serve sometimes in the generation of stones: at the very least the earth where they rot will be stained black. I have also often thought that rocks are very often of the color of the earth where they are generated, and those that are in sand are also very often of the color of the sands where they are found: Nevertheless white stones are often found in black earth, and that happens because the materials from which they have been formed have changed color in their decoction, which happens often to many minerals, and generally to all the fruits of the earth, which have a different color when

[148] *Noix de gale* in the original. Cotgrave gives "A Gall, also an Oak-apple."
[149] Cotgrave translates this as alder. Bescherelle says it is the ancient name for alder.

they are ripe than at their beginning. As for the colors of figured marbles, jaspers, porphyries, serpentines and other such kinds, their colors are caused by various drips of water that fall from the surface of the earth to the place where these rocks are formed: the waters coming from many and various places in the earth, in descending bring with them these various colors (243) which are in these stones. For as part of the water, in flowing will find some mine of copper or copperas, it will make green stains on the rock, falling drop by drop on it. Other drops will fall at the same instant which will pass through an iron mine and falling (as I have said) on the receptacle in which this stone will form, these drops will congeal yellow. Other drops will carry other various colors that will cause many patterns on the rocks.

Theory

If it were as you say, the patterns would all be round, as in porphyry: yet we see in jaspers, marbles and mixed rocks, patterns made according to strange designs: that proves that they are not made by dripping water, as you say.

Practice

If you had attended my lessons, you would have realized that what I say is true: for many men were there who are a little more learned than you are, and yet I showed them that the truth is just as I tell you, and there was never one who could contradict me. It is true that to make them understand my idea I made a drawing of it in their presence. It is true that if the drops that fall congealed as soon as they have fallen, they would all be round, (244) according to the size of the drop that falls: but since the material in congealing forms bumps, the materials that fall from many places at once, finding the surface uneven, are forced to flow into low places: and thus if three or four streams of water of various colors fall on a bump or little mountain, they will be forced to flow down from it, and in flowing each will form a vein of the color it carries: and in addition, as they flow quickly, by the violence of their descent, they will mingle as they whirl like two rivers meeting, and moreover another flow or two or three may take place on the same spot, which in jostling and pushing each other will not fail to make confused patterns. As for porphyry or other rocks with round patterns, they can be made where the waters fall, as the drops fall, and as they fall many little drops separate from the big ones, as we see in porphyry. I have also seen porphyry that had been made in another way which is that some sandy earth had congealed, and with it the sand that was in it, and when this porphyry was cut the whiter grains of sand served as a speckling. To understand how chalcedony and many kinds of jasper (245) have acquired their colors, one must examine clayey earths, and one will find that many of them have the same colors as chalcedony. Some clays also have patterns like those of agate. I shall leave the rest to say when I talk about these rocks.

Theory

You promised me a while ago to tell me why some rocks are harder than others; you would please me if you would talk about this.

Practice

It is an easy point to demonstrate: and to do so I shall send you nowhere but in the quarries of Paris, whose rocks are soft at the top, down to about ten or twelve feet, and these soft rocks are called rubble-stone because they are poorly consolidated: but underneath this rubble is rock called *liais* [150] which is so dense that it can be cut to any size desired, and these rocks are very hard, and are commonly made into steps for staircases, and also facings for monuments. This proof should suffice you: for you will be able to see in these rocks that the reason why they are harder underneath than at the top is none other than that the waters that go through the earth flow downward, and having found the bottom floored with some clayey earth, through which the waters could not pass (246) as quickly as they did above, they have been stopped; and when the first bed has been congealed it has served as a vessel to retain the other waters descending through the ground, and by this means these rocks always had ample water, which is the reason why they are much harder than those at the top. And you must note that the rocks at the top are soft only because the waters cannot remain in them until con-

---

[150] Cotgrave says "A verie hard free stone whereof staire-steps, and tombe-stones be commonly made." Bescherelle gives much the same explanation. There may be some connection between this word and the geologic term Lias.

gelation is complete. And this lack of water is due to two main causes; one is that which I have said, that the waters always go down and leave the heights, the other is that the ground is dried in summer by the power of the sun, and that is why it cannot produce stones in their perfection: and such upper stones could be called marcasites, because above metallic mines, and in many other places, imperfect metals are found, which are called marcasites because of their imperfection. And just as the rocks congealed in the lowest and most watery places are more perfect than the others, so we see that the most perfect metals are very often found in water, which must be pumped off with much work. It must therefore be taken as certain that there are two causes that give hardness to rocks, the one is the abundance of water, the other is long decoction: for many rocks can be generated (247) from water which nevertheless will not be hard. We have a very fine example of this in the plaster quarries of Montmartre, near Paris, for in these, there are certain veins of a plaster that is called *hif* or *mirrors* [151] that splits like slate, as thin as sheets of paper, and is as clear as glass. It is like a kind of talc; its diaphanousness or transparency easily shows us that the greater part of its essence is nothing more than water: nevertheless it can be calcined, and it is worked just like the other plaster. It must be concluded from this that too quick congelation cannot permit rocks to harden: And this we can know in places where plaster is found. For it is a sandy country and the ground is dry, and in this same place, next to the plaster quarries, are certain rocks whose stones are very light, soft, and clinging to the tongue, like *boliarmeny*,[152] and these rocks are very poorly condensed. That is how I prove that rocks that lack water too soon cannot be hard. To know well a rock that has lacked water during its formation: in the Bigorre country, there are no rocks, but only hard pebbles: the country is cold and very rainy: and there are many rivers for it is very near the mountains: therefore in the formation of rocks in this country there can be no lack of

[151] Common names for laminar gypsum or selenite. "Hif" was also spelled "gif" which may indicate a relationship with "gypse."

[152] A French adaptation of *bolus Armenus*. There is another variant, *bol d'Arménie*, in Palissy (1580, p. 337). Bescherelle's explanation is so interesting that a translation is given herewith: "Sealed earth, red ochreous clay . . . not only in Armenia but . . . in Tuscany, Sicily, France. Techn. Powdered red ocher and calcined gypsum with which gold beaters rub the leaves of gold leaf books to prevent the gold leaf from sticking together."

water: so they are forced (248) to make their masonry from pebbles, which cannot be cut, because of their hardness. In the Ardennes, the land is very sandy, and their quarries are of nothing else but this kind of earth: but because the country is very rainy, the rocks are very hard, sharp, and displeasing: so much so that those who build are forced to fetch soft rock from France, to cut the uprights of chimneys, capstones,[153] cornices, friezes and architraves: for they could not fashion their moldings from the rock of the country. The quarrymen who cut it do quite the opposite of those of Paris, for they take only the top, and when they have removed the least dense, and begin to find that which the Parisians call *liais*,[154] they are forced to leave it because it is too hard. The quarries I speak of are of such a kind as one seldom sees. For after a bed of rock a foot and a half or two feet thick has been found, there is another bed of sand under it, and all the rocks of this region are so made, and the sand that separates the beds of rock is as hard and as dense as the white stone that they fetch from France, to cut their window frames: which I find very strange, and cannot believe anything else except that the sand has started to petrify. In the forests of the Ardennes there are great quantities of pebbles of (249) many sizes and colors, which are found in greater quantity along the brooks that run through the valleys, because the rain water that comes down from the mountains brings with it the salt of rotten wood to the brooks of these valleys, which is another proof that rocks and pebbles cannot harden unless there is abundant water. And ordinarily the hardest ones are found in cold and rainy countries, as one sees for example in the Pyrenees, where fine marble is found. There is also some at Dynan [155] which is a cold and rainy region. In the mountains of Auvergne, crystal is found, and all this is accomplished only through abundant water and cold. It is well known that at Fribourg in Briscot,[156] the beautiful crystal is found in mountains in which there is snow nearly all the time: and according to what I have said of the Bigorre country, that only pebbles are found there, because the country is rainy and cold, the same can be said of a large portion of the regions

[153] Palissy uses the word *croisées,* an architectural term which Bescherelle explains as *croisement des nervures d'une voûte d'arête.* Keystone (of an arch) may be what is meant here.

[154] See note 150 on this word.

[155] Dinant, Belgium.

[156] Fribourg-en-Brigau.

bordering the Ardennes, and especially along the road from Messières to Anvers: the most marvelous thing I have yet seen. For along the Meuse River in the Liège region, this river flows between mountains that are of marvelous height; they are formed in the main of the same material as white pebbles, and other parts are gray, and so that you will not think the mountain is made (250) of various pebbles, I say that a large mountain will be only a pebble. And I say to you further that many of them produce neither trees nor plants; because of their great hardness they are useless: because they could not be cut to use in building, and under them, deep in the earth, are slate quarries: similarly the houses of Bigorre are roofed with slate, like those of the Ardennes: for they are quarried ordinarily in cool countries.

Theory

And tell me, I pray you, the cause of diverse weights.

Practice

A man of good judgment will understand it sufficiently by the causes I have given above, for the same thing that causes hardness causes the weight of stones: hence you can understand that it is nothing but water: for all light rocks, such as chalk and certain white stones, are light only because they have lacked water during their formation and these rocks have been left spongy and full of pores. And to prove it, take a pebble of chalk and soak it in water, after having weighed it, and when it is soaked, weigh it again; you will find by its weight that it is spongy, which has caused it to soak up much water.[157] If you soak a pebble or a piece of crystal, you will find that it does not soak up water (251) like a light stone, for it has had its fill of it during its congelation.

Theory

I pray you tell me the cause of the fixation of rocks. For I see some that are subject to calcination, and once calcined, are lighter than they were before, and if water is added to them,

---

[157] A somewhat similar, though more elaborate and accurate method of measuring porosity is in use today. See T. A. Pollard and P. P. Reichertz, Am. Assoc. Petr. Geol., Bull., vol. 36, No. 2, February, 1952, pp. 230–52, especially p. 231 and fig. 2, p. 233.

they fall into dust, and others are whitened and cleaned and liquefied, always holding together in the same mass.

Practice

There are two effects that cause the fixation of many rocks; one is the abundance of water, and the other is long decoction; and it must be noted that all rocks that are calcined are imperfect in their decoction. Here is in a few words all that I can say about the fixation of rocks. There are some regions or climates where the badness of the weather and impetuous winds, frosts and cold, cause the rocks and wood to have some sharpness, as we see by the iron mines of the Ardennes in the lands of the Duke of Bouillon. For just as I have said that the rocks of this place are sharp, rough or displeasing, similarly the iron that is made in the forges of this country is very sharp, rough and friable; and not only the iron feels the effect of the unpleasant air, but also the woods on the edges and limits of the forests are rough, hard, subject to warping, hard to work. Also grapevines (252) cannot be grown in this country, because there is very little summer. The lands of the Duke of Bouillon are well supplied with iron ore, but the ore is very fine-grained, and it must be dug up from deep underground, which is confirmation of what I have always said about metals that cannot be generated by fire. Just as some plants and fruits grow in one country and cannot grow in another, so in some climates the rocks are not the same as those of another climate: as also are not the clayey earths.

Theory

You have given me many reasons for the forms, colors, hardness and weight of rocks, which things were easy for me to understand, when you demonstrated them. But if now I had to instruct someone else on what you have shown me, I could not do it, having no proofs, as you had, while you were making your demonstrations: therefore I wish you had given me in a few words some fine conclusion, as you have done for metals and generative water.

Practice

If you remember the points I have taught you, you will remember that as the last conclusion on the effect of rocks, I proved before my hearers that the main material of all rocks was nothing else but congelative water, of which (253) crystal and diamond and all transparent rocks are made. And, if you remember, did I not show you certain agate rocks and others, that were pure in the upper part and cloudy in the lower part? Did I not say, with proofs, that all cloudy and colored rocks, of whatever color they may be, are cloudy or colored only by accident? Which is that rocks, among which are grindstones to sharpen irons, are made cloudy by sand that is mixed with the congelative water. Other rocks are made cloudy because of the earth that is mixed with the water; you have been able to understand the cause of this enough when I have spoken about the colors of stones: and to remind you of the proofs that I have put forth in my lessons, you must remember what I told you then. Consider the crystal that is in the rock, and you will understand that during its congelation its material is in the waters, as I have said many times: and when the waters are turbid because of earth, the earth always seeks the bottom, like the dregs in a puncheon of wine: and that is why the pure and impure water both congeal: but the upper part will be of pure and clean crystal, and the lower will be of turbid crystal. The same is true, as I have told you, of metallic matters, which always bring with them something that causes their impurity. (254)

ON CLAY EARTHS

Theory

You have so often mentioned clay earths, in talking about fountains and rocks, and yet I have not heard you say what clay earth is.

Practice

I have heard read some book by an author who, in treating of rocks and earths, says that argillaceous earth has taken its name from a village called Argis, and that because in this place were made the first earthen vessels, all earths suitable for making pots have since been called argillaceous earth, just as we call boliarmeny that is found in France bolus armenus: although it never came from Armenia. However, I have since heard from some Latin scholars that this was false, and that all earth suitable for making vessels is called argillaceous because of its sticky property: and they say that "argillaceous" means fatty earth. Such opinions have emboldened me to talk about it for I understand that on some subjects the Latins and Greeks can err just as much as the French. To illustrate, they call clay earth fatty earth: and it is far from being (255) fatty: for clay earth is used to remove fat, witness the cloth fullers: and some mercers have made it into cakes that they sell as a fat remover. It is very certain that clay earth has nothing to do with fatty earths, nor can it be confused with the fat made with water and oil. And the reason why clay earth removes fat from cloth is nothing more than that fat is its adversary. And just as heat removes humidity, so clay earth removes fat from the place where it is stronger.

Theory

What would you call potter's earth if not fatty earth? for I know very well that the birdlime which some call *besq* [158] is made

---

[158] A synonym for birdlime, according to Cotgrave.

up of fatty materials: some make it from the bark of a tree called holly: others use the seed of a certain plant that grows most commonly on apple trees: which seed is very viscous. Hence some call this plant *besq*. Now both of these are good for catching birds, and when it is handled the hands must be wet, otherwise it would stick to the hands: and yet when the French and Latins speak of clayey earth, they say that it is a viscous, fatty and sticky earth: and some have even written that clayey earth is a sticky, gluey and viscous earth. (256)

Practice

By your own words you admit that all those who speak thus understand it very poorly: for there is nothing more opposed to viscous materials than water. Now clayey earth is entirely made up of aqueous matter: therefore they can combine together. Clayey earth dissolves in water and all viscous and oily materials become harder. It would be much more correct to call it doughy earth and not viscous earth, because flour for making dough mixes with water as does clayey earth.

Theory

Well, then, what differences do you find among those that are suitable for making vessels?

Practice

Among clayey earths there is such a difference between one and another that it is impossible for any man to enumerate the contrasts between them all. Some are sandy, white and very lean: and for these reasons a strong fire is needed before they are cooked properly. This kind of earth is good for making crucibles: for it withstands a very hot fire: there are other kinds which, because they contain metallic substances, collapse and liquefy when they are greatly heated. I have seen some tilers' kilns whose arches were so liquefied that the roofs were (257) full of hanging forms like the icicles you see on the eaves-troughs of houses during freezing weather. There are other kinds which, when they are baked, either into tiles or bricks, the foreman must take great care not to take his work out of the kiln before it is thoroughly cooled: and what is more, those who work with it must stop up all the vents of their kilns as soon as their work is baked: for if it were exposed to the least bit of wind in cooling, the pieces would all be cracked. There is one kind at Savigny in Beauvoisis, which I think is like no other in France, for it withstands a marvelous fire, without being in any way damaged, and it has this advantage, that it can be shaped as finely and delicately as any other: and when it is fully baked, it takes a little glassy polish, which proceeds from itself: and this causes the pottery made from this earth to hold nitric acid as well as glass vessels. There are other kinds of earth that are black in their essence, and when they are baked, they are white as paper; other kinds are yellow, and when they are baked, they turn red. Some kinds are of evil nature: for they contain little stones and when the pottery is baked, the little stones in it turn to lime (258) and as soon as they are exposed to the humidity of the air, they swell, and cause the vessel to burst where they are enclosed: and that is because these stones have been calcined in baking: and by this means many vessels are lost, whatever great labor may have been lavished on them.[159] There are other kinds that are very good and stand fire well: but they are so weak and loose that they can only be made into light vessels, because when one wishes to shape it a little high, it collapses, not being able to stand up. As a general rule all clayey earths and particularly the finer ones are subject to bursting in the fire before they are done: for these reasons those who work with them are forced to raise their fire gradually: in order to expel the humidity that is in their work, so much so that if the pieces that are being fired are thick, and there is a quantity of them, the fire must be kept going sometimes three or four days and nights, and if once the work has begun to heat up and he who watches the fire goes to sleep and allows his work to cool, before it is perfectly fired, the work will undoubtedly be lost. And from such accidents tilers have suffered great losses. It will not be out of order for me to tell you another very curious secret, which is that many limeburners have also suffered great losses through a quite (259) similar accident: that is because as soon as the rock in the lime kiln starts to warm up, until it has its red color, and the flame has started to come through the rocks, if the one who tends the fire falls asleep, and on waking finds that the flame has gone down, and the heat lowered in part before the earth is calcined to the required point; if he should then put wood into his kiln again, and use all the

[159] George White calls my attention to the fact that the same thing happens today where glacial till is used to make brick or drain tile, e.g., in Ohio.

wood of the Ardennes forests, it is not possible for him to raise up his fire, nor to reduce his stone to lime, but he has lost all that he has put into it. I have known many who have become poor through such accidents. Those who work impatiently with the art of the earth often lose much through their impatience: for if they do not expel the exhalative humor that is in the earth gradually, and wish to raise up a great fire before it is out, nothing is more certain than that the heat and the humidity when they meet will generate a thunder, because of their enmity. For I know that natural thunder is generated by the same cause, to wit heat and humidity: because they are opposites, and cannot live together: for fire (being stronger) finding humidity enclosed in some parts of the earth, tries to expel it violently, as an enemy, and humidity, being pressed too hard, tries to escape in haste: but because (260) fire does not give it a chance to find the little exits through which it has entered, it is forced to flee, and in fleeing it bursts the rocks in which it is enclosed. I have seen long ago certain statue makers, instructed in the art of the earth only through hearsay, and rather new in the understanding of earths, who after making some statues came to put them into the kilns, to fire them, so they thought: but when they put on a full fire, it was rather funny (although everyone did not have something to laugh about) to hear these statues bursting and setting up a volley between them, like a great many musket and cannon shots, and the poor foreman very angry, like a man whose property is stolen from him: for when the day came to take the statues out of the kiln, the kiln was scarcely open than he saw some of them with split heads, others with broken arms and legs, so much so that the poor man had much trouble looking for the pieces: for some were as small as flies, and being unable to put them together he was often forced to make *nez de drapeau* [160] and other things with his statues. Men who are experienced in the art of the earth do not work so thoughtlessly, but first they try to learn the nature of the earth, and once they know it, they consider (261) the thickness of the work they wish to fire, knowing that the thickest is the most likely to burst in firing: so they are very careful not to fire it before it is quite dry. And when it is in the kiln, they keep the fire low for a longer time for the thick

---

[160] Literally, "flag-noses." I have been unable to find any explanation of this term, but one can guess that it may have meant the decorative finial at the top of the staff of a flag.

pieces than for the thin ones: and in applying fire gradually, they give humidity a chance to leave easily and without violence: and when the foreman knows that the moisture is gone, he lets the fire burn as high as it will, and then it plays about and enters freely, even inside the enclosed and shut parts of the work, made of earth: and in this way one can learn that in clayey earth there are two humors, the one evaporative and accidental, the other fixed and radical: the humid and accidental one is subject to evaporation and once it is evaporated, the radical one transmutes the substance of the earth into stone.[161] However, unless the moisture works on it first, that could not be done: for moisture must necessarily gather all the parts together, and serve as a putty to shape all kinds of pieces.

There are other kinds of earths which must not be heated gently for a long time; such earths are commonly coarse, sandy and spongy, and because they have open pores, (262) the moisture leaves them more quickly, when expelled by fire. There are other earths that are so dense, or have so few pores that because of this those who work with them are forced to add sand to them, to avoid having to heat them gently for a long time, to prevent the work from breaking. The reason why sand can cause the work to stand greater fire than when the earth is pure, is that it divides the subtle parts of the earth: and because its fineness would render it more dense and close packed, the sand gives it a few pores through which moisture will escape more quickly to make room for fire, its adversary. For these reasons, the potters of Paris put sand in all their work. Near Paris, there are three kinds of clayey earth; the finest comes from Gentilly, which is a village near Paris. But there are certain places there where in this earth are found great numbers of sulphurous and metallic marcasites, which causes the potters to have none of it, except to make brick or tile. The reason why they cannot work well with it is that when they bake their work, these marcasites give off a black and stinking vapor that blackens the work entirely and covers it with yellow and green. There is another kind of earth in a village near Paris, called Chaliot, from which tile is made; it is a little coarser than that of Gentilly; there are (263) a great many marcasites in it but they are of a different kind than those

---

[161] Substitute "free water" for "evaporative and accidental humor," and "combined water" for "fixed and radical humor" and the passage takes on a marvelously modern aspect.

of Gentilly. I tell you this to make you understand better that if, in so little distance, there are various kinds of earths, that should be an argument to make you believe that in the whole of a kingdom there can be a great many of very different kinds. I did not learn the differences between kinds of earths and their various effects without much expense and labor. Once I had discovered earth from Poitou and had worked with it a good six months before finishing a kilnful: for the vessels I had made were very elaborate and rather expensive. Now, while making these vessels from Poitou earth, I made a few with Xaintonge earth, which I had worked with many years before, and with which I had experience as to the degree of fire it needed: and thinking that all earths can be fired to the same degree, I baked my pieces of Poitou earth along with those of Xaintonge earth, which caused me great loss: for when I tried to enamel my vessels, as soon as they were exposed to moisture, it was an unpleasant joke for me: for every piece that was glazed dissolved and fell to pieces, as would a piece of lime (264) soaked in water, and yet all the vessels of Xaintonge earth were baked in the same kiln, with the same amount of heat, and for the same time as the others, and were in perfect condition. That is why a man who works in the art of the earth is always learning because of unknown natures, and diversity of earths. There are some clay earths that even though they have had reasonable baking and as much fire as they need, still when vessels of this earth are molded and exposed to fire, they will break as if they were not baked: which does not happen with other earths. There are some kinds that are so viscous and very fine that they can be stretched out like string. I have seen women working with this kind of earth, and to make pot handles they took a handful of it and holding it by one end with one hand, with the other hand they stretched it as long as they could raise their arms: And when that was done they dropped the hanging end without breaking the earth, and then cut it into pieces to make their handles. That cannot be done with sandy earths: for they are all short and weak. There are other kinds of very bad earths: for when they are baked a little too much, they are subject to burning, blackening and cracking, and the vessels (265) under them, pressed down by the weight of the ones on top, bend and warp at the mouth as if they were made of malleable material. There are clay earths in the Ardennes region that are very moist and take a long time to dry, are dangerous to burn, and that contain some substance like iron ore. I have sometimes found some of a kind that was very clean, fine-grained and easily worked, having the appearance of being very good; so much so that in the hope of using it, I made a few pieces from it, and put them in the hottest part of the kiln; but when I came to get my pieces I found that they had melted, and this earth had flowed into the ashes, like molten lead. Some ancient vessels are found of a red, polished earth, without any glaze and some call the vessels of this earth *barc* [162] vessels. I do not know why they are called this: but I do know that they were much used in ancient times. For great quantities of broken pieces of them are found in ancient cities: and many times they have been found in graves with coins of the emperors who reigned then, and that was done as a ceremony that has since been abandoned. If I wished to write down all the diversities of clay earths, I should never have done: you will learn more about it when I speak of the art of the earth: therefore I shall tell you no more about it for the present.[163] (266)

[162] "A kind of smooth red earth, whereof vessels were made in old time" (Cotgrave).

[163] An admirable section on the reactions of clays. When Palissy writes from first-hand knowledge, he is generally as clear, terse, and persuasive as can be. In this passage and a few others, his discourses are models of lucid exposition which have never been surpassed.

ON THE ART OF THE EARTH,
ITS USEFULNESS, ON ENAMELS AND FIRE

Theory

You promised me before to teach me the art of the earth: and when you gave me such a long talk on the diversities of clay earths, I was very happy, thinking that you wished to teach me the whole of this art; but I was quite surprised when instead of continuing, you told me to come back later in order to make me forget my affection for this art.

Practice

Do you believe that a man of sound judgment would thus wish to give away the secrets of an art that has cost dearly to the man who has invented it? As for me, I am not willing to do so unless I know a reason for it.

Theory

There is indeed no charity in you. If you wish thus to keep your secret hidden, you will carry it to the grave and no one will benefit from it, and thus your death will be accursed: for it is written that every man, according to the gifts he has received from God, should give to others: from this I can conclude that if you do not teach me what (267) you know of this art, you are misusing the gifts of God.

Practice

My art and its secrets are not like others. I am sure that a good remedy against a plague or some other pernicious disease must not be kept secret. The secrets of agriculture must not be kept secret. The hazards and dangers of navigation must not be kept secret. The word of God must not be kept secret. The sciences that serve the whole state must not be kept secret. But with my

art of the earth and many other arts, that is not so. Many charming inventions are contaminated and despised because they are
too common. Also, many things are highly prized in the houses
of Princes and noblemen that would be less prized than old
kettles if they were common. I pray you consider a little the glasses
that are so low in price because they are too common so that those
who make them live more poorly than the porters of Paris. The
profession is noble and the men who work at it are noble: but
many who are gentlemen because they practice this art, would like
to be commoners and have money enough to pay the income of
Princes. Isn't that the trouble of the glass makers of Périgord,
Limosin, Xaintonge, (268) Angoulmois, Gascongne, Béarn and
Bigorre? where glass making is so mechanized that they are sold
and auctioned in the villages, by the very men who peddle old
clothes and iron, so much so that those who make them and sell
them have a hard time making a living. Think also a little about
enameled buttons (such a charming invention) which at first sold
at three francs a dozen. Because those who invented them did not
keep their invention a secret, a little later, the lust for profit, or
the poverty of the people led to the making of such a large
quantity of them that they were forced to sell them for one *sol* [164]
a dozen, so that they are so despised that now people are ashamed
to wear them, and say that they are only for clods, because they
are too cheap. Have you not seen also the enamelers of Limoges
who, because they did not keep their invention a secret, saw their
art become so cheap that they have a hard time making a living
with the price they get for their work. I am sure that I have seen
figures d'enseigne [165] which were worn on hats, given away for
three *sols* a dozen, which *enseignes* were so cleverly welded to
the copper that no painting was more pleasing. And that has
happened not only once but more than a hundred thousand times,
and not only with these *enseignes,* but also with ewers, (269)
salt-cellars and all kinds of other vessels and other things that
they made: which is very regrettable. Have you not seen also
how the printers have harmed the painters and clever draftsmen?
I remember having seen the stories of Our Lady, coarsely printed
after the invention of a German called Albert [166] which stories

---

[164] A small coin worth a little less than one cent; one twentieth of the
ancient French pound or *livre*. See note 169 for the value of the pound.

[165] I have found no translation or explanation of this term.

[166] Does he mean Albrecht Dürer (1471–1528)?

came to be so despised, because of the great number that were made, that each of them sold for two *liars* [167] although the drawing was well done. Don't you see also how casting has hurt many clever sculptors, because after one of them has spent a long time making some figure of a prince or princess or other excellent figure, if it falls into the hands of some cast-maker he will make such a large quantity of it that the name of the inventor and his work will no longer be known, and these figures will be sold cheaply because of the work of casting, to the sorrow of the one who carved the first piece. I have seen such contempt of sculpture, because of casting, that the whole Gascongne country and neighboring places were full of cast figures, in pottery, that were sold in the fairs and markets for two liards apiece, from which it followed that when people were starting (270) to wear belts and other clothes *à la busque*,[168] one man was jailed and flogged because he went around the whole city of Toulouze, with a bale full of crucifixes, shouting "crucifixes, crucifixes, *à la busque*." You can easily understand by these examples and a thousand others like them, that it is better for one man or a small number of men to make a profit from some art while living honorably, than for a great many, who will harm each other so much, that they will be unable to make a living, save by profaning the arts, leaving things half done, as is commonly seen in all arts, whose number is too great: however, if I thought you would keep the secret of my art as jealously as it deserves, I would not hesitate to teach it to you.

Theory

If you will please teach it to me, I promise to keep it as secret as any man to whom you could teach it.

Practice

I should like to do much for you, and to advance you as willingly as I would my own child: but I fear that if I teach you the art of the earth, it would retard rather than advance you. That is because you need two things, without which it is impossible to do anything with the art of the earth. The first is that

[167] A small coin. Its value was at one time three *deniers* (pence) but varied from time to time.

[168] Bescherelle explains the expression: garments supported and stiffened by a framework. Cotgrave gives "Au vieux busq. After the old cut."

you must be wide awake, quick, sympathetic and hard working. Secondly, you (271) must have some capital, to bear the losses you incur in practicing this art. Now, since you lack these things, I advise you to look for some other livelihood that is easier and less hazardous.

Theory

I think you say these things not out of pity for me, but because you do not wish to keep your promise and to reveal to me the secrets of this art. For I know that when you first started to study this art, you did not have much money, to bear the losses and mistakes that you say can occur in working at this art.

Practice

That is true, I did not have much money; but I had means which you do not have. For I knew drafting. In my country I was thought to be more versed in the art of painting than I really was, which meant that I was often called upon to make drawings for lawsuits. Now, when I had such work, I was very well paid; also I worked for a long time as a glass maker, until I was certain I could make a living from the art of the earth: also, while I was learning this art, I taught myself alchemy, which you would have much trouble doing. That is how I spent the time that I devoted to learning this art. (272)

Theory

I know that you have borne much poverty and trouble in learning it: but that won't happen to me: because the reason of your trouble was that you had a wife and children. Now, since you had no knowledge of it before and had to guess, because also you could not leave your family to go and learn this art in some shop, also because you had no money to pay servants who could help you while you were learning this art. All these lacks have caused you the troubles and misery above mentioned. But that won't happen to me: because, according to your promise, you will give me in writing all the means of guarding against the losses and hazards of fire: also the materials from which you make enamels and their proportions, measures and composition. In this way, why should I not make fine things without running the danger of losing anything, since your losses will serve me as examples to guard and guide me in practicing this art?

Practice

Even if I used a thousand reams of paper to write down all the accidents that have happened to me in learning this art, you must be assured that, however good a brain you may have, you will still make a thousand mistakes, which cannot be learned from writings, and even if you had them in writing, you wouldn't believe them until (273) practice has given you a thousand afflictions. However, so that you may not have occasion to call me a liar, I will give you here in order all the secrets that I have found about the art of the earth, together with the composition and various effects of enamels; also I shall tell you about the various kinds of argillaceous earths which is a point you must note well. And, so that you may understand these things better, I shall give you an account starting right at the beginning of my interest in this art and thus you will hear about the calamities I have endured before attaining my goal. I think that when you have heard all this, you will have little inclination to devote yourself to this art, and I am sure that just as you now wish to acquaint yourself with it, so you will then try to flee from it: because you will see that nothing can be attempted or completed, to render it in beauty and perfection, without great and extreme labor, which never comes singly but is always accompanied by a thousand anxieties.

Theory

I am a simple man like you, and since these things were possible for you without any teacher, it will be much easier for me after I have had from you a complete exposition of how to go about it and the means by which you have succeeded at it. (274)

Practice

According to your request, know you that more than twenty-five years ago I was shown an earthen cup, turned and enameled with such beauty that I was immediately perplexed, remembering many things that some people had taunted me with, when I used to paint pictures. But seeing that they were going out of fashion in my country, also that glazing was not much in demand, I came to think that if I were able to make enamels I could make pottery vessels and other things of good design, for God had given me the knack of knowing something about drawing; and immediately, without thinking that I had no knowledge of clayey earths, I started to look for enamels, like a man who gropes in the dark. Without having heard of what materials these enamels were made, I crushed, in those days, all sorts of things that I thought could be used, and after having pounded and crushed them, I would buy a number of earthen pots, and after breaking them to pieces, I would put the things I had crushed on them, and after marking them, I would write down the drugs I had put on each one, as a reminder; then after I had built a kiln to my liking, I put these pieces to bake to see if my drugs (275) could produce some white color: for I was looking for no other enamel than white: because I had heard it said that white was the basis of all other enamels. Now, since I had never seen earth fired, and did not know at what heat this enamel would melt, I could do nothing in this way, even if my drugs had been good, for at one time my work had been heated too much, at others too little, and when these materials were too little baked or burned, I could not find out why I was making nothing good, but put the blame on the materials, although sometimes the work might have been good, or at least I could have got some hint toward achieving my goal if I could have controlled the fire according to the requirements of the materials. But still, in doing so I made a mistake even greater than the above: for in placing the pieces of my experiments in the kiln, I arranged them carelessly; so that with the best materials in the world and the best possible fire, it was impossible to do anything right. But, after making many mistakes, with much expense and effort, I would pound and crush new materials every day and build new kilns, at great cost in money and loss of wood and time. (276)

When I had thus blundered about unwisely for several years, with sadness and sighing, because I could achieve no part of my goal, and remembering the waste of money, I thought of sending the drugs I wanted to try out to some potter's kiln, to avoid such great expense; and having made up my mind about this, I immediately bought several earthen vessels, and after breaking them into pieces, as usual, I covered three or four hundred pieces of them with enamel and sent them to a pottery a league and a half away from my home requesting the potters to fire these experimental pieces inside some of their vessels; which they did willingly; but when they had fired their kilnful and drawn out my pieces, I had only shame and loss from them, for they included nothing good, because the potters' fire was not hot enough, also because my experimental pieces were not fired as they should be nor according to what I knew; and because I knew not why my experiments had not turned out well, I put the blame (as I have said above) on the materials: I would immediately make numerous new combinations and send them to the same potters, to be treated as before: Thus did I lose time, suffer confusion and sadness many times, always at great cost. (277)

When I realized that I could not in this way attain any part of my goal, I lay it aside a while, occupying myself with my art of painting and glazing, and pretended not to try any more to seek the secrets of enameling; some days later certain commissioners, appointed by the King, came to establish the salt tax in Xaintonge. They called on me to draw the islands and the country surrounding the salt pans of this region. Now, after this commission was completed and I found myself with a little money, I took up again the idea of searching for enamels, and seeing that I had been unable to do anything in my kilns or in those of the potters, I broke about three dozen brand new pots, and having crushed a great quantity of various materials, I covered all the shards of these pots with drugs brushed on: but you must understand that of two or three hundred pieces there were only three of each mixture: having done this, I took all these pieces to a glass works, to see if my materials and mixtures might not turn out well in the kilns of the glass works. Now, because their kilns are hotter than those of the potters, after putting all my experiments into the kilns, the next day when I had them taken out, I saw that part of my mixtures had begun to (278) melt, which caused me to be further encouraged to seek for white enamel, for which I had worked so hard.

As for other colors, I did not worry about them at all; this little showing which I had found then, made me work for two years more looking for white, during which two years I did nothing but come and go to the nearest glass works, trying to achieve my goal. God willed that just as I began to lose hope, and for the last time had gone to a glass works with a man carrying more than three hundred kinds of experiments, it happened that one of them melted within four hours of being put into the kiln which was so white and polished as to cause me such joy that I thought I had become a new man: and I thought immediately that I had complete mastery of white enamel: but I was far from my goal: this experiment was very fortunate in a way, but very unfortunate in another; fortunate in that it was the first step to what I have achieved and unfortunate in that it was not of the required dose or measure; I was so stupid in those days, that as soon as I had made this white which was singularly fine, I started to make earthen vessels, although I knew nothing of clay, and having taken seven or eight months to (279) make these vessels, I started to put up a kiln like that of the glassmakers, which I built with incredible labor: for I had to do the stone work alone, mix my mortar, draw the water for mixing it, and fetch the brick on my own back, because I had no money to pay a man to help me with this business. I baked my vessels for the first firing: but when it came to the second firing, I had sorrows and labors such as no man would believe. For instead of resting from my previous labors, I had to work for more than a month, night and day, to crush the materials from which I had made that beautiful white in the glassmakers' kiln; and when I had crushed these materials I covered the vessels I had made with them: this done, I lighted my fire at both openings, as I had seen the glassmakers do; I also put my vessels in the kiln, to melt, I thought, the enamels I had put on them: but that was an unfortunate thing for me: for although I spent six days and six nights in front of the kiln without ceasing to burn wood at both openings, it was not possible to melt the enamel, and I was like a desperate man: and although I was quite groggy from the work, I went and thought that my enamel contained too little of the stuff that was (280) supposed to melt the other materials, and so, I started to pound and crush this stuff, without, however, allowing my kiln to cool, so I had to do double work, pound, crush and fire up the kiln. When I had thus made up my enamel, I was forced to go and buy more pots, to try out the enamel: since I had lost all the vessels I had made: and having covered the pieces with the enamel, I put them into the kiln, keeping the fire high: but then another unfortunate thing happened which made me very angry, which is that when the wood was used up, I was forced to burn all the props that held up the plants in my garden, and when they were burned up, I was forced to burn the tables and the floor of my house, in order to melt the second mixture. I was in such anguish as I could not describe: for I was quite dried out because of the work and the heat of the kiln; for more than a month my shirt had not dried on me, and moreover, to console me I was jeered at, and even those who should have helped me, went about the town shouting that I was burning up the floor: and thus I was made to lose my credit, and I was thought to be crazy. Others said that I was trying to make counterfeit money, which was an evil thing that made me dry up on my feet; and I went about the streets hanging my head, like a man ashamed: (281) I had debts in several places, and usually two children being nursed and could not pay for it; no one helped me: but on the contrary they jeered at me, saying: he richly deserves to starve to death, for he neglects his trade. All this news reached my ears when I passed in the street: nevertheless I still had some hope, which encouraged and sustained me, for the last experiments had turned out fairly well, and I already thought I knew enough to earn my living, although I was still very far from it (as you will learn later), and you must not mind my telling it at length, to make you more attentive to what may be useful to you.

When I had rested a while, regretting that no one had pity on me, I said to myself, what are you sorry about, since you have found what you were looking for? Now get to work and you will shame your detractors; but my soul answered, you have nothing to carry on your work with; how will you feed your family and buy the things you need to go through the four or five months required before you can enjoy the fruits of your labor? Now as I was in this sad and puzzled mood, hope gave me a little courage, and having thought that it would take me a long time to make a kilnful all by myself, to shorten the time and (282) gain a little of it, and to bring out more quickly the secret of the white enamel that I had found, I hired a common potter and gave him certain designs, so that he could make me some vessels according to my ideas, and while he was doing this I worked on a few medals; but it was a sorry business: because I had to feed the potter in a tavern, on credit: for I could not do so in my home. After we had worked for six months and had to fire what had been made, I had to build a kiln and pay off the potter, to whom, for lack of money I had to give some of my clothes as salary. Now, because I had no materials to build my kiln, I started to pull apart the one I had made like those of the glassmakers, so as to use its materials. Now, because this kiln had been heated so much for six days and nights, the mortar and the brick in it had been liquefied and vitrified so much, that in demolishing it I cut and incised my fingers in so many places that I was forced to eat with my fingers wrapped in bandages. When I had torn down the kiln, I had to build another, not without effort: for I had to fetch water, mortar and stone with no help and no rest. This done, I put my work through the first firing, and then by borrowing or otherwise I (283) found money for the materials to make enamels, to coat my work, which had gone through the first firing safely: but when I had bought my materials, I had to do work that I thought would kill me. For after many days during which I tired myself pounding and calcining my materials, I had to crush them without help, with a hand mill, which it usually took two strong men to turn: the desire I had to attain my goal made me do things that I would have thought impossible. When these colors were crushed, I covered all my vessels and medals with the enamel, then after putting and arranging them all in the kiln, I started the fire, hoping to make three or four hundred pounds [169] from the batch, and kept up the fire until I had some indication and hope that my enamels were melted and the batch was safe. The next day, when I took out my work, after putting out the fire, my sorrow and pain were so heightened that I lost all countenance. For although my enamels were good and my work was well done, still two accidents had happened to the batch, which had spoiled everything: and so that you may guard against them I shall tell you what they are: and after these, I shall tell you about a number of others so that my bad luck may be your good luck and (284) my loss may be your gain. It is because the mortar I had used to build my kiln was full of pebbles which when hot (when my enamels began to liquefy) burst into many pieces, making many loud noises in the kiln. Now, as the fragments of these pebbles flew against my work, the enamel, which was already liquefied and sticky, caught these pebbles and stuck them to all parts of my vessels and medals, which without that would have been fine. Thus, knowing that my kiln was hot enough, I let it cool until the next day; then I was so saddened that I could not describe it to you, and not without reason: for my kilnful cost me more than 120 écus.[170] I had borrowed for the wood and materials, and had borrowed for part of my food while making this work. I had kept my creditors in hopes that they would be paid out of the money I would get from the pieces of this kilnful, which

[169] Note that these were French *livres* or pounds. Bescherelle gives its value as 0.9876 francs (of around 1906, not 1956) but notes that it varied. The livre was divided into 20 sous or sols.

[170] "A crown in money" according to Cotgrave, who also lists several varieties.

caused many of them to run to me as soon as I began to unload
the kiln in the morning. In this way my sadness was doubled; for
as I drew out my work I was given nothing but shame and confusion. For all my pieces were dotted with little pieces of pebbles
that were so well stuck to them and bound into the enamel, that
when the hand was passed on them, the pebbles (285) cut it like
a razor; and although the work was spoiled by this, still some
people wanted to buy some at low prices: but because that would
have been a mockery and a loss of honor for me, I completely
broke up the whole kilnful and went to bed from melancholy, not
without reason, for I no longer had means to support my family;
in my house I got nothing but recriminations; instead of being
comforted I was cursed; my neighbors, who had heard about this,
said that I was nothing but a fool and that I should have had
more than eight francs for the work I had broken up, and all these
things added to my sorrow.

When I had stayed in bed for some time, and had thought that
if a man should fall into a ditch, his duty would be to get out of
it, I began to do a few paintings, and by many means I worked
hard to earn a little money; then I said to myself that all my losses
and dangers were over; and that there was nothing now that could
prevent me from making fine pieces: and I started (as before) to
work at this art. But in firing another batch, I had an accident
which I had not anticipated: for the violence of the fire's heat
had thrown a quantity of ashes against my pieces, so that wherever
the ash had touched, (286) my vessels were rough and poorly
polished, because the liquid enamel had mixed with the ashes: in
spite of all these losses, I continued to hope that I would re-
establish myself through this art: for I had certain potters make
me a large number of earthen lanterns [171] to enclose my vessels
when I put them into the oven: so that the lanterns should protect
my vessels from the ash. The idea was a good one, and it still
serves me today: but after I had overcome the ash hazard, I made
other mistakes and had other accidents so that when I had a kilnful it was either baked too much or another time too little, and
entirely spoiled because of that. I was so new that I could not
judge what was too much or too little; at one time my work was

---

[171] Palissy used these lanterns, for which the English term is saggers, to
protect his finer pieces while he was working in Paris. Some of them were
found during excavations at the Tuileries in 1865. See France (in Palissy,
1880, p. xvii, footnote). Saggers are still used by potters at the present time.
According to the *Shorter Oxford Dictionary* the English term dates from 1768.

baked in front and not behind: the next time, when I tried to prevent such an accident, I would burn it behind and the front would not be baked: sometimes it was cooked on the right and burned on the left: sometimes my enamels were put on too thin, and sometimes too thick: which caused me heavy losses: sometimes when I had enamels of various colors in the kiln, some were burned before the others had melted. In short, I blundered thus for fifteen or sixteen years: when I had learned to guard against one danger, I encountered another that I would never have thought about. During that time I built many (287) kilns which caused me great loss before I learned the way to heat them evenly; finally I found a way of making a few vessels of various enamels intermixed like jasper: that kept me fed for a few years; but while I lived on these things, I was always trying to go further with cost and investments, as you know that I still do at present. When I had invented a method for making rustic pieces,[172] I had greater pains and more trouble than formerly. For having made a certain number of rustic ewers and fired them, some of my enamels turned out fine and well melted, others were poorly melted, others were burned, because they were made of various materials that were fusible to various degrees; the green of the lizards was burned before the color of the serpents had melted, also the color of the serpents, crayfish, turtles and crabs had melted before the white had attained any beauty. All these mistakes have caused me such labor and mental anguish that before I had made my enamels fusible at the same degree of fire, I thought I would be at death's door: also as I worked at such things for more than ten years my body was so wasted away that my arms and legs had no form or trace of muscles, but on the contrary my legs were like (288) sticks: [173] so that the laces with which I tied up my stockings fell down to my heels with the rest of my stockings as soon as I walked. I often went for a walk in the meadow of Xaintes thinking over my misery and troubles. And above all that in my home itself I could obtain no patience, nor do anything that was considered good. I was despised and jeered at by every-

[172] The rustic pieces referred to are ewers and basins with castings of natural foliage and animals. The term rustic is approximately equivalent to naturalistic in this context and does not mean rough or clumsily naïve. See the illustrations by Delange and Borneman in Sauzay (1862).

[173] Palissy says that his legs were *toute d'une venue* meaning, as he has just explained, that they had no muscles on them and were therefore straight and thin.

one: nevertheless I was always making a few vessels of various colors, which fed me more or less: but in doing so, the diversity of the earths with which I hoped to advance myself did me more damage in a short time than all the previous accidents. For, having made many vessels of various earths, some were burned before the others were baked: others took the enamel and proved very suitable for working: the others disappointed me in all my undertakings. Now, because my enamels did not turn out well in the same thing, I was disappointed many times: from which I always got troubles and sorrow. However, my hope made me work so vigorously at my project that many times, to amuse those who came to see me, I made an effort to laugh, although privately I was very sad.

I pursued my project in such a way that I earned much money with one part of my (289) work, which turned out well: but I suffered another affliction related to the above, which is that the heat, cold, winds, rain and leaks in the roof spoiled most of my work before it was fired; so much so that I had to borrow lumber, lath, tile and nails to establish myself. Now, very often when I had nothing to build with, I was forced to make do with branches and other greenery. Now, as my means increased, I would tear down what I had built and rebuild it a little better; which meant that certain tradesmen, such as hosiers, cobblers, policemen and notaries, a whole lot of old women, all of them without thinking that my art could not be plied without a large building, said that I did nothing but build and tear down and blamed me for something that should have called forth their pity, since I was forced to use the things that were necessary for my sustenance to build the commodities necessary to my art. And what is worse, the motive of these jeers and persecutions came from those of my household, who were so unreasonable as to wish me to work without tools, which is more than foolish. Now, the more this was unreasonable, the more the affliction was great for me. For several years, having nothing to roof over my kilns, I was every night at the mercy of rains and winds, with no succor, (290) aid or consolation, except for the owls hooting on one side and the dogs howling on the other; sometimes winds and storms sprang up which blew so hard over and under my kilns that I was forced to leave everything, losing my labor; and it happened often that having left everything, without a dry rag on me, because of the rains that had fallen, I went to bed at midnight or at dawn, dressed like a man who has been dragged through all the mud holes of the city; and in retiring thus, I stumbled about without light, and falling on one side or another, like a drunkard, filled with great sadness: because after having worked a long time I saw my labor lost. Now, in retiring thus dirty and wet, I would find in my bedroom a second persecution worse than the first, which makes me wonder now that I did not die of sadness.

Theory

Why are you giving me such a lament? it is rather to turn me away from my intention, than to make me get closer to it; you have really made me a fine speech about the mistakes that are made in the art of the earth, but that only serves to scare me: for you haven't said a thing about enamels. (291)

Practice

The enamels I use in my work are made of tin, lead, iron, steel, antimony, *saphre*,[174] copper, *arène*,[175] *salicort*,[176] *cendre gravelée*,[177] litharge, and Périgord stone. These are the very materials from which I make my enamels.

Theory

Fine, but the way you say that teaches me nothing. For I have heard before from what you said that you lost a great deal before you managed to find the exact dose for your enamels: therefore you know well that if you do not tell me the dose, it would be useless for me to know the materials.

Practice

The mistakes I made while I found out the dose for my enamels taught me more than the things that were easy to learn: therefore I judge that you should work to find this dose, just as I have done; otherwise you would esteem the knowledge too lightly, and perhaps that would cause you to despise it: for I am certain that

[174] See note 145 on this word.
[175] Coarse sand. Bescherelle explains that arène is midway between sand and gravel.
[176] See note 90 on this word.
[177] Literally, gravelly ash, but it has a special meaning, given by Cotgrave: "Ashes made of the burnt lees or dregs of wine." Bescherelle gives the same meaning but says it is also made from grape pips, the grapes themselves, or grapevine wood.

no one in the world takes lightly the secrets and the arts save those who get them cheaply: but those who have learned them at great cost and labor do not give them away so lightly.

Theory

You make me prize things marvelously (292) high: if it were some great science, which were in great demand, you would make it sound very fine: seeing that you prize so highly a mechanical art: which one can easily do without.

Practice

There's a statement that now makes me think that you are unworthy of knowing anything of the secret of this art: and since you call it a mechanical art you won't know anything more about it through me. It is well known that in this art there are some mechanical parts, such as kneading the clay: there are some who make vessels for ordinary kitchen use without regard to proportions; they can be called mechanical: but as for the regulation of fire, it cannot be compared with mechanical measures. For you must know that in order to make a successful batch of work, especially when it is enameled, the fire must be regulated with such careful skill that if it is not well done, you are very often disappointed. As for the right method of filling the kiln, it requires a special geometry.

Item, you know that in many places earthen vessels are made which are contrived with such geometry that a large vessel is supported on a small base, even when the clay is still soft; do you call that mechanical? Don't you know that compass measurements cannot be called mechanical (293) because they are too common, also because those who work at it are poor; nevertheless the arts that require compasses, rulers, numbers, weights and measures must not be called mechanical. And so, since you wish to put the art of the earth on a par with the mechanical arts, and scarcely prize its usefulness, I now wish to make you understand how much greater it is than I could tell you. Think a little how many arts would be useless, even completely wasted, without the art of the earth. The gold and silver refiners would have to go out of business, for they could do nothing without kilns and earthen vessels: since no stone or other material can be found to use in melting metals except earthen vessels.

Item, the glaziers would have to go out of business: for they have no means of melting the materials of their glass except in earthen vessels. The goldsmiths, smelters and smelting of any kind or species whatever, would be wiped out, and not one of them can do without pottery. Look also at the forges of the blacksmiths and locksmiths, and you will see that all these forges are built of brick: for if they were made of stone they would soon be burned out. Look at all the kilns, you will find that they are made of clay, even those used for clay, all make their kilns out of clay, such as the tilers, brickmakers (294) and potters. In short, there is no stone, or mineral, or other material that can be used to build a glassmaker's or lime kiln or others above, that can last for a long time. You see also how common pottery vessels are useful to the state, you see also how great is the usefulness of pottery for roofing houses: you well know that in many countries slate is unknown and there is no roofing material save tile; how useful do you think pottery is to bring water to fountains? It is well known that water passing through pottery pipes is much better and cleaner than that which passes through lead pipes. How many cities do you think are built of brick because they have had no way of obtaining stone? How highly do you think our ancestors prized the usefulness of the art of the earth? it is well known that the Egyptians and other peoples have built many splendid buildings through the art of the earth, many emperors and kings have built great pyramids of clay, to perpetuate their memory, and some of them did this fearing that their pyramids would be ruined by fire, if they were made of stone. But knowing that fire has no power against buildings of baked clay, they had them built of brick, as witness the children of Israel, who were (295) terribly oppressed while making the bricks for these buildings. If I wished to write down all the uses of the art of the earth, I should never have done: therefore I leave it to you to think about its other uses. As for its esteem, it is now despised, but it has not always been so. The historians assure us that when the art of the earth was invented, vessels of marble, alabaster, chalcedony and jasper fell into disrepute: and many earthen vessels have even been consecrated to the service of temples.

HOW TO FIND AND KNOW THE EARTH CALLED MARL [178]

*With which barren fields are fertilized, in countries
and regions where it is known: a matter of great importance
and necessary to those who own property.*

Theory

I remember having seen a little treatise which you had printed
during the first troubles,[179] in which are set down many natural
secrets, and even some agriculture: however, although you have
spoken at length about manures, still you have said nothing about
the earth called (296) marl: I am well aware that you have promised in your book to see if some of it could be found in Xaintonge
and other places where this earth is still unknown. I have en-
quired many times whether you might not have written some
other book in which you might have mentioned this earth: but
I have not found any: so if you know something about it, do
not hide it from me: it would not be fair of you to bury a secret
so useful to the state.

Practice

It is true that I promised, in the book you mention, to search
for marl in the Xaintonge country, for at the time I lived there
and expected to spend the rest of my life there; and because
there is no knowledge of marl in this country, and I had seen
some in Armaignac, I should have been happy to improve and

[178] American readers should not identify Palissy's marl with the material
so named in the United States and Canada. The marl of France and England
is a soil consisting of clay and carbonate of lime. Many European marls are of
marine origin but in America the term is restricted to lake deposits. The
French word *marne* is related to that of the River Marne in whose basin
marl is abundant.

[179] The reference here is to the *Recepte véritable* (1563).

render a service to the country where I lived: and for these reasons, I have tried to gain full knowledge of this earth: however well it may be known and common in other countries as it is in Brye and Champagne, I should not deign to speak of it: because the farmers who use it do not care to know why it makes the ground fertile: and although the reason need not be understood by all, still doctors and all physicians, philosophers and naturalists, will gain much by reading about the causes and reasons which I shall give you (297) in pursuing our subject.

Theory

I pray you first explain to me what marl is.

Practice

Marl is ordinarily a white earth that is taken from under the soil, and usually pits are dug to get it out in the same way as water wells, and in the places where this earth is used it is spread over barren fields, in the same way as manure is spread, first in little heaps, then it must be spread over the fields, as with manure, and when barren lands are manured with this earth, it is enough for ten or twelve years: some say that in various regions nothing need be added for thirty years. Some of these marls are found at the top of the pit and extend downward for a number of *toises.* In other places and regions, one must dig down more than four or five *toises* before finding the top of it. That is what I have been able to learn from those who use marl. However I have heard someone say that marl is scarcely any use on a field during the first year after it is applied, which I find very strange.

Theory

Why do you find it strange (298) that they say that the first year that land is marled it produces nothing? If you had considered the reason that can stimulate the vegetation of fruits you would not find such a thing strange: for no one in this world can make me believe that marl can aid generation save because of the heat that it contains: for we see that nothing can vegetate in winter, and no seed would ever germinate, except because of the heat coming from above by the power of the sun: although the sun causes the vegetation of all things, still, when it is too hot it dries out moisture, and plants cannot grow: the sun, therefore, is life and when it is too strong it is also death: in such a case, marl is the cause of the germinative or vegetative generation of plants, because of heat: but when it is freshly drawn one must believe that its heat is so great that it burns seeds. That is why the generation of seeds that are sown in the soil the first year cannot grow.

Practice

Really, your reason is weighty and very easily persuades those who have no feeling for natural things: but with me such an argument will never suffice.

Theory

I will give you another one now to which you (299) can oppose no legitimate argument, and even if you wished to deny it, the humblest ploughman of the Ardennes will confound you. You must necessarily admit that stone, burned in red-hot furnaces, when it is reduced to dust by the ardor of the fire, nothing remains in it save earthiness filled with an igneous power, and for these reasons it is called lime: because it is warm, so warm that it has often happened that when such stones have been brought into houses on straw, these houses have burned down, by the movement of certain dripping waters that have fallen during times of rain on this lime: and just as stones of this lime are dissolved by the moisture that they encounter when they are removed from the kiln, so, in the same circumstances, marl stones when they are taken from the trench happen to dissolve and crumble to dust like lime stones. I have another fine argument and sufficient proof to conclude what I have said, which is that since the lands around the Ardennes forest are cold because of the snows and frosts of this country, the farmers of certain regions, when they are short of manure, have thought of fertilizing their land with lime, in the same manner and form as they are usually fertilized with manure: and by this means they have made the lands fertile, which previously produced (300) nothing. Since lime causes such good by its heat (as the farmers say that lime warms the land and causes seeds to germinate), may I not conclude thereby that marl can be of no use to fields save because of its warmth?

Practice

Good reasons, like the one you tell about, will always be accepted as good, providing there are no better ones than yours: and although your arguments have every appearance of truth, I shall give you truer reasons than yours, and first, concerning what you say that marl earth dissolves in moisture like lime, to this I reply that all earths do this, when they are dry, and particularly all argillaceous earths: and as for the other reason that you might put forward, that marl is as white as lime, to this I reply that there is gray, black, and yellow marl, by which colors I prove the argument challengeable.

Theory

I do not know what objections you might have against my statement: for we know that the reason why manure helps the vegetation of seeds is because of its warmth and if that is true for manure, so it must be for marl and lime.

Practice

Then you wish to state and conclude that manure (301) is warm?

Theory

And do you wish to deny such an obvious fact? do we not know that sheets of lead are consumed and reduced to ceruse in manure, because of their great heat? Do we not know that much dyeing of silk is done in warm manure? Do we not know that many alchemists use warm manure to hatch the eggs of their essences? Don't even pigs give us evidence of the warmth of manures? for very often manure piles serve them as stoves or steam baths to warm themselves.

Practice

All this is very badly thought out and does not convince me. We know that when hay and straw are moistened by water, they rot, and in rotting, putrefaction causes a great heat in the straw and hay until the dissolution of the radical essence is complete, and when this is done, the manure no longer has any warmth. We know also that baked lime chunks generate a fire, which fire lasts in them until they are broken up and pulverized, and then there is no more heat in them; we know that boiling water is hot while it is moved or touched by fire, but afterwards, when it has rested away from the fire, it is more subject to freezing than water (302) which has not been heated. We know also that a wound or concussion, due to an accident, will raise a bump in the injured part, will be warmer than usual because of the accident and the putrefaction that occurs, as I have told you for straw or hay, which heats up by the accident of putrefaction, and not because heat is always in it. We also know that two pebbles or other hard materials (when they are struck against each other) will generate *bluettes* [180] or sparks of fire: still that does not mean that pebbles are warm: but it does mean, as I say, that accidents generate uncommon heats: from which it must be concluded that there is some other cause that makes seeds germinate. After I had very closely examined the earth called marl, I have found that it was nothing more than a kind of argillaceous earth, and if that is so, it is the contrary of the reasons you have alleged: for it is certain that argillaceous earth is cold and dry, as you may have heard me mention as we talked about metals and minerals, while proving to you that in many argillaceous earths there are marcasites, even metallized and petrified wood: and if marl were warm, argillaceous earth would be warm also, and all that I have written about earths, rocks and metals would be false. We must therefore begin with this and finally conclude that marly earth is a kind of clay, which (303) after being exposed to weathering for many years, has cooled or frozen, even at the first frost: and even if it had been warm in the matrix of the earth it could not serve to warm the soil a single year. I say as much for manure and lime; it is easy to conclude that since the land is improved by marl for ten or thirty years, this is not caused by the heat that is in it: for in taking out this marl in many places, some of it cannot dissolve by weathering, nor by rains, until the frost has worked on it, which frost, finding marl stones as hard as chalk, will make them dissolve and reduce them to powder, as often happens with soft rocks, which are called *jolices*,[181] about which I have talked above; and to end all discussion, I say to you that marl was earth before it was marl, that argillaceous earth and the beginning of chalk rock were first marl, and I say further that the chalk that is still in the matrix of the earth will become white stone, and I'll tell you something else which it will be harder for you to believe, that wherever there are rocks subject to calcination, they

----

[180] A synonym of sparks.

[181] "A kind of soft and tender stone which in frostie weather falls into dust" (Cotgrave). Bescherelle gives "Jollyte" which he says is hydrous silicate of alumina and iron, mixed with a little magnesia, resembling fahlunite and found in Bavaria.

have been marl before they were rock: for otherwise, after calcining they could not improve barren fields.

Theory

I never saw a man so set in his (304) opinions as you are; do you think you will find men so foolish as to believe the ideas you have put forth? You will find many who will jeer at them and think you destitute of all reason: for my part, I have decided to believe nothing of what you say if you do not give me easy and intelligible proofs, through which you can make me believe that some cause, other than the heat of lime, marl and manure, aids the vegetation of seeds. For, as I have told you, since marl scarcely benefits fields during the first year, it is a sign, as I have said, that the heat in it is too great and prevents its action.

Practice

You are mistaken and you do not understand what you say, for it is not the usual thing, nor everywhere, that marl is more effective the second year and the following ones than the first: but regarding this you must note a peculiar and weighty point, which you may have understood by the following statement, which is that marl is reduced to chalk or some other rock by a long decoction, and when a marl begins to pass its decoction, it hardens in such a way that rains cannot reduce it to the required amount, but instead it remains in the fields in little pieces without liquefying in the earth, and for this reason it cannot give flavor to the earth until it is dissolved and liquefied, and inasmuch as this cannot (305) be done soon enough during the first year, frost will have brought about a little later the dissolution of the marl, which then begins to putrefy, and once it is dissolved and liquefied, it will aid the generation of the seeds presented to it. Here is a point that you must keep and hold as certain: that is very easy to understand in Valois, Brie and Champagne, in which regions this marl is found in abundance, even more so than chalk, which was formerly marl and has been reduced to chalk rock by its long decoction. You were able to understand some of these reasons from my treatise on stones.

Theory

And I ask you, if it is true, as you say, that chalk earth was originally marl, then chalk could be used as marl providing it is well pulverized; for if you are right, the same virtue that was in the marl is still in the chalk.

Practice

You have reasoned very well, but since the chalk is lapified, it could not dissolve, and it would not suffice to pulverize it, also it would cost too much to do so, and truly if frost could dissolve it it could be used as marl: and as witness of what I say, I refer you to what I have said above, that lime rock when dissolved by fire serves to marl or manure (306) the soil.[182] If you should wish finer evidence, you must look still further and look into the cause of the differences in colors that exists in marls. The cause of white marls proceeds from its long decoction; as for the black ones, there may be many reasons for them, of which the main one is that it is not long since the materials have begun to congeal, and such marls are easier to dissolve: they may also contain some rotten wood or minerals that may have stained the materials black. As for the yellow ones, the ores of iron, lead, silver and antimony, all these minerals can stain marl yellow: that is why they are of various colors.

Theory

And since you say that the heat of marl, manures, and lime is not the activating cause of seminal vegetations, please explain to me by what virtue marl might activate these barren soils.

Practice

When I told you that generative virtue must not be attributed to the heat of marl, I did not wish by that to deprive marl of all heat: but I wished thereby to destroy the foolish notion of those who want to attribute everything to heat: I say everything internally and externally. We know well that salt is warm internally, and for these reasons it is said to aid (307) in genital generation: and yet in cold weather you will find salt as cold as water or rocks; it must therefore be concluded that its heat cannot operate unless it is moved by a counter-heat, for example in the seminal phenomenon; we must therefore argue further and look for the

---

[182] Palissy's acuity shines forth refreshingly here. He knows that "chalk rock" could be used just as easily as marl but that it cannot be because no good pulverizing machinery existed in his time; it was easier to burn it than to crush it, as can be done profitably nearly four centuries later.

essential, motive and operating cause in this fact, and something hidden will be found that man cannot understand.

Theory

I beg you, if you know something about it, do not keep me in suspense, but explain to me clearly what you think about it.

Practice

If you had opened wide your ears when you read the earlier parts of this book, you would have easily understood it: for I have told you before that there is a fifth element, which the philosophers have never known about; and this fifth element is a generative water, clear or limpid, subtle, mixed indistinguishably with other waters, which, when it is brought in with ordinary water, hardens and congeals with the things that are mixed with it, and just as ordinary water rises upward by the attraction of the sun, either as clouds, exhalations or vapors, so the second water which I call the fifth element, is carried with the other: and when (308) ordinary water happens to flow downward along the valleys, either in rivers, streams or springs, or as rain, I say that however it descends, wherever it stops, something is formed, and particularly by this means the pebbles and rocks and quarries are formed, a very certain thing as you have been able to understand by reading my discourse on rocks: now, let us come to the main point, let us see how that can happen. After you have thoroughly understood that there is a generative water and another that is exhalative, and as you will easily understand that congelative water is generative, the one I call the fifth element, that when it is moved about by water contained in some receptacle, or resting place, it, being thus at rest, will congeal and form some rock according to the size of the material which is in it and it will take the form of its container; and after it has thus congealed the ordinary water sometimes will be absorbed by the earth and will descend lower or else will evaporate and go off as vapors into clouds, and leave behind its companion, because it can no longer carry it. Here is a principle that must make you understand that before marl was marl, it was earth into which the two waters have penetrated and rested a while; and while at rest, the generative water, having found its rest, has congealed, and the vaporative water has gone on, or has evaporated, (309) as I have said above, and the earth in which the congelative water has stopped has hardened and there-

fore whitened by the effect of this congelative water which has
united with it: and that is why when earth is reduced to marl by
the action of generative water, the earth that is then carried to
the fields and is called marl, it is not this that makes the soil fruit-
ful, but rather the congelative water that has stopped in the
earth: which water, having stopped for the reasons I have given,
hardens and whitens the soil, and when seeds are sown into the
soil converted into marl, they do not take up the substance of the
soil to aid in their vegetation, but rather feed on the generative
and congelative water, which I call the fifth element, and when the
seeds, over many years, have drawn out the generative water, the
marly soil is as useless as the dregs of any decoction that might
have been made, and the same is true of manure and lime.

Theory

Then you wish to conclude that vegetative seeds soak up this
fifth element which you call generative water, as a man might suck
up water or wine through the bunghole of a cask, and allow the
dregs to settle at the bottom of the cask?

Practice

You speak truly and none of it must be doubted, but we must
(301 err. pro 310) make a closer examination, for vegetative seeds
could not attract the generative water, unless it is moistened by
ordinary water, and you must note that when soil is moistened
by rain, dew, or otherwise, that plants take up ordinary water with
congelative water; which ordinary water prevents too sudden a
congelation, and that is why wheat and other seeds remain green
until they are ripe and when they have died and the stem stops
its pumping and no longer needs food, the exhalative water goes
away and the generative water remains: and as the decoction of
plants is achieved, their color also changes, as happens in rocks
and in all kinds of minerals, as I have told you about minerals in
my other treatises, that every kind of fruit changes color as it
ripens, according to which I have always said, in speaking about
the fifth element, that although it is a liquid, and among other
waters that it is the one which nourishes straw and hay, and all
kinds of trees and plants, even man and animals, and I have even
told you that human and animal bones are hardened and formed
by this fine generative substance; and as you see that in the
beginning marl is a soft and mobile earth and then becomes a

harder marl, and from marl changes to chalk, and from chalk to rock by the virtue of (311) this water, so human and animal bones (which are a kind of rock and break when they are dry as rock) these I say are made of the same water as above. At first very soft, as I have told you for marl, then they become hard as rock when they have achieved their decoction and maturity, and just as you see that rocks and pebbles, generated and formed of this congelative water, endure fire and cannot be burned, but vitrify instead, you see also that this generative element I have told you about cannot be consumed in straw and hay, for if you burn straw, hay or wood, all the ordinary water will go up as smoke, but this generative water that has sustained, nourished and grown the hay and straw, will remain in the ashes and cannot be consumed, but will be vitrified in red hot kilns, from which ashes glass can be made that will be transparent and spotless, as the generative water was before its congelation; and if that is true of wood ashes, of rocks which because of this generative seed suffer the effects of fire, also you see likewise that nothing resists fire better than the bones of many animals; so you have seen me many times burning sheep foot-bones, and however great the heat of a kiln, it is impossible to consume them by fire, nor likewise eggshells; which must (312) lead you to believe that God has so ordered nature that the bones have attracted and usually attract more of this generative water than do the other parts; and as I have said elsewhere, it must not be doubted that there must be a lot of it in the eyeballs, and because it is moistened and accompanied by exhalative water, that prevents the eyeball from being petrified. We have mirrors and eyeglasses as evidence that there is some affinity between eyes, glasses and mirrors, and it must not be believed that anything can be polished or serve as a mirror or eyeglasses save by the admirable virtue of this fifth element, that binds other materials to itself, and makes them hard, spotless and polishable by the efforts which the Lord has ordered them to make. Another proof, do you believe that the shellfish in the sea, in ponds and freshwater streams have no knowledge of this element? Then how could they build their shell, in the water, and how could the shell harden and dry up in the midst of moisture, if they could not pick out the congelative material in the best of waters? You know that these great purple shells and whelks have shells as hard as stone or harder, and yet the material was liquid and unseen by us before the fish had built its house. In conclusion, we must come to this point, as I prove in the (313) treatise on metals, that crystal is made of this generative water in the midst of ordinary water, that this seed or generative water not only serves in the generation of stones, but also is the substance and generation of all living and vegetative things, according to human understanding, following the admirable order and virtue that God has willed in nature. You have heard previously that there is no kind of stone that is not transparent in its main form, and that the cloudy ones are so only by accident: because in the material there is earth or sand that congeals and hardens with it, and that is why material that was formerly transparent is now dark; however there is no stone so dark but cannot be made transparent by means of fire, because the main element about which I have talked so much makes things fixed and transparent, as it is itself transparent by nature: this cannot be easily verified, except by practical men, and theory certainly has nothing certain to say about these things. I have put forward all these proofs for you so that if you have barren lands, you should work hard to find marl in your property to manure the sterile soil, so that it may yield abundantly fruits in their season, and in so doing you will be a good family man, and like a beacon for lazy ones; you will be a good example, and the neighbors will take pains to follow in your footsteps. (314)

Theory

I pray you do me this favor—teach me the way of knowing the marl you talk about: for if I knew how to recognize it, I should not fail to exert all my strength until I knew if it were possible to find some on my property.

Practice

I do not believe that those who first bettered their soil with marl did so by means of imaginative theory: but I suspect that those who first made the discovery found it without looking for it, as many other sciences offered themselves spontaneously, as you may think that molding may have been invented through the steps of a man who walked barefoot on fine sand or on clay, in which clay or sand the form pressed in wrinkles, hollows, bumps and depressions of the form of the entire foot: this, I say, is enough to have produced the first invention of molding and printing, and accordingly, it is easy to believe that when marl was first known, it was by means of some ditch or trench, as when in throw-

ing the earth from the depths of ditches on top of the neighboring field, it was found that the wheat sown in this field was much
thicker where the earth from the ditches had been thrown; seeing
which, (315) the owners of the field may have taken the next year
some earth from this ditch and having spread it over the entire
field, they discovered that marl was as good and better than
manure. The first discovery of marl may also have come about in
digging wells for water, and somewhere it happened that when a
deep well had been dug, the earth from it was thrown all over the
soil surrounding the pit of the well, and after the field had been
ploughed and sown, what was not being looked for was found,
that is, that the seeds thrown on the parts of the field covered with
earth from the well were found to be thick, fine and healthy.
Here are two effects that may have enlightened the first people
to use marl, and I dare tell you and assure you that both are likely
and can still serve as the first step in places where marl has not
yet been used, and I shall give you an invincible argument, which
is that sometimes marl is found right at the beginning, or very
near the surface of the earth, and in digging down toward the
center of the earth, no marl can be found before a pit fifteen or
twenty feet deep has been dug; sometimes more than twenty-five,
and once the top of this marl is reached, it must be taken out like
water from a well, with much labor. That is why I have told you
and assured you that once marl has been found (316) by chance in
digging wells and trenches, after the discovery is made it has been
searched for so deeply in the countries where it is known and
used. It must therefore be concluded that finding marl cannot be
learned by theory, no more than hidden waters without springs,
and that just as clay is sometimes found near the surface and
sometimes must be searched for deep down, so is marl found, as
I have told you above. If, then, you wish to find marl, I advise you
to remember the example of a good Norman family man, who
lived in a Norman parish, took great pains in cultivating his land,
and yet was forced every year to go and buy wheat outside the
parish, for the whole parish was infertile, and no one harvested
wheat for his own use; and when prices went up, and the men of
this parish went to buy wheat in the nearest town, the other
parishes cursed them, saying that they were responsible for the
high price of wheat. It happened that this good family man, whom
I told you about at the start, thought one day of taking a hatful
of white earth that he found in a ditch and he carried it to a

spot in a field he had sown, and marked the place where he had put this earth, and when the seed had grown he found that the wheat was thick, (317) green and healthy far more than in any other part of the field: seeing which the good man next year manured all his fields with this earth, which bore fruit abundantly; and after his neighbors and all the people of his parish were told of this, they hastened to find this marl, and after manuring their fields, they harvested more abundantly than any other parish. Here is the way to look for marl, the most certain I can think of, and to give you better the means of looking for it and knowing it, I want you to understand thoroughly that marl is nothing more than a soil that has rested a very long time, while it was constantly moistened by the waters that it retained, so much so that all petrifiable things within it have been reduced to fine earth: which earth, being purified of all corruptible impurity, has retained within it one of the two waters, to wit the congelative one, and this congelative water having united with the earth, the latter by this means has been hardened: not as much as rock, although it is a beginning of hard rock, but since it has been mined before its perfect decoction, it dissolves with the rain and frost, after it is taken from the place where it had formed: and since it is imperfect rock it leaves the water that has (318) congealed it in the place where it is dissolved or broken, and the water that held it together is liquefied in the field and gathered up, absorbed and picked up by the seeds that are sown there, as I have told you above: but because this topic is very important I have wished to repeat the same thing with a more intelligible example, which is (the better to make you understand it) that pork or the flesh of a pig, will not lose its shape because it is salted, and when it is desalted it will still keep its form, as you see often that in a pot there may be many pieces of fresh meat, among them and in the pot a piece of pork that will give flavor to all the others that are fresh, and all the stock in the pot will be salt because of the salt that was in the pork, and yet the pork will keep its form. The distillers will extract from cinnamon its flavor, its smell and power, without destroying the form of the cinnamon: so you can understand by this that just as the pork has not salted the water in the pot by its power, but because of the salt in which it was steeped, which salt has been extracted from the pork by the power of the water without taking away the form of the pork: so the seeds attract to themselves the salsitive power of the marl, which is this generative water, and when all the salsitive power has been attracted by the seeds, the marl is nothing more than a barren soil like the bark of the cinnamon, after the essence has been drawn out of it. I (319) will tell you another secret which is that salt could never preserve pork meat, nor convert it to salt pork, nor therefore any other meat if, in the first place, the salt were not dissolved; and if the salt merely touched instead of liquefying, it could not penetrate inside, nor prevent rotting. That is why you can understand that marl which has already begun to petrify, if it is not first dissolved on the field, the seeds could not draw anything out of it, no more than meat could from salt that could not dissolve or liquefy. I am trying as hard as I can to make you understand that any rock, if it could dissolve by rain or frost, could serve as manure for fields: because all rocks are formed, held up and hardened by the same fifth element, which accompanies all things from beginning to end; and there must be many things that fear neither fire, nor water, nor any injury of time, as witness the clay earths that have been caused by its action, and remain in water undamaged, and when made into vessels or bricks, endure the fire of furnaces; and even furnaces are made out of them.

Theory

You have just given me many reasons; still I am not satisfied concerning the best way (320) of finding this marl quickly.

Practice

I can give you no quicker way than that which I would wish to use myself: if I wished to find some in some province where it is not yet known, I would search out all the pits that potters, brick and tile makers use in their work, and from each pit I would manure a part of my field to see if the soil would be improved; then I would want a very long auger, which auger would have a hollow tube at its tip, in which I would house a stick that would have at the other end a handle through it like an auger, and this done, I would go through all the ditches of my property, into which I would plant my auger to the full length of the handle, and after taking it out of the hole, I would look into the recess to see what kind of earth it had brought up, and after cleaning it, I would take out the first handle and put in another much longer one and would put the auger back into the hole I had made, and deeper into the earth with the second handle, and thus, with several handles of various lengths, one could know what the deeper earths were; and not only would I want to probe into the ditches of my properties, but also in (321) all parts of my fields, until the tip of my auger should have brought up a sample of marl, and having found some trace of it, then I should wish to dig at that spot a pit such as one would dig for a well.

Theory

All very well, but supposing there were rock under your land, as happens in many places, where all the lands are underlain by rock?

Practice

That would really be too bad, but still in many places the rocks are very soft, especially when they are still in the earth: therefore it seems to me that a boring auger would pierce them easily, and after the boring auger one could put in the other auger, and thus, one could find marl, even water for wells, which very often could rise higher than the spot where the auger has found them: and that could be done providing they come from higher up [183] than the bottom of the hole you have dug.

Theory

I find it very strange that you should say that if rock prevents me from piercing the soil, then the rock must also be pierced; and if it is rock why should I pierce it, seeing that I am looking for marl? (322)

Practice

You have misunderstood, for we know that in many places the earth is made up of various beds, and in digging into them, one sometimes finds a bed of earth, another of sand, another of rock and another of clay: and commonly the soil is so made up in distinct beds. I shall give you an example to serve you for all that I could ever tell you about them: look at the clay pits near Paris, between the boroughs of Auteuil and Chaliot, and you will see that to find the clay, one must first remove a great thickness of

[183] A casual statement on the cause of artesian wells, and possibly the first correct explanation of the phenomenon.

soil, another thickness of gravel, and then one finds another thickness of rock and under this rock, one finds a great thickness of clay, from which all the tile for Paris and nearby places is made. It is not only in this place that clay is taken from under rock: but in many other places. If you remember well the discourse of the treatise on rocks, you may have understood that the clay having attained its perfection, has served as a receptacle to retain the congelative waters that have caused the rock which is above it.

Theory

We talk about finding this marl, and you tell me about clay: it seems to me that this is beside the point.

Practice (323)

You misunderstand it badly; I have told you above that congelative water not only has acted on the soil to reduce it to marl but has also acted on clay and in rock and wood, even in all generative things, even in living things: do you believe that the generative seed of humans and animals is an ordinary exhalative water? I dare tell you that just as human seed bears with it the bones, flesh and all the distinct parts of the human form, so in plant seeds are carried the trunk, branches, leaves, flowers, and fruits, the powers, colors, odors, and all this by an order which the admirable providence of God has ordered; and you must not find it strange that I should cite you the example of clay to serve you in the matter of marl: for some time ago I traveled through Valois and Champagne, where I saw many fields adorned with many heaps of marl, arranged like piles of manure, and as it was raining on the marl that was in large and small lumps, I saw that they were dissolving under the falling rain: so I took one of these lumps, which was liquefied like dough, and after kneading it in my hands, I made a number of *trochisques* [184] out of it, which I baked in a strong fire, and when they were done, I found that they had hardened in the same way as clay: (324) so I learned that both of them could do the same thing, if not everywhere, at least in some places.

Theory

True, but clays are of various colors and are most commonly gray, and marl is white: therefore these things cannot agree.

[184] Large pills or lumps.

Practice

Truly, marl is commonly white in Valois, Brye and Champagne, yet I have good evidence that in Flanders and in Germany, even in some parts of France, it may be gray, black and yellow, as I said at the beginning: hence I advise you not to tarry over color: for gray or black marl can become white during its decoction; and just as there is white marl, so also there are white clays. I remember going from Partenay, as I went to Bresuyre in Poitou, and from Bresuyre toward Thouars, but in all these regions, the clays are very white, and therefore the pebbles which are very numerous in this region: which leads me to believe that the clays of these regions could also serve as marl, and particularly the one used by the drapers to full and degrease cloth. But let us see also that the crucibles of the goldsmiths, which come from Anjou, near Troye, and many other places, are made from a very (325) white earth similar to marl. In lower Burgundy, there is a certain village where clay quite similar to marl is dug up, and I believe it is just that: nevertheless it resists fire, so well that all the glaziers of most of the Ardennes use vessels made from this earth; and even the glaziers of Anvers, who work in crystal glass, are forced to send for it, although it is very expensive, because it lasts a long time in hot furnaces. I have seen a well dug in the Ardennes country, where before finding water, it was necessary to dig through a very great thickness of earth, and after the earth, a rock bottom of great thickness was found, and after the rock a clay as white as chalk, which I tested, and found good for making vessels: nevertheless, although it has not been approved, still I believe it to be a perfect marl. If I could ply my trade while traveling about, I could give much advice about these things, which would be very useful to the state: still, here is an open road: if you are curious about your property, you can search by the methods I have told you about; in searching, you will find things more surely than I could tell you: for it is commonly said that it is easy to add to something that has been invented: therefore science reveals itself to those (326) who seek for it.

Theory

And will it not be sufficient for me to seek marl by its feel to the hand? Since marl is a fatty earth, like clay, and since clay is recognized by feeling it with the hands: for some people, if they feel wet clay, say here is a fatty and viscous earth: hence the Latins say that clay earth means fatty earth.

Practice

You have very poorly remembered what I said in the book on earths: I have told you that the Latins and the French misuse the term, when they call clay a fatty earth: for if it were fatty, it would be impossible to dissolve it with water or frost: for all fats and oleaginous viscosities resist water and cannot have any affinity with it: but on the contrary, clay and marl remove all greasy, viscous and oleaginous stains: for these reasons the fullers use them to degrease cloth.

Theory

I find in some of your statements a rather obvious contradiction; for you have told me before that even the rocks are caused by the very matter that aids in the generation of seeds: and yet I have seen countries where all the lands are encrusted with rocks and stones, and such lands (327) have very little soil over the rock, and the seeds planted there can scarcely grow, but on the contrary the wheat remains low, with very small ears, because the plant cannot get nourishment from the rock.

Practice

Have you not heard a statement I made to you that if salt could not dissolve, pork, fish and all kinds of meat could not be salted, if the grain of the salt remained entire without dissolving or diminishing? If the country that is thus rocky is of such nature that the rains that fall on it, having in them so great a quantity of congelative water, which, falling from above, makes a crust as it increases the rocks covered with a little earth, that does not argue against my statement: for I have told you that since the water is congealed and reduced to rock, the seeds can draw no liquid from it, unless the rock is first dissolved, as I have told you that meat could not take anything from the salt unless it is dissolved and diminished. That is an entirely certain conclusion.

Theory

Nevertheless I have seen many forests in mountainous areas, in which the trees are marvelously large, although their roots are in nothing but rock, with a very little soil over the surface of the rock, and the roots of these trees run through and among the rocks of the (328) mountains.

Practice

If you had noted well what I told you in treating of rocks, you would not have put forward such an argument: for you must understand that tree roots cannot pierce rock. You must therefore believe that the trees had taken root before the earth where they are had congealed, and as the trees in growing have taken up much generative water, they have distributed it as much to the leaves and fruits, as to the branches and the roots: and because the leaves and fruits fell under the trees, they eventually rot, and in rotting (as do the grasses of the forests) they give up in their putrefaction the ordinary and the generative water to the soil, which is caused among the leaves and fruits: and some time later, by the power of the sun, the ordinary water is evaporated, and the generative water then turns to rock the earth that has been formed by the leaves, fruits and other forest plants: for otherwise what you say could not be done: because if you examine the roots of trees you will find none without as much root as branches: for otherwise, it could not survive the struggle that it wages against the wind.[185] And if you wished to study the reason why trees have such twisted roots, you will find that the cause is nothing else but that just as men (329) look for the easiest mountains, roads and paths, so the roots in their growth look for the easiest parts of the earth, the softest and least rocky; and if there is some rock in front of the root, it will leave the rock in its path and turn to the right or to the left; because it could not pierce the rocks in its way.

Theory

And yet the branches of trees, which meet no obstacle in the air, are just as twisted and forked as the roots: and yet the air is no harder in one place than in another. There must necessarily be a reason other than the one you have given.

Practice

As for the roots, I have told you the truth: but as for the branches, there is another reason, which is that the branches in furthering their expansion, each one seeks the liberty of the air,

---

[185] One of the rare instances where Palissy gives a wrong explanation of a natural phenomenon, possibly because of too little observation.

and grows away from the others as much as it can, so as to have air in abundance; and for this reason, the branches avoiding each other's vicinity cannot ascend directly, which you can know through walnut, pear and apple trees and many other kinds of trees, because in their first growth the stalk will grow straight up until the strength of the roots rises abundantly, which causes it to fork, (330) growing several branches, like an overflowing stream. I see these reasons in many examples, first because I have seen oaks, walnut trees, chestnuts and many other kinds of trees, planted in the country, among which I have never found one that grew directly upward, like those in forests, surrounded by other trees that prevent them from spreading out in every direction. I have never observed also that forest trees were abundantly fertile, like those of the open, nor also that their fruits were as tasty as those of trees that have air and sun at will: from which it is easy to conclude that forest trees surrounded by other trees, not enjoying the sun and air to right and to left, are forced to grow upward to seek the air and the sun that they desire for their nourishment and growth. And as I was seeking to understand these causes, I sometimes went through a forest three leagues wide, and in order to make the road easy, the trees had been cut, all through the forest, over a path eight or ten *toises* wide: passing through this forest, I noticed that all the trees to the right and left of this path, had grown a great many branches toward the side of the road; and toward the forest there were very few, (331) which gave me sure knowledge that the trunk of the tree took pleasure in growing toward the road, because it was the airiest part: I noticed also that the trees on the edge of the forest threw, bent or inclined themselves toward the fields, as if the other trees were annoying them: and truly there are very often many fruit trees, either in gardens or in other places, that are bent because of the shade of their neighbors, other trees whose nearness they dislike.

Theory

By your statements you mean that after the leaves, fruits and branches of trees and plants are rotten they can be reduced to stone.

Practice

I have said that, and much more, as you may have understood from my discourse on metals, that not only rotten things can be lapified, but on the contrary cannot be petrified before putrefaction, as you have seen for wood and shells, and I dare tell you moreover that there is no kind of earth which cannot naturally petrify by the action of the fifth element about which I have talked so much above.

Theory

And tripoli, what is it? Can it be petrified?

Practice

Not only tripoli, but also ocher, boliarmeni, and all those minerals that are lapified, (332) such as *sanguine*,[186] *orcane*,[187] and black stone: all these are no more than petrified desiccative and astringent rocks, like a kind of sealed earth.

Theory

And what is it you called sealed earth?

Practice

Sealed earth is also called *terre lemnie;* [188] some give it this name, from the place where it is taken: and you must note that the earth is nothing more than a kind of marl or clay that is taken from deep in the earth, as clays and marls commonly are: it is said that this earth is very astringent, and that by its action it protects against poison and staunches the flow of blood by its astringent power: and for these reasons the people of the country where it is found go one by one to open the pit, or the hole through which they go down to get some, and having taken as much as they want, they close the hole until the next year: for the reason that they have tribute of this earth. They open the pit with great pomp and ceremony. The country where this earth is found is now occupied by the Turk, which means that he makes a profit on it, and this earth is sold in *trochisques* marked with the arms of the Turk. That is why it is called sealed earth, and it would seem to me better to say stamped earth, and because it is called marked or stamped earth, that leads me to believe that it is soft when (333) it is dug up, as clay usually is: for although it

---

[186] Literally, bloodstone, but, as Palissy explains elsewhere, there are many kinds.

[187] A variant spelling of *arcanne*, which is red ocher.

[188] Lemnos earth or Lemnian earth. Compare Palissy's account with that of Agricola (Hoover and Hoover, 1912, p. 31).

is hard enough to be carried often in great lumps on the shoulders, nevertheless it is moist, so that it can easily be stamped. Let us now look into the reason for its usefulness; whence can such a property come? If you had thoroughly understood the statements I have made on congelations, you would know that the power of this earth comes from nothing more than ordinary and congelative waters, which, having seeped through the soil, until they found some rock to stop them where the waters have stopped, the subtle and fine earth that was there retained the virtue of the congelative water, and there an association and ligature took place, that is, that the earth and water produced a moderate decoction and beginning of petrifaction, and in doing so have allowed to run, go down or evaporate the ordinary water, and there remained in the earth only the congelative water which has lost in congealing the color and appearance which it had before, and has taken the same color as the earth with which it had united; and because it has not yet attained its perfect decoction or petrifaction, it is certain that when it is taken by mouth, the virtue of the congelative water in it will dissolve from the heat and moisture of the stomach, and then, when these materials are liquid, the body uses the congelative material that was in the earth, and the earth is (334) eliminated in the usual manner. That should lead you to believe that this congelative water is of salsitive nature, as I have explained to you above, that the venom of serpents is cured by spittle, because of its salt. I have told you above about an island full of serpents, aspics and vipers that are on an island belonging to the lord of Soubise. I have also told you that those who are bitten by mad dogs are cured by sea water, and even some by old pork, and this is done only by a salsitive virtue. I have explained to you enough (in talking about salts) that all salts are not mordicative or acrid, so as to explain to you that I do not mean by that that the salsitive virtue of salty earth comes from common salt: but rather I merely wish to say that its action is caused only by a salsitive virtue.

Theory

Pray tell me if it would be possible to find in France some earth with the same properties as the one you talk about: because in your discourses you make no distinction of the materials that cause the congelation of rocks, marls, and clays; and since you attribute the virtue of sealed earth to the same cause as that which congealed the earths, stones and marls of this country, why is it that earths with the same properties could not be found in France, seeing that they have the same cause? as (335) I have said.

Practice

I cannot give you any reasons against it, unless it is that in warm countries fruits, or at least some of them, are much better than in cold countries, as you see that in France, from Paris northward, *pompons*,[189] melons, oranges, figs and olives cannot be grown, nor many other kinds of fruits that grow in warm regions, and even grapes cannot ripen, as they do in the southern parts of France, in Champagne and Picardy. You know also that spices and sugar cannot grow in France, as they do in warm countries. You know that cassia and all aromatic gums come from warm regions, even rhubarb and other simples used in medicine. It is easy enough to believe that the sun gives some more powerful virtue in some regions than in others, and we even see that in a single region, the same kind of plant will thrive wondrously better than another that is grown in the same country. I have given you as an example the grapevines of La Foye-Moniaut, which are between St-Jehan d'Angely and Nyort, which yield wine no less esteemed than hippocras; and quite near there, there are other vines whose wine never ripens perfectly, which is (336) esteemed less than that of wild grapes. From this you can believe that the two soils are unlike in properties, although they resemble each other in color and appearance. Nevertheless, I do not wish to conclude from this that there could not be in France any *lemnie* earth that could produce the same effects as sealed earth; and I shall argue about this that the first vessels made were made, as some say in *argis*,[190] and since then all the others that are made are called vessels of argillaceous earth; also that earth similar to that of *argis* is found in all countries, so it is not hard to believe that *terre lemnie* could also be found. I shall use another, more reliable argument: that in the Marennes islands and in Foye-Moniaut, wine is made that has the sweetness and goodness of

---

[189] "A Pompion, or Melon" (Cotgrave). George W. White informs me that "pompion" was the word for pumpkin in American Colonial writing, 1610 to 1630.

[190] Apparently the name of a place, but it does not have a capital initial either in the 1580 or 1880 editions.

hippocras and that its goodness comes from a salsitive virtue which we call tartar, and that in the Narbonne and Xaintonge country, common salt is made, and although the salsitive virtue of *lemnie* earth does not come from common salt, still, just as in one part of France the grapes and some other fruits carry a sweetness as great as that of dates, figs, and other fruits from warm regions, I have concluded that *lemnie* earth could also be found in some place, and that it would have the same properties as that which comes from Turkey, about which we have talked. I shall give you (337) still another example: you know that the ancients held *bol d'Arménie* [191] in great esteem, because of its astringent action: and yet, ever since it has been used in France, even that which is produced in this country, and although it is found in several regions of France, still it is called by the same name as that of Armenia, as you see that the Latins call it bolus armenus, in French boliarmeny. We have still another kind which is more desiccative than the above, from which painters make drawing pencils, which they call bloodstones; it is quite good for drawing portraits from nature: it is very fine-grained. There is another kind of bloodstone, which is very hard; because of its hardness, it can be cut and polished like jasper or agate, although it is not as hard: some people have had these stones cut to use in burnishing or polishing gold and other things. If you examine this stone closely you will know that there is no difference between the two kinds of bloodstone, except that one is petrified because it has received more congelative water which has made it heavier and harder, and the other, from which red pencils are made, has remained soft, and is still parched because it has lacked water before its perfect decoction. And because the beginning of our subject was only to talk about (338) marl, I tell you now that in many places marl can be used to make white pencils, to draw in white, just as bloodstone is used to draw in red.

Theory

I find here a very strange thing, which is that you contradict so many millions of men, dead as well as living, in what they all say and hold as a sure thing, that marl and clay are fat, and that the soil is improved because of the fat in the marl; and

[191] Bolus Armenus, or boliarmény. According to Bescherelle, a synonym of "sealed earth." See note 152.

you, like a confirmed stubborn one, wish to prevail over all of them.

Practice

If you had carefully examined the statements I have made to you above in speaking about drinkable gold, golden tonic, greases and waters, you would know by them that once men are convinced of a false opinion, it is hard to take it out of their heads: the same is true of those who have little concern for the effects of nature. Do you not remember that long ago I brought together in Paris some of the most learned doctors, surgeons and other naturalists, who have all granted me that philosophers and physicists, past and present, had erred in writing about the golden tonic, drinkable gold, metals, waters, and rocks, and in many other instances, of which you know I have lectured, and I have not found a man to contradict me: (339) however, there was an alchemist who was rumored to have tormented himself searching for the increase of metals, to make money through it. He was very displeased that I should talk about drinkable gold, because he contended that he could dissolve gold to give color to silver, which is impossible, except on the surface, as a trick: and as you know that the tongue speaks of the abundance of the heart, this one, aroused by my statements, waited until the others had left, and then came to tell me that he knew how to make two kinds of drinkable gold. His passion had caused him to misunderstand me: for I had not said that gold cannot be made drinkable, because I know several ways of dissolving it, but I said that even if it were liquefied it would never be assimilated by the human body, to serve it as a tonic, because it cannot be digested. And to return to the pursuit of rooted false opinions on the earths that they call fat, I shall put forward the same reason I have given when speaking about clays, which is that in these earths there are two waters: one is ordinary and exhalative, enemy of fire, the other is congelative and causes earth, which is merely dust, to hold together in one mass and harden by fire: I would ask all these dictionaries, if the radical humor that joins the particles of the earth together are fatty, could it stand fire? is it not well known that any thick, oily grease burns in fire? do we not know also (340) that drapers degrease their cloth with clay or marl; if it were fatty, how could it remove grease? There are some who, to prove that it was fat have said that many wells have marl at the bottom, wishing to prove thereby that it was fat: but such a proof is not good, for we know that all kinds of clay hold water while they are underground, but when they are dug up from their pit, they could not hold water save while they are soft as paste: but after these earths have been dried, they immediately dissolve when put into water; and if it were fat, as is said, it could never dissolve in water, any more than suet, wax, *poix-raisine* [192] and other fatty things. It is very certain that if you take two pieces of marl or clay and have two containers, one full of oil, the other of water, and that in each container you put a lump of marl or clay, the one that you put into the oil will never dissolve, but the one you put into the water will crumble and dissolve like a piece of lime, for we know that fat and oily materials are repelled by water, and that these earths are made up of aqueous matter, hence they cannot join or mingle: Those who call marl (341) and clay fat must therefore seek other reasons than the ones they put forward. If they called them pasty earths, they would speak much better and would speak the truth, for we know that flour and water have such an affinity that as soon as they are mixed, they are converted into a pasty mass. They should therefore be called pasty earths, and not fat or viscous.

Theory

I find it strange that you say that not only putrefied things can be reduced to stone, but also any thing, without losing their form; how is it possible that the water you talk about can enter into solid bodies if first they are not softened by putrefaction?

Practice

How dare you say the contrary of what I have said, seeing that when I spoke to you of the essence and form of stones, I have shown you many shells reduced to rock, although the shells were formerly as solid as a glass vessel could be, or one of some metallic material.

Theory

It might be, then, that nothing is porous, and if that were so, vessels could not contain water or any other material whatsoever, and yet the contrary is evident.

[192] See note 77 on this word.

Practice

I do not doubt that all things are (342) porous, but those things that are made of the most condensed materials have such fine pores that liquids cannot pass through them visibly, except by some accident: as you have seen long ago that when I wished to grind my colors in winter I would heat the pestle and when I placed it hot on the marble, this pestle, by its heat, drew water from the marble, although the marble seemed to be quite dry: there is an argument that must persuade you that marble is porous, through which pores the heat of the pestle attracted moisture. Another example: You well know that arms and blade-smiths when they wish to harden weapons and blades, heat them until they are red hot, then they cool them in water; then the cutting edge of blades and weapons becomes much harder. I ask you if iron or steel, when they are thus tempered, did not take up some substance to the center and throughout, could they be hardened by the action of water? Of course not: for if the blade or the armor hardened only at the surface, that would be useless. It must then be concluded that when arms are hot, they are penetrated by and attract some kind of water, other than the exhalative one, which holds together and strengthens; and to show this, to make you understand better (343) that armor is not strengthened by the exhalative waters, you must understand that to temper armor, some people have many secrets; some will put salt in the water in which they wish to temper their armor, some will put vinegar, others will put lime chunks, others will put glass finely ground; and you must not doubt that ground glass can serve to harden iron or steel; I do not say that it can do so as glass, but when it is well ground, the salt of the glass liquefies in ordinary water, and then the armor that is tempered in it makes use of this liquefied salt, which it attracts to strengthen itself, and not common water, for it cannot be fixed. In the time of the late King of Navarre, two goldsmiths from Geneva brought to the court of this King a war club and a cutlass, to make which they had worked for two years, adorning and enriching or carving these pieces: and because they were marvelous and very costly, they had spared nothing in order that this war club and cutlass should be wrought of good material, and in such case tempered in certain waters that hardened these weapons: I do not know if they were tempered by the magnificent Maigret, who had spread the rumor that in searching for the generation of gold, or philosopher's stone, he had found a water that hardened armor marvelously; (344) not knowing, then, who did the tempering, I shall continue with my subject which is that the cutlass I speak of was so well tempered that it would cut andirons or *landiers* [193] of iron like wood without damaging the cutlass: here are proofs that should give you enough to understand the statements I have made to you about marl, that just as seeds are nourished by it through the effect of ordinary water, so are metals. I shall give you still another good example in confirmation of what I have told you, about what causes the goodness of marl; thus it causes the congelation of rocks. There are certain iron forges in the Ardennes, in the village of Daigny and Givonne, other forges in the village of Haraucourt, which are at most two leagues away from each other, yet in the forges of Haraucourt white earth, taken fairly deep in the ground, is put in with the iron ore to help it melt, and at Dagny and Givonne, they use for the same reason rock which is used in making lime, which they call Castile stone, which they break up to help their ore melt, as I have said. Do you see in this an obvious proof, since the salt of trees helps everything to melt, there is a salsitive virtue in rocks, and therefore in soils that are not yet lapified, like the one (345) that is used at Haraucourt, since it has the same effect as the rocks of Dagny and Givonne.

Theory

You seem to contradict yourself in that you sometimes say that the rocks are congealed by the virtue of salt and afterwards you say that it is a water.

Practice

It seems to me that you have a very hard head, for I remember having told you before that sea water is not usually called salt, although it is salty: but it is rightly called water until it is congealed, and then it is called salt; icy water is not so called before it is frozen, but when it is frozen it is called ice: milk is not called cheese before its congelation, similarly I cannot call the things above otherwise than according to the form that they have when I speak of them after writing the above. I find sure evidence against those who say that marl scarcely improves fields in the

[193] A kind of andiron; see note 41.

first year; it is certain that it does so as well as the following year, providing it is put on the fields before winter has begun, because marl is useless if it is not first dissolved by frosts. I have also been informed by the people of Champagne, Brie and Picardy, that in some places the marl is (346) nothing more than chalk, and since in many parts of these regions stone is lacking, and they are sometimes forced to make walls out of chalk, when they find some pit where it is well condensed and reduced to chalk; this cannot be done in all marl pits because some can be dug up only in little pieces, and some even are still liquid and mudlike. And as I have said before, they are not all white, but on the contrary there are some of various colors. Have you not considered seeds which, when they are placed in a vial full of water, develop and move about in the water, although the vial is well sealed? and yet we take it for granted that all living things could not live without air; then it must be that the water and the vial are both porous, for otherwise the animals enclosed in them could not live. I say the same for fishes of the sea and rivers, that if the water were not somewhat porous, the fishes could not live. Have you not considered that when the weather is damp, and that it sometimes rains or snows on the windows, they will be wet through, on the inside, within the room: do you think that the sun could pass through window glass if it were not porous? Certainly not; likewise fire could not go through metal pots and kettles, if they were not somewhat porous; [194] you see also that although egg shells are well condensed, still when they are put on coals, certain little drops of water come out of the shell from inside the egg. (347)

[194] Palissy may have been the first to propound the theory that solids are porous, even window glass. In 1580 the idea must have sounded preposterous, but the learned potter is upheld and surpassed by the physicists and chemists of our day.

COPY OF THE LABELS

Placed under the marvelous things which the author of this book has prepared, and arranged in order in his cabinet, to prove all the things contained in this book: for some would not want to believe; in order to convince those who will take the trouble to come and see them in his cabinet, and having seen them, will leave convinced of all the things written in this book. [195]

Just as all kinds of metals, and other fusible materials, take on the shape of the hollows or molds in which they are placed, or thrown, even when thrown into the earth take the shape of the place where the material is thrown or poured, so the materials of all kinds of rocks take the shape of the place where the material has congealed. And just as metallic forms are unseen until they are out of the mold, in which the material has congealed, so it is with stony materials, (348) which in their first essence are liquid, fluid and aqueous: and in order to forestall the calumnies that could be uttered through ignorance or malice, having seen no more than my writings and flat drawings: for these reasons, I say, I have placed here as evidence a great number of stones through which you will easily be able to know that the reasons and proofs of my treatise on stones are true. And if you are not entirely devoid of sense, you will admit it after having had the demonstration of these natural stones: which I have illustrated in my book, because all those who see the book will not have the chance of seeing these natural things: but those who will see them in their natural forms, will be forced to admit that it is impossible for

[195] Palissy's teaching methods were revolutionary for his time. Not only did he use specimens to illustrate his lectures but he expected his readers to visit his museum, book in hand, to do laboratory work, as we would call it now, to verify his statements. In this he was so much ahead of his time that nearly three centuries were to elapse before his method was generally adopted.

them to have taken the forms that they have unless the material was once liquid and fluid.

If you wish to understand the above, go inside the quarries whence have been taken quantities of rocks, or other minerals. If these quarries still have standing roofs, you will find in most of them certain hanging wicks formed by the waters that daily descend through the earth, on the roofs [196] of these rocks. And the waters that have flowed to right and to left, against the minerals of these rocks, will give you clearly to understand the proofs that you will see below. Because you will know (349) that the waters, which have congealed since the stones have been taken out of these rocks, are not similar, either in color, form or hardness, to those of the main quarry.

Also, in looking at the above, you will know that there is an infinite number of stones that have two essences, and others that have been formed by additions, all by liquid material, as you will understand easily by the proofs which I have placed here for you in rows.

And because I have said that all rocks are diaphanous and transparent in their first essence: you must therefore understand, that those you see here are cloudy, because ordinary water, mixed with congelative water has brought earth or sand with them, which sand or earth, having congealed with the crystalline material, makes it cloudy, even gives it its color, whether sand or earth; as you can see clearly by these patterns, in considering their forms.

You can also judge by these rough and unpleasing forms that they have nevertheless been formed by fluid materials, in such a way that you can easily judge which end was up or (350) down, as if it were a metallic material.

You can also know by the other next stones that they have been formed with the flat side down, and that they have been made at different times, and by congelative additions, and not by growth, as some say: the additions are evident enough in these stones.

You see also that the rocks of plaster,[197] talc and slate peel and disaggregate in sheets like a book: and this because the materials

[196] "Quarries with roofs" appears to be a misnomer, yet there are many places around Paris, and elsewhere, where an open quarry is continued into a maze of tunnels when the overburden is too great to remove and the stone must be "quarried" by digging into the hillside.

[197] By his description of the cleavage that follows, it is obvious that his "rock of plaster" is selenite.

have fallen at various times, through the earth, and therefore the congelations taking place at different times, they cannot join together as well as if the material had been congealed all at once; therefore, as you see, there is sometimes some earth or sand between two congelations.

By these stones you can easily learn that they are formed at several times and various congelations added by distillating materials.

All these kinds that you see filled with pebbles and various kinds of shells, have been formed in the earth in some spot covered with water, and are stones of double essence: for the shells and pebbles that are in them, had been formed before the mass and their formation, for these reasons, is heavier and harder than the mass. And some time after the exhalative waters have departed, leaving there the (351) congelative water. The latter has lapified and petrified the muds in which were shells and pebbles. And since the soil was already parched because of the absence of exhalative waters, the main mass is softer and lighter because of the number of pores that are in this mass.

And you must not think that nature has formed these shells without subject: but on the contrary you must believe that they have been formed by living fishes like other animal natures, and must never believe that these things were made at the time of the Flood: for even though some are found on mountains devoid of water: still when their shells took their form, there was water in which were many living things, which were caught and enclosed when the mud hole was reduced to stone: you will understand this better as you continue the reading of the following signs.

You see here a great number of pieces of wood reduced to stone, which is petrified in water like the shells, and this wood has been petrified at the same time as the mass of the rock to which this wood is attached, and the whole thing has not been made out of water, and cannot be.

You see also certain pieces of wood that have been petrified in congelative water, from which all things are started and without which nothing can say, I am. That is why (352) I have called it the fifth element, although it should be called the first one.

To make you certain that all things are porous, as I have written in my book, consider this great number of shellfish that I have put before your eyes, which are now all reduced to stone; and this by virtue of the congelative water that has penetrated all through these shells, changing them from one nature to another, without taking away anything of their form.

And because many people are convinced of a false opinion, saying that the shells reduced to stone have been brought in at the time of the Flood, throughout the earth, even on top of the mountains, I have answered and disproved such an opinion by an article above, and in order the better to verify the writings in my book, I have placed before your eyes all kinds of petrified shells, which have been found and taken from among a hundred million others, which are found daily in mountainous places, and in the midst of the rocks of the Ardennes: which rocks, full of shellfish, have not been made or generated since the mountain was made; but you must believe that before the mountain was made of rock, that this place, where these shells are found, was then water or ponds, or other water bodies, where these fishes lived and fed.[198] That is why you can easily know that I have (353) told the truth, when I said that there were in unsalty soil three kinds of water just as in the sea: for otherwise the same fishes that live in the sea, and multiply their houses one by one, they have done likewise in the mountains where the shells of these fishes are found to be quite like those of the sea.

And in confirmation of the above: Look at all these kinds of fishes which I have put before your eyes, you will see a number whose seed has been lost, and even now we do not know what they should be called; but that cannot prevent it from being obvious to all that the form of these gives us clearly to understand that they were once alive, and these forms cannot be made in any way except by living things.

It must suffice you by the following articles, that the proofs are all evident, that all rocks are at first liquid, fluid and crystalline material. Similarly, metallic materials are also fluid, aqueous and crystalline. And just as cloudy rocks are so because of the addition of earth and sand mixed in among the essential material, so metals can in no way appear diaphanous or crystalline: thus they are impure because of the materials intermixed with the pure essence: which intermixed materials (354) render the metal impure, brittle and friable: which could not be if there were not

[198] Palissy here returns to the subject of fossils and their origin. His explanation is ingenious, original, and close to the truth. One more step in this chain of reasoning and he would have arrived at the right explanation.

opposition of earths or sands or other interpositions: and even sulphur is an enemy of metals after their congelation. For this reason it must be driven out by the refiners, like an excremental material.

And in order to well prepare your ears to hear and your eyes to see, I have put here certain rocks and ores of all kinds of metals, to make you understand a peculiar and very weighty point, which is that through these metallic rocks placed before your eyes, you will be able easily to understand that all the alchemists past and present have erred in trying to build through the destroyer: in that they have tried to make through fire that which is made with water, and through heat that which is made with cold: which has led me to place these obvious proofs before your eyes.

Note well this little argument, well proved by the thing itself, and look well at all metallic ores, you will find on the surface of the metal an infinite number of points, naturally cut into facets, as if they had been carved artificially: the majority of which points is formed of crystalline materials, or to say it better, of crystal, which has caused me to know directly and to be sure that never did points form naturally out of water: but (355) certainly all materials congealed in water have an upper surface with triangular, quadrangular or pentagonal forms, I say formed by a marvelous nature, just as it is given to plants to keep a certain order, as you see that roses and gooseberries form prickly spines for their defense: also metallic and stony materials form a sort of armor, or protective body over their surface, in the shape of pointed rocks: as it is given to several fishes to form many scales, as you see in crayfishes and many other kinds of fishes.

Do look and see if I am a liar, don't you see many samples of gold and silver ore that show you obviously that they were formed in water? Among others, do you not see one in which the first layer is of rock, which shows you clearly that the rock was first to congeal? And after that you see another layer of silver ore. And in third place there is a layer of crystal formed into diamond points, and since I tell you that these pointed and faceted forms cannot be made out of water, you will admit therefore that the silver ore, which is below the crystal, was also congealed in water, as you will know as you continue to examine these things. (356)

You see also by these other metallic rocks certain points like the ones named above: and yet in these there are several kinds of metals: such as gold, silver, lead and copper, which things are also impure, because of the sulphurous earths and other excrements that cause metals to become brittle and friable. And when these excrements are dissipated and separated by the action of fire, then these metals are tractable and malleable: as one sees in coined metals.

Now here is an article that must make you stop to consider and believe all the above. Look at the slate that I have put here before your eyes, which is full of marcasites, formed in the shape of a square die. It is certain that the slate has been congealed in water, and that before its congelation, the metallic material that was concealed in the water has been separated from the water: like oil which has no affinity for water; and the materials of these marcasites, which are formed of metallic materials, in congealing and dividing from the water, have formed into pentagonal faces, and have taken on their color as they congealed. And it must necessarily be that the marcasites were formed and congealed before the formation of the slate.

Don't you see these crystalline rocks which I have placed here, as evidence of the rarest and hardest (357) demonstration in my book? For although these rocks are as clear and crystalline as pure water, still, within them there is metallic material, which can in no way be seen in the mass unless the metallic material be made known by testing with a good hot fire, as you see by a piece of the same material that has turned a silvery color after its fusion test. And by this you must be assured and believe firmly that metals are intermixed with and unseen in water until they congeal.

Do note that metallic materials are unseen in the earth, in waters, and are so liquid and subtle that they penetrate through bodies or corporeal materials, as the sun does through window panes: for otherwise the metallic waters could not reduce any form into metal, if the form were not first dissipated. We see, however, that many shells of fishes are metallic and changed in substance, because they have soaked in metallic materials, as you see at present many pieces of wood which have been reduced to metal because they have soaked in water in which there were metallic waters.

You see clearly that all these forms of shells reduced to rock have formerly been living fishes, and because (358) the memory and use of all these species has been lost, yet by the other species that are now living, and are also reduced to rock, we can easily know that nature makes none of these things without purpose, as I have said above. And for these reasons, I have put aside a group which as you see is formed in spiral lines: I have seen one that was sixteen inches in diameter.

I have put this rock before your eyes to make you understand that all I have said about earthquakes is true: for you see in this rock the effects of air and water moved by fire: for although the rock is large, still it is formed of very little material: because the three elements have blown it up and made it spongy in such a way that you see that if the material were condensed at is was before it was exposed to fire, it would be a hundred times smaller than it is now: but because it was liquid and boiling when the fire caused it to be tormented, it has suddenly congealed, and the air that kept it swollen by the action of the fire has remained in it until now. And that is why this rock is so light that it floats on water, like all other light objects.

Just as I have told you that metals are unseen in waters, so they are in the ground, before their congelation: and for these reasons, I have put before your eyes this large (359) piece of pottery which was made in the form of a large vase: but when it was touched by fire, it liquefied, and collapsed, and entirely lost its form, so that if it had been forged while hot, it would have spread out without breaking, as do malleable things. Must you not believe through this that there is some unseen metallic material in the earth from which these vessels are made? for otherwise it should have broken rather than bent.

Do you see these fish-forms called *availlons:* [199] they were found in a field near the forests of the Ardennes: and the part of the soil in which they were found is very hollow at the surface: which has led me to believe, as above, that formerly water gathered there more than in any other part of the field, and these fishes were born and grew and lived there as if they had been in the sea. In the Ocean sea on the coast of Xaintonge, is found a great quantity of these fishes. And as I have said above, the water of this field has evaporated and dried out, and the muds and the fishes, of which an infinite number is found, have been reduced to rock.

And in another field I have found an infinite number of fishes which we call cockles, with which the *Michelets* [200] decorate their

[199] A colloquial name for *Venus borealis.* See also note 42.
[200] A colloquial name for pilgrims to Mont-Saint-Michel.

bonnets or hats when they come from Saint-Michel. And the reason why the shells are not white (360) like the others, is because there is iron ore in them, and in the earth which they inhabited.

Do you not see here fruits reduced to rock, by the same causes as I have deduced above?

All the rocks that you see in this place are agates or chalcedony which were formerly clay, as you will see on the next shelf.

Examine a little these lumps of earth which have the appearance of agate or chalcedony, and you will know that they were about to be reduced to rock, and nothing more was needed except the decoction by which rocks are brought to perfection.

Look here a bit: here are two rocks that have retained the form of grasses on which the material has fallen before it congealed.

There are fishes and other animals that have rocks in their skulls, which are formed from liquid materials, like the others.

By these horny rocks, which are hollow inside, I prove that they have been full of exhalative water, during the time of their formation.

These rocks which you see thus full of holes are formed by the muds of the sea, in which are many fishes called angel-wings: [201] these are long, like knife handles, armed with two shells: and when the mud is reduced to rock, these fishes die in it, and the rock has (361) remained pierced.

And to show you that all things formed in water are in facets and otherwise not, look here at copperas and vitriol, saltpeter and all other kinds of salts that are covered with water while they congeal. [362]

[201] See previous note (129) on this word.

EXTRACT OF THE MAIN MAXIMS [202] CONTAINED IN THIS BOOK

The number at the end indicates the page: those that have none are for the most part collected from the entire discourse, without being related to a particular place.

Although all philosophers have concluded that there are only four elements, there is a fifth, without which nothing could say, I am.   125–126, 127, 128

Never has man understood the effects of water or fire.   12

Those who say that the waters come from the sea and return to it are mistaken.   34–35

All springs and rivers of fresh water are caused only by rain water.   34 & 47

Modern fountain makers daily make mistakes, not understanding the effects of waters enclosed in underground pipes. The ancients, for these purposes, invented aqueducts.   12 & 15 [363]

All pumps and machines for raising waters cannot last because of the violence of water.   2

Without the violence of water moved by fire, there could be no earthquakes.   23

There are two kinds of water, the one exhalative and the other congelative and germinative.   126

Just as the seminal water of all living things is different from urine, so exhalative water is different from congelative water.

All human substances are started by aqueous materials; even the materials of hard seeds cannot generate unless they are first liquefied: for otherwise they could not absorb or attract some of this congelative material which I call the fifth element.

Just as all kinds of plants, even all living things, are in their

[202] This page and all those that follow it are unnumbered in the 1580 edition.

the mountains, and that there should be a well enclosed pipe from the high seas to the summit of the mountains; if the pipe should start only at the edge of the sea, the water would never rise higher than the seashore: and if the pipe which brought the water of streams to the tops of the mountains should ever burst, it is certain that the entire world would be submerged.   40–41

If the congelative water were not carried by the ordinary one, it could not act either.

If all the water of the earth were congelative in nature, soon the earth would be reduced to rock.

If in man there were no other water than the ordinary one or urine, he could never generate stones in his body.

Many waters generate the stone in those who drink them, because within the ordinary water there is a quantity of congelative water. [366]

Just as clear water is suitable for receiving all colors, so white earths can also receive them.

In the sea there are three kinds of water, the ordinary, the salty, and the vegetative or congelative ones.

The truth is opposed to and mocks at the stupidity of many who maintain that ice forms at the bottom of the river Seine.   156

Among all visible spirits, there is none more certain than ordinary water which is testimony that all exhalative minerals are composed of aqueous materials and for these reasons they are sublimatory.

Although the land and the sea daily produce new creatures and various plants, metals and minerals, nevertheless as early as the creation of the world, God put into the earth all the seeds that are in it and ever will be: inasmuch as He is perfect, He has left nothing imperfect.   90, 103

Just as all smells, colors and powers are unknown in the earth: so all lapific and metallic materials are indistinct and unknown in the waters and the earth, and this until they are reduced to some form by an unknown congelation.
                                                108, 121, 124

All those who seek to generate metals by fire, wish to build with the destroyer.   93 [367]

Just as in all seminal materials of all living things the bones

and hair cannot be distinguished from the flesh, so no
one could know metallic materials before their formation
or congelation.   121–122

If anyone could distinguish the colors, tastes and powers which
plants can attract and separate from the earth, I would say
that it would be possible for such a man to make gold and
silver.   120, 135

Metals have no color, but are like water before their congelation and decoction.   91, 105

Never has man known either sulphur or quicksilver before it
had started to generate, any more than colors and odors extracted from the soil by plants could be seen before the
plants had attracted them.   114, 121, 137

If metallic materials were not fluid and liquid, it would be
impossible for them to form the monstrous stones which I
have placed in my cabinet.   125, 126, 130

By the action of metallic materials while they are still fluid,
the body of man and beast and fishes, and of all kinds of
trees and plants, can be reduced to metal.   131, 203 [368]

Gold may be stewed in various ways, but not to serve as a
tonic.   138

Stew gold any way you will, even though the stomach of the
patient to whom you give it is as hot as a red hot furnace,
the heat of the stomach, instead of distributing the gold
stew to the nutrifying members, will fuse it into an ingot:
for otherwise gold could not be stable.   143

Metals can be increased by art, but not legitimately.
                                              95, 96, 97, 98, 99

Antimony is an imperfect metal which causes vomiting in the
two parts of man, because of the natural heat of the
stomach which causes it to be evaporated: which noxious
exhalation disturbs all the vital spirits.   145, 146

Through many kinds of marcasites, I prove that all metals are
generated from liquid materials.   111, 112, 122, 131

Those who have written that metals grow in the mines like
the trees, have understood nothing and have spoken against
the truth.

Those who say and have written that invisible spirits kill
men in the mines, have erred.

All the alchemists who are and have been in this world, have

been mistaken in thinking that they could hold back the
spirits moved by fire in closed vessels.   132
Even though an earthen vessel or one of any kind of metal
[369] whatsoever were as thick as a mountain, and there
were some spiritual or exhalative material within the vessel,
it is inevitable that this vessel will burst if it is touched by
fire, unless the vessel has some vent for the escape of the
spiritual or exhalative material inside.   133
It would be easier for an alchemist to return to its first state a
pounded and crushed egg, or a pulverized chestnut or nut,
than to generate metals.   102
Just as oil in water separates from it in little rings, as also do
suet and all kinds of fats, so lapidary and metallic materials
can separate from ordinary water.   109, 119, 126, 134
Just as air has dimensions and occupies space, fire does likewise in molten metals, and for these reasons molten iron
and other metals shrink as they congeal.
Even as God has commanded the surface of the earth to busy
itself producing and germinating things that are necessary
to man and beast, it is certain that the interior of the earth
does likewise, producing many kinds of rocks, metals and
other necessary minerals.   90
Those who say that the rocks were created at the very beginning of the world are mistaken and do not understand
[370] the matter.   195
And those who say that rocks grow are likewise mistaken.   195
Those who think that rocks acquire their full hardness as
soon as they are first formed, do not understand the matter.
                                                      245, 246
Those who say that earths and rocks have taken on their color
at the very beginning of their existence do not understand
the matter.
Just as fruits of all kinds change color when they ripen,
similarly rocks, metals and other minerals, even clays,
change color during their decoction.   122
The material of all rocks, both the common and the rare and
precious ones, is crystalline and diaphanous.   199
All colored and cloudy rocks are cloudy or colored only by
accident which happened to the diaphanous material before the congelation of these rocks.   253
All clays are the beginnings of rocks.   301

There is no rock in this world, nor any living thing which, if
it could be dissolved, would not serve as manure or marl to
make soil productive.

Those who have written that the shells found in rocks date
from the Flood have erred clumsily.   211, 212 [371]

Just as the bones of man give him form, so the rocks give
form to mountains.   47, 197

To the degree that they are hard, dense or compact, stones
will take a beautiful polish.

If rocks did not exist, there would be no mountains.   47

Some rocks and rock bodies are hollow because of air enclosed when lapidary materials were brought in and congealed above the enclosed air and borne up by it.

Certain other rocks and rock bodies are hollow because they
have been covered by soil which has prevented the distillating material from condensing; of this kind are the mill-
stones from La Ferté sous Jouarre, which bear witness to
this.

Chalk and marl are imperfect rocks that have lacked congelative water before their perfect congelation.   308, 309, 311

The same is true of all soft rocks and because of their imperfection they can be calcined, being unable to withstand
fire.   247

All hard rocks are so through two necessary conditions: one
that they should have water in plenty during their congelation and formation: the other that they should not be
removed from their place until their congelation is completed.   245 [372]

If plaster, otherwise called *gyp* and alabaster were left in the
ground they would become hard rocks, providing the
bottom where they lie can hold water, otherwise they would
not.

If the main material of all rocks were not a pure and transparent water, diamond, crystal, emeralds, rubies and garnet
could never exist, nor could any diaphanous rocks.

All horned rocks are so only by accident and are formed in
the ground, according to the place and mold in which the
liquid material happens to stop and to congeal.   228

All rocks are formed from fluid and liquid materials.   199

All rocks or materials formed in facets or points are congealed in water.   111, 112, 200, 267

The number of the various kinds of salts is infinite.   115, 153

There is nothing which does not contain salt.   163, 164

Those who say that common salt harms seeds are in error.
170, 171, 172

Salt is the cause of the flavor of all kinds of fruits and plants.   165, 168, 194

The salt in all plants, metals and minerals causes the virtue that is in them.   164, 168, 194

Salt whitens all things.   165, 168, 194

It gives tone to all things.   168, 194 [373]

Makes all things transparent.   169

Causes the action of mirrors and spectacles.   194, 312

It causes friendship and generative virtue.   168, 194

It is cause of the voice and incorruption.   168

It attracts dyes.   177

It takes from the one to give to another.   177

And as it gives tone to metals, so it does to the songs and hymns made by humans, even makes glad men and animals.   169, 194

Without salt it is impossible to make glass.   168, 194

Common salt is an antivenom.

Without salt no blade would have strength to cut or even to be hardened.   168, 177, 194

It is impossible for the tongue to find flavor in anything, unless it is first dissolved and attracts some part of the salt which is in the thing that it touches.   147, 148

In the bark of the wood is contained almost all the salt of the tree.   166

If there were no salt in wood-bark it could not tan leather, nor clean cloth and would be useless in lye.   166

If there were no salt in straw and hay, manures could in no way improve the soil.   169

If it were not for the salt in spices, embalmed corpses would putrefy.   167, 194

Without the effect of salt nothing would have an odor.   164 [374]

Sealed earth [203] has no power against poison except because of the action of salt or congelative water.   331

The ashes of all kinds of wood, trees and bushes are suitable

[203] Sealed earth or boliarmény. See note 152 for an explanation of these terms.

for making glass because of the salt which is in these woods
through hay and straw.   168
If there were no salt in rocks, they could not be used, when
calcined, by the tanners to prevent rotting of leather.
The shells of marine fishes are very good for making lime,
and this is evidence of the saltiness that is in them.
The salt of grapes destroys copper, turning it into verdigris.
There is in human things a beginning of form held up by the
fifth element, and otherwise all natural things would re-
main jumbled up together without any form.   128
The number of the various kinds of clay is incalculable.   156
The effects of these earths are marvelous, even indescribable.
                                                            257, 258, 259
All earths can become clays.
Those who say that clay is fat and viscous do not understand
it.   254, 255
The same material which causes all earths to become clay, is
the very thing which makes marl [375] produce and grow
fruits in barren soils.
By the methods set down in this book, marl can be found in
all provinces.
All things, however compact and dense they may be, are
porous.
The mummy of moderns is nothing but carrion.   167
The *plombusti* [204] of moderns is not made as it should be.
Architects and sculptors take occasion to glorify themselves
only in that they know how to imitate the inventions of
pagans, and wish to be honored as inventors.
The vainest works of man are the most esteemed.
Things from which the tongue cannot draw flavor cannot
serve to nourish the body.   147
As the body is subject to corruption, it wishes to be nourished
with corruptible things.   146, 147
If there were none of the fifth element mentioned above in
the eyeball, spectacles could not aid sight.   312
Just as God has ordained that in each seed there are all the
materials required for the generation of new ones to come,
just as in the seed of the egg is included the white, the yolk,
and the shell, and in nut trees beneath their shell, the tree,

[204] Compare with plumbostibe, a synonym of Boulangerite, according to
Bescherelle.

leaves and branches: which unseen materials appear at their maturity: similarly the flesh, the [376] bones, the blood and all the parts of man are contained and enclosed in one,[205] and as God has ordained the separation of stony materials by hardness, similarly the materials of the bones of man and beast are hardened, and in part through lapidary material: which can be seen through eggshells and foot-bones of sheep and many other animals, whose bones resist fire better than any rock that can be found.

The mithridate of the ancients was composed of only four simples.   153

The three hundred simples which the moderns put in their mithridate could not blend together: just as all the colors of a painter ground together could not make a beautiful color.   150

As also a bouquet of all kinds of flowers could not smell as good as a single rose.   150

Many meats ground together could not be as tasty as a capon alone.   150

Without the action of moisture, nothing could be corrupted or putrefied.   178

In well-sealed sepulchers, the bodies keep forever in the form they had when put in: because of the air that is enclosed with them.

All trees and other plants would climb straight up during their growth if it were not for the accidents which I have set down in this [377] book.   330, 331

Just as the rivers and brooks are crooked because of the mountains, so the roots of all trees and plants are twisted only because of the position of the stones or earths which are harder to pierce in one place than in another.

328, 329, 330, 331

Marly earth is harmful to plants not sown by the farmer [206] and will not permit them to sprout among the sown wheat.

Sulphur *la gème,*[207] *poix-raisine* and bitumen are nothing more than congealed oils.

In many regions and places where the soil is unsalty far from

---

[205] This is the doctrine of the "homunculus," commonly accepted until the nineteenth century.

[206] More simply, weeds, but I have preserved Palissy's expression.

[207] "Tarre, or Pitch" (Cotgrave).

the sea, even in the highest parts of the Ardennes, the same seed exists as in the sea for the formation of all kinds of fishes, as I certify and prove by the lapified shells that exist in millions in this Ardennes country and in many other places, which can be seen in this book.

Winds are caused only by a compression of the air.

There are very few things in this world that cannot be made transparent by art.

Marl is a natural and God-given manure, harmful to all plants that grow by themselves, and generative to all seeds that have been sown by the farmer. [378]

EXPLANATION OF THE MORE DIFFICULT WORDS

Acrimonie (acidity) [208] is said of biting things that sting the tongue: such as some kinds of salts, as copperas or vitriol.

Additions (additions) are the materials added to rocks and metals, congealed and attached to the original mass at various times.

Aigres (brittle) are things that are broken easily with a hammer.

Alizes (dense) are close-knit things, such as pebbles and crushed bread, which has not been allowed to rise, and all things that are so well condensed that they have no visible pores.

Altérées (parched) are the imperfect rocks, such as chalk, plaster, and all light rocks, that have lacked water before their perfect decoction.

Amalgame (amalgam) is what the alchemists call gold, when it is dissolved and mixed with quicksilver.

Antimoine (antimony) is an imperfect metal, a beginning of lead and silver.

Appositions (inclusions) are intermixed earthy materials that lodge between two [379] congelations of rocks and metals and in this place render the mass softer and less pure.

Aqueducs (aqueducts) are water pipes for which the ancients built many arches, to carry water.

Attraction (attraction) is meant of attracting dye or the virtue of something, as boiling water attracts the color of *brésil*,[209] and alum attracts the saliva of man.

Bitumen (bitumen) is a kind of tar with which ships are greased to resist rotting: and although some people use it in certain mixtures, such as *jesme*,[210] grease and *poix-raisine*,[211] still it is found in a natural state in certain regions.

---

[208] In this section, the original French word is given, followed by a translation in parentheses.

[209] "The wood Brasill" (Cotgrave). A kind of wood used in dyeing which gave a red color (Bescherelle). See note 100.

[210] A variant spelling of *gème;* see note 206.

[211] Rosin? See note 77.

Calciner (to calcine) is said of all things that are turned to lime or dust by the action of fire.

Circonférence (circumference) is the line around a round or square figure, and all figures.

Concasser (to crush) is said of things coarsely pounded.

Concatenées (linked) is said of things bound together, related to each other.

Congeler (to congeal) is said of all things that harden after melting: as water hardens when cold.

Décoction (decoction) is used for metals that have attained their perfection: as also of rocks when they are perfectly hardened: like nut-shells.

Diaphane (diaphanous) is said of all clear things, through [380] which one sees the things that present themselves before the eyes.

Dilater (to dilate) is said of things that spread out on one side and another: as of overflowing rivers, trees and plants, as one sees in pumpkins and cucumbers.

Dissoudre (to dissolve) is said of things that lose their form: such as ice and snow, when they feel mild weather.

Esmail (enamel) is an artificial stone composed of many materials.

Esmailler (to enamel) is said of things that are painted with enamel liquefied on the work.

Espirale (spiral) is a line made by an arc in turning, in the form of a snail shell.

Esprits (spirits) *ou matières spirituelles* (spiritual materials) is said of things that rise when heated: like water from a wet cloth.

Evaporer (to evaporate) is said of liquids, which are made to rise by the action of fire.

Fixes (fixed) are things that endure fire until they melt: as do glass, gold, silver and other metals.

Fossiles (fossils) are the mineral materials, to recover which the earth must be dug into.[212]

Frangible (breakable) is said of brittle and breakable materials.

---

[212] Palissy's definition of fossil is similar to that of Agricola but that does not mean that Palissy had read his predecessor, for this meaning had widespread acceptance until after 1800. Palissy here simply gives the literal meaning of a term derived from Latin which may not have been obvious to his reader.

Fusibles (fusible) are the things that liquefy or melt in the heat of fire: as lead, tin and other metals. [381]

Imbiber (to soak up) is said of things which, because they are parched, drink up liquid materials.

Incliner (to tilt) we call it inclination when vessels are tilted to one side, to draw the liquor from something, to leave the dregs at the bottom of the container.

Lamines (plates) are little tablets of lead or other metal which have been forged for calcination or for other uses.

Lapifier ou pétrifier (to lapify or petrify) is said of things which in their first state were earth or water, or wood, which have been turned to stone.

Liquides (liquid) is said of all things that are clear like water, or like glass in a furnace.

L'ocre jaune (yellow ocher) is a seed and beginning of iron, and eventually turns into iron, when it is sufficiently watered and nourished by the waters, so you see rusty iron returning to the color of ocher.

Luter (to lute) the distillers and those who make acid call lut the earth with which they cover their glass vessels, so that they will resist fire, which they could not do otherwise.[213]

Maléables (malleable) are the things that endure the hammer without any breaking: as do gold, silver and other workable metals.

Marcassites (marcasites) [214] are imperfect metals. Their materials sometimes form in square fashion, [382] like dice, when they are congealed and formed under water.

Marne (marl) is a natural manure, which is taken from mines, and sometimes very deep underground, like stone and metal quarries.

Mordicatives (mordant) are called the things that bite the tongue, almost enough to cut it.

Obliques (oblique) are crooked lines.

Oléagineuses (oily) are things of the nature of oil, and they agree with it: as does wax, sulphur, *poix-raisine* and several other things.

Peintures et teintures (paints and dyes) are different: because dyes are all transparent, having no body: and they color inside

[213] The process is discussed at length by Agricola, Biringuccio, and Ercker.
[214] Here, as elsewhere, Palissy's marcasite is pyrite.

as well as outside: which paints cannot do, because they have body.

Pentagones (pentagons) are figures with five corners, Hexagons have six, Heptagons have seven and so on for the others.

Pétrifier (to petrify) is said of things that have been formed as wood, shells, or other plants in their first state, and since have turned to stone.

Pyramides (pyramids) are figures pointed at the top, in imitation or semblance of fire, from which the word pyramid is derived.

Quadrangle (quadrangle) is a square form and is called quadrangle because of its four corners. [383]

Salsitive ou salsitives (salty) are the things that bite the tongue, like salt, alum and calcined rocks.

Saphre (cobalt oxide) is an earth taken from gold mines, which is a fixed earth as much as gold itself, and from it is made a blue color, in enamel work.

Sel commun (common salt) is the one we usually eat, which is distinguished from the others: for there are many kinds of it.

Souffleuses (literally "blowy") [215] are the things that will not accept melted metals, as earth, porous sand, that retain enclosed air, the latter preventing metals from taking exactly the form of the things that are put into them.

Sousterreines (underground) are the things that are under ground, like pipes through which fountains are fed.

Sublimer (to sublimate) is said of things that rise up in smoke, when they are touched by fire.

Sulphurées (sulphurous) are all materials related to sulphur: as are metals and all kinds of marcasites.

Superficies (surfaces) is said of things that surround some round or square mass, or other form, as if one had gilded a piece of silver and the gilding were only on the outside.

Ténébreuses (cloudy) are the rocks that one [384] cannot see through, as one can see through crystal and glass.

Terrestres (terrestrial) are the materials that cannot be evaporated or sublimated by the action of fire.

Triangle (triangle) is a figure with three corners.

Trochisques (disks) are round figures like pills that are then made flat by a compression exerted on the upper part.

---

[215] Literally, "blowy." By context, the meaning here is spongy or porous.

Varenne (varenne) [216] is an earth ordinarily of a russet color (which is of somewhat argillaceous nature), from which are made molds for all sorts of molten metals and to build furnaces and to lute glass vessels.

Visqueux (viscous) is the same thing as sticky.

Vitrifier (to vitrify) is said of things that takes a polish and the luster of glass when they are strongly heated in furnaces.

[216] Cotgrave explains the term, much as above, but has no English equivalent for it.

THE END

ANNOTATED BIBLIOGRAPHY

The following list of publications by and about Palissy does not pretend to be complete. An extensively annotated bibliography by Audiat (1868, pp. ci–clxxii) should be consulted for works published before that date. In this list, notes are given on the location of various editions and copies in American and Canadian libraries for the most significant items, that is, books and reprints of rare articles. Articles in serial publications, easily available in most of the larger libraries, are not annotated, as the *Union Serial Catalog* and its supplements give this information. The bibliography also includes references cited in the text but not directly concerned with Palissy. The information on holdings in American libraries was kindly supplied by the Union Catalog Division of the Library of Congress, and by the National Library of Canada for Canadian holdings.

Adams, Frank Dawson (1938). *The Birth and Development of the Geological Sciences.* Baltimore, Williams and Wilkins Co., reprinted 1954, Dover Publications, Inc., 506 pp., illus.

Agricola: see Bandy and Bandy (1955), and Hoover and Hoover (1912).

Albutt, Sir Thomas Clifford (1919?). "Palissy, Bacon, and the Revival of Natural Science." *British Academy, London, Proceedings,* 1913–14, vol. 6, pp. 233–47.

Audiat, Louis (1864). "Bernard Palissy." Saintes, Fontainier, éditeur, xxi [1] + 358 pp., illus., frontispiece (port.); Les Oubliés, II.
Yale University; Union Theological Seminary, New York; Bibliothèque de la Législature de la Province de Québec, Québec, P. Q., Canada.

—— (1868). *Bernard Palissy; étude sur sa vie et ses travaux.* Paris, 480 pp.
Harvard University; Wellesley College; Princeton University; New York Public Library; University of Pennsylvania; Boston Athenaeum; Bibliothèque Saint-Sulpice, Montréal, P. Q., Canada.

—— (1897). "Palissy à Sedan." *Bull. Soc. historique et Revue de Saintonge et d'Aunis,* vol. 17, p. 114.

Ballot, Marie Juliette (1924). *Documents d'art. Musée du Louvre. La Céramique française, Bernard Palissy et les fabriques du XVIème siècle.* Paris, A. Morancé, 37 pp., 48 pls. (part col.).
Library of Congress; Boston Public Library; Walters Art Gallery, Baltimore;

John Crerar Library, Chicago; University of Illinois; Cleveland Museum of Art; Oberlin College Library; Ohio State University; Philadelphia Museum of Art; Harvard University; Yale University.

Bandy, Mark Chance, and Jean A. Bandy (1955). *De Natura Fossilium (Textbook of Mineralogy) by Georgius Agricola, Translated from the First Latin Edition of 1546.* Geol. Soc. Am., Spec. Paper 63, xiii + 240 pp., frontispiece.

Bescherelle, aîné (n.d., circa 1906). *Nouveau Dictionnaire National.* 3rd edition.

Biringuccio, Vannoccio (1540). *De la Pirotechnia. Libri X dove ampiamente si tratta non solo di ogni sorte et diversita di minera . . .* Venice.

———— (1942). *The Pirotechnia of Vannoccio Biringuccio,* Translated from the Italian with an Introduction and Notes by Cyril Stanley Smith and Martha Teach Gnudi. New York, xxvi + 476 pp., illus.

Borlé, Edouard Th. (1927). *Observations sur l'emploi des conjonctions de subordination dans la langue du XVIᵉ siècle, étudié spécialement dans les deux ouvrages de Bernard Palissy.* Paris, Société d'édition "Les Belles Lettres," xx + 261 pp.

University of California; University of Illinois; Indiana University; New York Public Library; Princeton University; University of Michigan; University of North Carolina; University of Wisconsin; Harvard University; Yale University; New York University, Washington Square; University of Pennsylvania; Bibliothèque Saint-Sulpice, Montréal, P. Q.; University of Toronto.

Braun, E. W. (1907). *Essay on Bernard Palissy.* Allgemeines Lexikon der bildenden Künstler, Leipzig, vol. 26.

Brieux, Eugène, and Salandri, Gaston (1880). *Bernard Palissy, drame en un acte, en vers.* Paris: Tresse, 50 pp.

Boston Public Library; Harvard University; Oberlin College.

Brightwell, Cecilia Lucy (1858). *Palissy the Potter; or The Huguenot, artist, and martyr.* New York, Carleton & Potter, 235 pp.

Harvard University.

———— The same, another edition. New York, Phillips & Hunt.

New York Public Library.

———— The same, another edition. New York, Nelson & Phillips; Cincinnati, Hitchcock & Walden (1859?).

Library of Congress; Cleveland Museum of Art; University of Toronto.

———— (1858). *Palissy the Huguenot Potter, A true tale.* Philadelphia, Presbyterian Board of Publ., 169 pp., front., plates.

New York Public Library; State Teachers College, West Chester, Pa.; Oberlin College.

———— (1858). The same, another edition. London, The Religious Tract Society.

New York Public Library; Bibliothèque générale, Université Laval, Québec, P. Q.

———— (1859). The same.

University of Illinois; St. Lawrence University, Canton, N. Y.; Detroit Public

Library; New Hampshire State Library; Cincinnati Public Library; Presbyterian Historical Society, Philadelphia.

———— (1859?). The same.
Yale University.

———— (1860). The same. Philadelphia.
Brooklyn Public Library.

———— (1864). The same. Philadelphia.
American Sunday School Union, Philadelphia; University of Tennessee Library.

. ———— (1865). The same. Boston & Chicago.
Boston Public Library.

———— (187–?). *Bernard Palissy; the Huguenot and Potter.* Edinburgh, W. Oliphant & Co., 92 pp.
Harvard University.

Burty, Philippe (1886). *Bernard Palissy.* Paris, Librairie de l'Art, 56 pp.
Harvard University; Yale University; University of Michigan; Library of Congress; University of Chicago; Walters Art Gallery, Baltimore; Peabody Institute, Baltimore; Cleveland Museum of Art; Free Library, Philadelphia; University of Pennsylvania; Princeton University.

———— (1889). The same. *Artistes célèbres.*
Yale University; Peabody Institute, Baltimore; Bibliothèque générale, Université Laval, Québec, P. Q.

Cotgrave, Randle (1611) 1950. *A Dictionarie of the French and English Tongues.* University of South Carolina Press, Columbia, S. C., 1950; reprint of the 1611 London ed., "Printed by Adam Islip." Pages unnumbered.

Dangibeaud, Eutrope (1863). *Saintes au XVIᵉ siècle. L'atelier de Palissy.* Evreux, Auguste Hérissey, 16 pp.

Delécluze, Etienne Jean (1838). *Bernard Palissy, 1500–1589.* Paris, Dupont & Cie, 32 pp. Reprinted from the *Revue française* (décembre, 1838).
Boston Public Library; University of Michigan.

Dumesnil, A. (1851). *Palissy le potier de Terre.* Paris, Librairie nouvelle, 142 pp.
Harvard University; Wellesley College; Boston Public Library; Yale University.

———— (n.d.). The same. Paris.
Peabody Institute, Baltimore.

Dupuy, Ernest (1894). *Bernard Palissy, l'homme, l'artiste, le savant, l'écrivain.* Paris: Société française d'imprimerie et de librairie, viii + 342 pp.
Bibliothèque générale, Université Laval, Québec, P. Q.

———— (1902). The same.

Harvard University; Yale University; University of Michigan; University of Wisconsin; University of Pennsylvania; Princeton University; John Crerar Library, Chicago; Duke University; Bibliothèque Saint-Sulpice, Montréal, P. Q.

Enjubault, Emile (1858). *L'Art céramique et Bernard Palissy*. Moulins, iv + 178 pp.
Not located in any American or Canadian library.

Ercker, Lazarus (1580). *Treatise on Ores and Assaying*. Translated from the German Edition of 1580 by Anneliese Grünhaldt Sisco and Cyril Stanley Smith. Chicago, The University of Chicago Press, 1951, xxxiii + 360 pp., illus.
Geoffroy, Gustave (1881). *Bernard Palissy*. Paris, in-12.
Cited by Ballot; not seen.

Hanschmann, Alexander Bruno (1903). *Bernard Palissy der Künstler, Naturforscher und Schriftsteller*. Leipzig, T. Weicher, vi + 231 pp.
Library of Congress; John Crerar Library, Chicago; Boston Public Library; University of Wisconsin.

Hoover, Herbert Clark, and Lou Henry Hoover (1912). *Georgius Agricola, De Re Metallica, translated from the first Latin Edition of 1556*. Reprinted 1950, Dover Publications, Inc., New York, xxxi + 638 pp., illus.
Larroumet, Gustave (1893–96). *Etudes de Littérature et d'art*, vol. 3, pp. 29–53.
Yale University; Library of Congress; University of Pennsylvania; Library Company of Philadelphia; University of Cincinnati; Oberlin College; University of Michigan; Drexel Institute of Technology, Philadelphia; University of Wisconsin.

Lasteyrie, Ferdinand de (1865). *Bernard Palissy, sa vie et ses oeuvres*. Paris, in-8.
Cited by Ballot; not seen.

Leroux, Désiré (1927). *La Vie de Bernard Palissy*. Paris, Librairie Ancienne Honoré Champion, 129 pp., 5 pls.
Princeton University; New York Public Library; The Ohio State University; University of Wisconsin; Harvard University.

Morley, Henry (1852). *Palissy the Potter. The Life of Bernard Palissy, of Saintes, his labours and discoveries in art and science, with an outline of his philosophical doctrines, and a translation of illustrative selections from his works*. London, Chapman & Hall, 2 vols.
Library Company of Philadelphia, Ridgeway Branch; Edgar Fahs Smith Memorial Library, University of Pennsylvania; Cleveland Institute of Art; Library of Congress; Cleveland Museum of Art; Yale University; University of Wisconsin; Toronto Public Libraries, Reference Division; University of Toronto.

——— (1853). The same, first American edition. Boston, Ticknor, Reed & Fields.
American Entomological Society Library, Philadelphia; Library Company of

Philadelphia, Ridgeway Branch; University of Pennsylvania; John Crerar Library, Chicago; Library of Congress; McGill University, Montréal, P. Q.

———— (1855). The same, second London edition. Chapman & Hall, 2 vols., 494 pp.

Newberry Library, Chicago; John Crerar Library, Chicago; University of Virginia; Swarthmore College, Swarthmore, Pa.; Free Library, Philadelphia; University of Michigan.

———— (1869?). The same. London, Cassell, Petter, & Galpin (The Belle Sauvage Library), viii + 320 pp., front.

Yale University; University of Texas; University of Tennessee; University of Toronto.

Palissy, Bernard (1563). *Recepte véritable par laquelle tous les hommes de la France pourront apprendre a multiplier et augmenter leurs thresors, Item, ceux qui n'ont jamais eu cognoissance des lettres pourront apprendre une philosophie necessaire a tous les habitants de la terre. Item, en ce livre est contenu le dessein d'un jardin autant delectable et d'utile invention qu'il en fut onques veu. Item le dessein et ordonnance d'une ville de forteresse, la plus imprenable qu'homme ouyt jamais parler, compose par Bernard Palissy, ouvrier de terre et inventeur des Rustiques Figulines du Roy et de Monseigneur le duc de Montmorency, Pair et Connestable de France, demeurant en la ville de Xainctes. A la Rochelle, de l'imprimerie de Barthelemy Berton, 1563.* 130 pp.

Not located in any American or Canadian library. Few copies, perhaps only two, are known to exist. Dupuy (1902) notes that one copy, in the "Bibliothèque de l'Arsenal," bears the date 1564.

———— (1563). *Architecture et Ordonnance de la grotte rustique de monseigneur le duc de Montmorancy.*

Not located in any American or Canadian library. See also 1919 reprint, below.

———— (1580). *Discours Admirables, de la nature des eaux et fonteines, tant naturelles qu'artificielles, des metaux, des sels et salines, des pierres, des terres, du feu et des esmaux, avec plusieurs autres excellens secrets des choses naturelles, plus un traite de la Marne fort utile et necessaire pour ceux qui se meslent de l'agriculture, le tout dresse par dialogues esquels sont introduits la Theorique et la Practique. Par Bernard Palissy, inventeur des rustiques figulines du Roy et de la Royne sa mere. A Paris, Chez Martin le Jeune, a l'Enseigne du Serpent, devant le college de Cambrai.* [16], 361, [22] pp.

University of Illinois; University of Wisconsin; Harvard University; Yale University.

———— (1636). *Le Moyen de devenir riche et la maniere veritable par laquelle tous les hommes de la France pourront apprendre à multiplier leurs thresors et possessions. Avec plusieurs avtres excellens secrets des choses naturelles, desquels iusques à present l'on n'a ouy parler, par Maistre Bernard Palissy de Xaintes, Ouurier de terre et Inuenteur des Rustiques Figulines du Roy. Paris, Robert Fouët,* [16], 255 pp.

A reprint, with additions and excisions, of the *Recepte véritable*. See note after next item.

———— (1636). *Seconde partie dv moyen de devenir riche, contenant les Discours Admirables de la nature des eaux et Fontaines, tant natvrelles qv'artificielles des Fleuves, Puits, Cisternes, Estâgs, Marez et autres Eaux douces, de leur origine, bonté et autres qualitez. De l'alchimie des métaux, de l'Or potable, du Mithridat, des glaces, des sels vegetatifs ou generatifs, du sel commun. Description des Marez salans. Des pierres tant communes, que précieuses. Des causes de leur genera-tion, formes, couleur, pesanteur et qualités d'icelles, des terres d'argille, de l'art, de la terre, de son vtilité, et du feu, de la marne, et le moyen de les cognoistre. Par M. Bernard Palissy, Inuenteur des Rustiques Figulines du Roy.* Paris, Robert Fouët, [16], 526 pp.

This and the preceding item are a reprint of Palissy's two main works, but both of them were considerably altered by the printer. This edition is justly criticized by Cap (1844) because of the ridiculous change in title and the suppression of everything that might have offended the clergy at the time and for additions to the text which were not written by Palissy and add nothing to it. Apparently not in any American or Canadian library.

———— (1777). *Les Oeuvres de Bernard Palissy revues sur les ex-emplaires de la Bibliothèque du Roi, avec des notes par M. Faujas de Saint-Fonds, et des additions par M. Gobet.* Paris, Ruault, 734 pp.

Free Library, Philadelphia; American Philosophical Society, Philadelphia; John Crerar Library, Chicago; Library of Congress; University of Pennsyl-vania; Harvard University; Yale University.

———— (1844). *Oeuvres complètes de Bernard Palissy, édition con-forme aux textes originaux imprimés du vivant de l'auteur; avec des notes et une notice historique par Paul-Antoine Cap.* Paris, J. J. Du-bochet, xxxix + 437 pp.

The title, with its insistence on faithfulness to the originals, implies a criti-cism of previous editions. The notes have been praised for their scholarly character.

Duke University; Cornell University; Peabody Institute, Baltimore; New York Public Library; Library of Congress; Corning Glass Works Library, Corning, N. Y.; University of Michigan; Harvard University; Yale University.

———— (1863). *Discours Admirables de l'Art de la Terre, de son Utilité, des Esmaux et du Feu.* Geneva, J.-G. Fick, viii + 44 pp.

Harvard University; Princeton University; Yale University.

———— (1880). *Oeuvres de Bernard Palissy, publiées d'après les textes originaux, avec une notice historique et bibliographique et une table analytique par Anatole France.* Paris, Charavay frères, xxvii + 499 pp.

This edition was prepared to appear on the three hundredth anniversary of the publication of the *Discours Admirables*. It has been criticized by Audiat (see next item) on minor points. It is the most common edition of Palissy's works in American libraries.

Indiana University; University of Chicago; Boston Public Library; Princeton University; Western Reserve University; Haverford College; University of Illinois; Brown University; Harvard University; Yale University; University of Michigan; The Ohio State University; University of Wisconsin; Bibliothèque générale, Université Laval, Québec, P. Q.

―――― (1888). *Les Oeuvres de Maistre Bernard Palissy. Nouvelle édition revue sur les textes originaux par B. Fillon, avec une notice historique, bibliographique et iconologique par Louis Audiat.* Niort, L. Clouzot, 2 vols., CCVIII + 144 + 280 pp.
This edition has the most extensive and most satisfactory notes and introduction of any French edition. It corrects several errors of previous writers on Palissy and gives the most extensive bibliography on the subject up to the year 1888.
Yale University; University of Pennsylvania; Peabody Institute, Baltimore; John Crerar Library, Chicago; Princeton University; Boston Public Library; U. S. Department of Agriculture Library; Bibliothèque Saint-Sulpice, Montréal, P. Q.: University of Toronto.

―――― (1919). *Architecture et ordonnance de la grotte rustique de monseigneur le duc de Montmorancy, Connestable de France. Premier Livre du célèbre potier demeuré inconnu. Réimprimé d'après l'édition de La Rochelle, 1563.* Paris, Librairie Damascène Morgand, Edouard Rahir succr., 38 unnumbered pages.
University of Michigan.

―――― (1922). *Recepte véritable par laquelle tous les hommes de la France pourront apprendre à multiplier et augmenter leurs thrésors* (with a note by C. Corbière). Strasbourg, J. H. E. Heitz (Bibliothèque française), xxvi + 178 pp.
The Ohio State University copy bears the inscription *Bibliotheca Romanica 279/281. Bibliothèque française, Oeuvres de Bernard Palissy, Recepte veritable* and the full title at the beginning of the text, after the introduction by Corbière.
Harvard University; Yale University; University of Michigan; The Ohio State University.

Pimier, L. (1934). "Bernard Palissy, rocailleur, soutenier et décorateur de jardins." *Gazette des beaux-arts,* 1934, vol. 2, pp. 8–29.

Salles, Jules (1856). *Etude sur Bernard Palissy, sa vie et ses travaux, précédée de quelques recherches sur l'art céramique.* Nîmes, B. R. Garve, 11 + pp.
Harvard University.

Sauzay, Alexandre (1862). *Monographie de l'Oeuvre de Bernard Palissy, suivie d'un choix de ses continuateurs ou imitateurs dessinée par MM. Carl Delange et C. Borneman et accompagnée d'un texte par M. Sauzay et M. Henri Delange.* Paris [Impr. de E. Martinet], 38 pp., 100 col. pls., port.
This magnificent folio, with its one hundred colored plates, shows the work of Palissy and his contemporaries and successors. It has been criticized by Audiat for not showing clearly the authorship of each piece but the criticism seems unjustified because of the doubt concerning many of these works which existed at the time and continues to the present day.
Philadelphia City Institute Branch Free Library; Peabody Institute, Baltimore; Philadelphia Museum of Art; Cleveland Museum of Art; Boston Pub-

lic Library; Princeton University; Grosvenor Library, Buffalo, N. Y.; Library of Congress; Brown University; The Ohio State University; Newberry Library, Chicago; Free Library, Philadelphia; Yale University.

Scudder, Antoinette (1934). *The Henchman of the Moon, a poetic drama in five acts.* Chicago, The Bookfellows, 110 pp.
A play, one of many, on Palissy.
Yale University; Free Library, Philadelphia; Boston Public Library; Library of Congress.

Tainturier, A. (1863). *Terres émaillées de Palissy, inventeur des rustiques figulines.* Paris, V. Didron, 136 pp.
John Crerar Library, Chicago; Boston Public Library; Peabody Institute, Baltimore; Walters Art Gallery, Baltimore; Harvard University.

Tapia y Rivera, Alejandro (1944). *Bernardo de Palissy o el heroismo del trabajo; biodrama original en dos partes y cuatro actos. . . .* San Juan, P. R., Imprenta Venezuela, 147 pp.
Harvard University; New York Public Library; Library of Congress; Yale University; University of British Columbia, Vancouver, B. C.

Thompson, H. R. (1954). "The Geographical and Geological Observations of Bernard Palissy the Potter." *Annals of Science,* vol. 10, no. 2, pp. 149–65.
Weiss, Nathanaël (1896). "Bernard Palissy à Sedan, d'après quelques documents inédits, 1572–1576 . . ." 15 unnumbered pages, illus. *Bull. Soc. Hist. Protestantisme français,* Oct., 1896.
Yale University (a reprint).

Willett, E. E. (1876). *Resources: A Treatise on "Waters and Springs." Written by Bernard Palissy, in 1557. Translated by E. E. Willett, 1876.* Brighton, D. O'Connor, published by W. J. Smith, [5], 39 pp.
Library of Congress.
The translation is an abridged version of the 1580 (not 1557) first chapter of the *Discours Admirables* which leaves unexplained many doubtful translations, particularly for words that have no modern English equivalents.

Zimmermann, Volkmar (1915). *Die Syntax des Verbums bei Bernard Palissy. Beitrag zur Kenntnis der französischen Sprache des 16. Jahrhunderts. . . .* Halle (Saale), Heinrich John, 79 pp., Inaug.-Diss., Leipzig.
Library of Congress; Harvard University; Yale University.